D1264122

PRACTICAL OPTICAL
CRYSTALLOGRAPHY

PRACTICAL OPTICAL CRYSTALLOGRAPHY

N. H. HARTSHORNE, Ph.D., M.Sc.

Formerly Reader in Chemical Microscopy, University of Leeds

A. STUART, M.Sc., F.G.S.

Emeritus Professor of Geology, University of Exeter

NEW YORK

AMERICAN ELSEVIER PUBLISHING COMPANY, INC.

Printed in Great Britain by the Pitman Press, Bath.

PREFACE

This book is an introduction to the study of the optical properties of crystals in transmitted light by means of the polarising microscope. In many respects it follows the treatment in our larger work *Crystals and the Polarising Microscope* (Arnold, 3rd edition, 1960), but it deals only with true crystals and the simpler practical techniques. The ground covered should, however, be sufficient for the needs of most students of geology, ceramics, and crystallography, and of many other users of the polarising microscope in these fields and in chemistry. We hope also that those needing eventually a more advanced treatment, or primarily interested in quasi-crystalline materials (fibres, polymer films, liquid crystals, plant cell walls, etc.) may find the contents of the book useful as a foundation on which they can build.

The practical methods described are those which are applicable to mounts of crystalline material between a slide and cover slip lying on the ordinary stage of the microscope, or to single crystals mounted on some simple form of apparatus by means of which they may be rotated about a horizontal axis. In experienced hands the scope of these methods is considerable. In describing them we have been at pains to show the beginner exactly how to proceed, by giving full practical details (Chapter 7), and also a number of illustrative examples (Chapter 8). In these examples we have aimed to show how to extract the maximum amount of optical information from whatever orientations the specimen naturally presents, as well as how to circumvent any limitations imposed by these orientations. It is our contention that from the outset a student should be trained to do this, and not be allowed to think he can get by, using a look and say method.

In Chapter 3 we have paid considerable attention to the principles of the correct illumination of the specimen, and the methods by which this may be established. The polarising microscope, like any other microscope, will only give the best results if the user understands and applies these principles. Too often a student is given a microscope without any guidance in these matters, and he 'muddles on', regarding the instrument simply as a super hand lens with the added complication of polars.

Many beginners in the use of the polarising microscope will have a sufficient grounding in elementary optics to need no introduction to the idea of light as a wave motion, the phenomenon of interference, and the properties of simple lenses. In our experience, however, this is by no means always the case, and we have therefore thought it desirable to include sections on these subjects. Those readers who feel that they are not in need of such preparation can easily skip these passages without losing the thread of the main theme of the book.

A.S.
N.H.H.

1964

CONTENTS

vii

1   THE MORPHOLOGY OF CRYSTALS

Crystals are composed of atoms which are arranged in an orderly manner in a three-dimensional structure, the fundamental characteristic of which is that in any given direction identical elementary units (*units of pattern*) are repeated at regular intervals. A two-dimensional section through such a structure will present a repetitive array of units similar to those shown by many wall-paper and fabric designs.

The unit of pattern in a crystal may contain a single atom, as in certain elements, but more usually it contains a group of atoms. The nature of this group varies with the type of substance; it may, for example, be a molecule or a small number of molecules, or it may consist of positive and negative ions in equivalent amounts. If, however, we disregard the actual composition of the unit, and consider only some representative point in it, such as its centre of gravity, then the arrangement of all such points in the structure constitutes what is known as a *space lattice*, the properties of which may be summarised as follows:

1. the line joining any two points, when produced in either direction, will pass through a series of points spaced as were the original pair;

2. all parallel lines passing through points in the lattice present a similar spacing of points.

In such a lattice *each point has a similar environment*, and the structure is homogeneous.

Bravais in 1848 proved mathematically that there can exist only 14 different types of space lattices. These are shown in Fig. 1.1. Experimental determinations of countless crystal structures by the method of X-ray analysis, developed originally by W. H. and W. L. Bragg in 1913, have shown that all the structures are based on one or other of the 14 Bravais lattices.

It is evident that a space lattice can be divided into elementary cells in many different ways, as shown in Fig. 1.2. The cells shown in Fig. 1.1 are those selected by Bravais himself on the basis of the following principles.* The cell with the shortest sides and if possible

* They are not in all cases the ones now preferred by X-ray crystallographers.

1

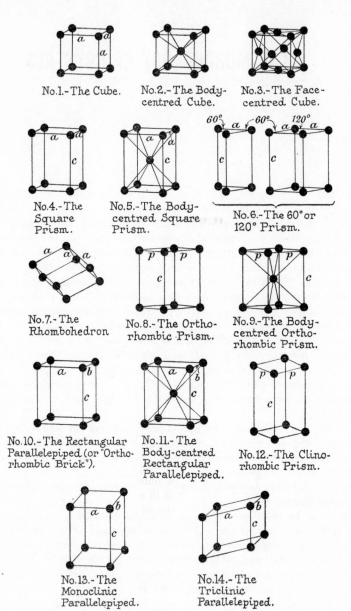

Fig. 1.1. The Fourteen Space Lattices. (Bravais Cells.)

No. 7. Angles $a : a : a$ equal but not 90°.
No. 8. Diagonals of top and bottom faces unequal.
No. 12. Diagonals of top and bottom faces unequal, and these faces not at right angles to the vertical faces.
No. 13. Angle $a : c = 90°$; angle $b : c$ not 90°.
No. 14. Angles $a : b : c$ unequal and not 90°.

of regular shape was chosen. In most cases this results in a cell which is a parallelepiped defined by 8 corner points without any additional points inside it or on the faces (Nos. 1, 4, 6, 7, 8, 10, 12, 13 and 14 in Fig. 1.1). Such cells are true *unit cells* containing the equivalent of one lattice point. (Each corner point is common to eight similar cells and counts only $\frac{1}{8}$ to any particular cell. Since there are eight corners to a cell it contains the equivalent of $8 \times \frac{1}{8} = 1$ point.) In the cells

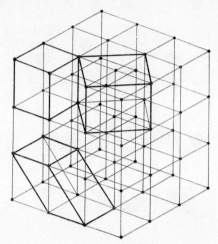

Fig. 1.2.

selected for the remaining lattices, there is an additional point at the centre or, in No. 3, in the middle of each face, and they contain more than the equivalent of one point. They are termed *compound cells*, and were chosen by Bravais in order to bring out more clearly the relationship between the lattices and the external symmetry of crystals based on these lattices.

In illustration of the above, Fig. 1.3 shows a portion of the structure of the salt sodium chloride, NaCl. This consists of an equally spaced array of sodium ions (small black spheres in the figure) and chloride ions (larger spheres) in equal numbers. Both the sodium ions and the chloride ions have the face-centred cubic arrangement (No. 3, Fig. 1.1), and since they are present in equal numbers this must be the lattice on which the structure as a whole is based.

The unit of pattern is a true unit cell of the structure, such as the parallelepiped ABCDEFGH (Fig. 1.3). This has a chloride ion at each corner and a sodium ion, J, at the centre. A little consideration will show that the whole structure is built up by the close packing of such cells, and that their centres lie at the points of a face-centred cubic lattice. Each cell contains the equivalent of $8 \times \frac{1}{8} = 1$ chloride ion (since each chloride ion is common to 8 cells) and 1 sodium ion, the one at the centre, which belongs wholly to the cell.

Two points about the unit cell of the structure may be noted. The first is that instead of defining it as a parallelepiped with chloride ions

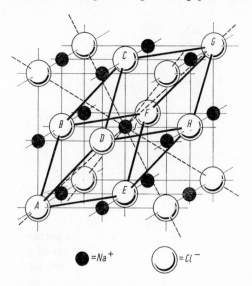

$\bullet = Na^+$ $\bigcirc = Cl^-$

Fig. 1.3

at the corners and a sodium ion at the centre, we could have chosen an exactly similar one with sodium ions at the corners and a chloride ion at the centre; it would have made no difference to the final result. The second is that the parallelepiped is in fact a rhombohedron (since all its edges are equal) and this might suggest that the lattice to which the structure conforms ought to be No. 7 (Fig. 1.1) as well as No. 3. It is indeed geometrically a special case of No. 7, with apical angles between the edges meeting at A and G equal to 60°, but this angle is a direct result of the essentially cubic symmetry of the structure, and the correct assignment is therefore to No. 3, i.e. to the lattice with the higher symmetry. A similar apparent ambiguity is shown by the inclined cell outlined at the bottom left-hand corner of the cubic lattice in Fig. 1.2. This cell is a special case of the Bravais cell No. 13 (Fig. 1.1) with an acute angle $b:c = 45°$, but since this angle results directly from the cubic symmetry, the correct assignment is to the cubic lattice No. 1.

The Bravais cells can be classified according to the symmetry of their shape into seven groups which correspond to the seven *systems* into which crystals have been divided on the same grounds. The characteristics of these crystal systems are described in detail later in this chapter, but for the present it is sufficient to state that they are strictly defined in terms of crystal symmetry, each system however being characterised by *crystal axes* (p. 7) which in most cases have the same relative lengths and directions as the three edges meeting at a corner of the appropriate Bravais cell.

The correspondence between Bravais lattices and crystal systems is as follows:

BRAVAIS LATTICE NUMBER	CRYSTAL SYSTEM
1, 2, 3	Cubic
4, 5	Tetragonal
6	Hexagonal
	Trigonal*
7	Trigonal
8, 9, 10, 11	Orthorhombic
12, 13	Monoclinic
14	Triclinic

* Hexagonal crystals are based on Lattice No. 6, but trigonal crystals may be based on either No. 6 (e.g. quartz) or No. 7 (e.g. calcite). X-ray analysis is necessary to decide the lattice of a trigonal crystal.

The fact that each chemical substance (laboratory product or natural mineral) has its own architectural structure means that every substance is unique in the sum of its crystallographic properties. In particular the angles between corresponding faces of two crystals of the same substance will be identical.† This constancy of interfacial angles has been used by Federov and some of his followers, notably Barker,‡ to identify substances by morphological means alone. In the cubic system, however, morphological identification is not possible, since all substances in this system exhibit identical angles between corresponding faces. But even in such cases, difficulty is not encountered in differentiating between substances when other properties like specific gravity, cleavage, hardness, colour and refractive index are taken into account.

† Slight imperfections of growth in the best crystals result in differences of perhaps a few minutes of arc between values of corresponding pairs of faces, and averages of a number of values are usually given in the literature.

‡ Barker, T. V., *Systematic Crystallography*. Murby, London 1930. Porter, M. W., Spiller, R. C., *The Barker Index of Crystals* (see Appendix p. 314).

The Measurement of Crystal Angles. The angle between two crystal faces may be stated in two ways, either by means of the included angle between the faces, or by means of the angles between the normals to the faces. The term 'interfacial angle' as used in crystallography always refers to the latter or *polar* angle, and is the value used in the construction of the various kinds of crystal projections (see e.g. Chap. 6). The included angle is often measured under the microscope as an

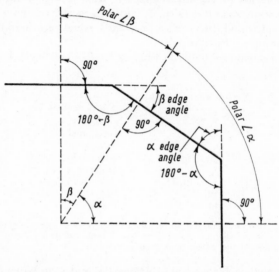

Fig. 1.4. Horizontal section across three vertical faces to show the relationship between included ('edge') and polar angles.

'edge angle' or 'profile angle' (p. 157). Fig. 1.4 shows the relationship between the included and the polar angles. It will be seen that they are supplementary.

The interfacial angles of crystals are measured by instruments known as *goniometers*. The simplest form of these is the *contact goniometer*, which is a semi-circular protractor with a movable arm pivoted at the centre of the circle. When the two faces enclosing the angle to be measured are fitted closely to the base and the movable arm of the instrument, the value of the angle may read off directly on the graduated half circle.

Contact goniometers are now only used on large crystals with dull faces, which do not lend themselves to examination upon a *reflecting goniometer*. This extremely accurate instrument, of which there are now various types, was invented by Wollaston in 1809. In the ordinary 'single circle' type, the crystal to be measured (which need not be larger than about 1 mm. in average diameter, but must have smooth, well-developed faces) is mounted on a stout needle attached to the spindle of a graduated rotatable drum, which can be read to one minute of arc by means of a vernier. The needle is provided with lateral and tilting adjustments, by means of which any *zone* of the crystal may be brought parallel to the axis of rotation of the drum. (A zone is a group of faces, produced if necessary, the intersections of which are parallel lines, see p. 247.) This having been done for one zone, parallel light from a collimator, fitted with a slit, is directed at the crystal and by turning the drum, is reflected from each face of the zone in turn into a telescope provided with cross-hairs, the reading on the drum being taken every time the image of the slit coincides with the intersection of the cross-hairs. The differences between these readings give the angles between the normals to the faces.

With the above type of reflecting goniometer a new setting of the crystal is required for each zone. (The angular relationships between the different zones can be calculated, because some faces are common to more than one zone.) There are more complicated 'two circle' and 'three circle' types by means of which all the interfacial angles can be measured with one setting of the crystal.

Crystal Axes, Face Indices, and the Law of Rational Indices. The relative positions of crystal faces and the angles they make with one another are described by referring the planes in which the faces lie to three (or four, see p. 8) axes along which the various planes make known intercepts. These axes which, as stated on p. 5, are in most cases parallel to the edges of the appropriate Bravais cell, are selected morphologically by the directions of intersection of three prominent faces (produced if necessary) meeting at right angles, or as nearly so as possible, in a crystal corner.

The general case where none of the angles between any pair of axes is a right angle, as in the triclinic system, will be taken. In Fig. 1.5, XOX′, YOY′ and ZOZ′ represent the three axes intersecting at O. They are parallel to the three pairs of pinacoid faces (Fig. 1.17, p. 21 and p. 17 for definition) which make up the simple crystal. The axes are arranged in the conventional way, the XOX′ or *a* axis pointing to the left front of the observer, the YOY′ or *b* axis pointing to the right of the observer, and the ZOZ′ or *c* axis being arranged vertically. The angles between the axes are designated α, β and γ, α being between the axes *b* and *c*, β lying between *a* and *c*, and γ between *a* and *b*. The

three planes containing the axes divide the space occupied by the
crystal into eight parts known as *octants*.

For each substance a face is selected, which is inclined to all three
axes, and makes intercepts on them which are as nearly equal as
possible. Such a face is ABC in the figure, the intercepts on *a*, *b* and
c being OA, OB and OC respectively. The face chosen is called the
parametral plane, and its intercepts, expressed in terms of the intercept

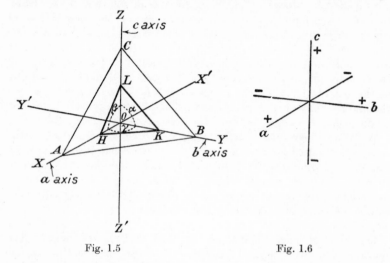

Fig. 1.5   Fig. 1.6

on *b* as unity, are called the *parameters*, or *relative lengths of the axes*
of the crystal. These intercepts are usually given the same symbols,
a, *b* and *c*, as the axes to which they respectively refer. The ratios
a:b and *c:b* are called the *axial ratios*, and these are equal to *a* and *c*
respectively since $b = 1$. The axial ratios and interaxial angles of a
crystal are collectively termed its *crystal elements*.

Four axes are convenient in defining the positions of the faces in
crystals of the hexagonal system (and may be used for crystals of the
trigonal system too); this case will be dealt with later (see p. 28).

The parameters or relative lengths of the axes having been defined,
the position of any other face on the crystal may be fixed by means
of its intercepts on the axes, *expressed in terms of the parameters*. For
example, in Fig. 1.5 the face HKL makes intercepts on *a*, *b* and *c*
respectively of $\frac{1a}{3}, \frac{1b}{2}$ and $\frac{1c}{2}$. These may themselves be taken as the
symbol of the face, as was proposed by Weiss in 1818. A much more

convenient way of expressing the face symbol is that of Miller (1839), who obtained it by taking the reciprocals of the intercepts and clearing away fractions by multiplying throughout by a small integer. The symbol of the face HKL in the figure would be $\frac{3}{1}, \frac{2}{1}, \frac{2}{1}$ or 3,2,2. These numbers or *indices* are conventionally placed in brackets without

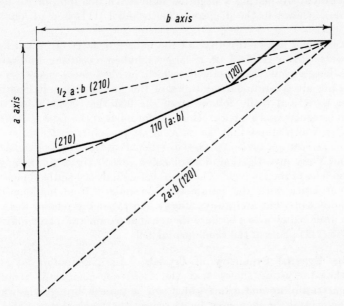

Fig. 1.7. Illustrating the law of rational indices. The heavy lines are traces of three vertical prism faces of the crystal and their intercepts are shown by the dotted lines.

commas, thus—(322). To state the case generally, if *hkl* are the Millerian indices, the intercepts along the axes are $\frac{a}{h}, \frac{b}{k}, \frac{c}{l}$.

It will be seen that the symbol for the parametral plane is (111), and that all parallel faces have the same indices, because the ratios of the intercepts in each case will be the same. The intercept on an axis to which a face is parallel is infinity, and the corresponding Millerian symbol is 0. For example, the faces which in Fig. 1.17 (p. 21) were used to determine the directions of the crystal axes will therefore have symbols as follows: front face, (100); right side face, (010); top face, (001).* Faces which cut the horizontal axes and are parallel to the vertical axis will have the general symbol (hk0). Fig. 1.7 will make this clear.

In order fully to describe the faces of a crystal, it is necessary to attribute different signs to opposite ends of the same axis. This is shown in Fig. 1.6. Where a face makes a negative intercept, the fact is indicated by placing a negative sign above the appropriate index figure as shown in the diagram. The symbol ($11\bar{1}$) is read 'one one bar one'.

It is found in practice that all the indices of faces are small *whole numbers*, chiefly 1, 2, 3 or 4, larger numbers occurring but rarely. This means that the intercepts which inclined faces make on the axes are always rational multiples of the parametral unit length of those axes, and really follows from the fact that crystals are built upon a regular space lattice. Hence is formulated the *Law of Rational Indices*, which states that *the ratios of the intercepts on the axes made by any face can always be expressed as rational multiples of the parameters.*

The X-ray investigation of a substance reveals the absolute lengths of the sides of the unit cell. The ratios between these lengths sometimes do not agree with the parameters determined from goniometrical measurements, but are always simply and rationally related to them. This discrepancy arises because the selected parametral plane may not be the (111) plane of the fundamental cell.

The External Symmetry of Crystals. An examination of well-developed crystals shows that the faces are commonly arranged symmetrically around a line which can be passed through the centre of the crystal, or they may be so placed that each face is balanced by a similar one opposite to it. The symmetry of crystals is often masked by the unequal development of the faces (p. 35), but will be revealed if drawings and projections based solely on the interfacial angles are made. In the following treatment of symmetry, ideally formed crystals are considered. The symmetrical disposition of crystal faces can be described by means of the following *elements of symmetry:* (i) *simple rotation axes,* (ii) *planes of symmetry* and (iii) *rotation-inversion axes.*

A *simple rotation axis* is such that repetition of parts of the crystal takes place by rotation around it. For example, if the eye is placed

---

* These faces are often called the *a*, *b* and *c* faces respectively, i.e. the *a* face is that which intercepts the *a* axis only, and so on. Other letters are conventionally used to denote other faces, e.g. *m* and *p* for prism faces, *o* for pyramidal faces, and sometimes the Millerian indices are prefixed by the appropriate letter, thus 'the *a*(100) face', etc.

above the vertical axis of a hexagonal crystal, a rotation of 60° about this axis will cause the crystal to display an exactly similar aspect. This is shown in Fig. 1.8 *a*, the heavily lined segment moving from position 1 to position 2. Six such movements are possible in 360°, and the vertical axis of the crystal is therefore said to be a *hexagonal*,

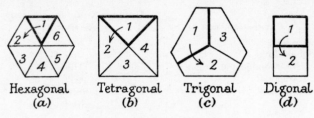

Hexagonal	Tetragonal	Trigonal	Digonal
(*a*)	(*b*)	(*c*)	(*d*)

Fig. 1.8. Axes of Symmetry.

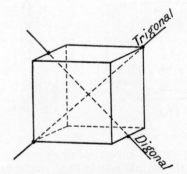 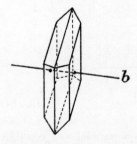

Fig. 1.9. Digonal and Trigonal Axes of Symmetry of the Cube.

Fig. 1.10. Digonal Axis of Symmetry of a Monoclinic Crystal.

or *six-fold*, axis of symmetry. Only three other kinds of such axes of symmetry exist in crystals, namely, *tetragonal* or *four-fold*, *trigonal* or *three-fold*, and *digonal* or *two-fold*, the angles of rotation necessary to repeat a part in these cases being 90°, 120°, and 180° respectively.

The line joining the centres of two opposite faces of a cube is a tetragonal axis, as is also the vertical axis of a tetragonal crystal (Fig. 1.8 *b*); the vertical axis of a trigonal crystal (Fig. 1.8 *c*), and also the line joining two diagonally opposite corners of a cube (Fig. 1.9) are trigonal; the lines joining the middles of two diagonally opposite edges of a cube (Fig. 1.9), and the *b* axis of a monoclinic crystal (Fig. 1.10) are digonal axes.

A *plane of symmetry* can be described as a plane which divides the crystal into two parts, so that one part is the mirror image of the other, each plane, edge, or solid angle having its counterpart on the opposite side of the symmetry plane. The highest number of planes of symmetry displayed by each crystal system is given below.

CRYSTAL SYSTEM	HIGHEST NUMBER OF PLANES OF SYMMETRY
Triclinic	None
Monoclinic	One
Orthorhombic and Trigonal	Three
Tetragonal	Five
Hexagonal	Seven
Cubic	Nine

Fig. 1.11 shows examples of such planes. A plane of symmetry is

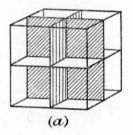 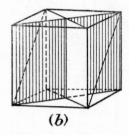 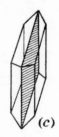

(*a*)   (*b*)   (*c*)

Fig. 1.11. Planes of symmetry.

always parallel to a possible face of the crystal and at right angles to a possible edge.

An *inversion-rotation axis* is such that a crystal face is turned about an axis through 120°, 90° or 60° and then inverted through the centre of rotation. Only these three types of inversion-rotation axes exist. A four-fold inversion axis is shown in Fig. 1.15 *a*. If the (111) face is turned through 90° in a clockwise direction about the vertical axis and then inverted through the centre, the ($\bar{1}1\bar{1}$) face of the tetrahedron results. It will be seen from the figure that a four-fold inversion axis is equivalent *morphologically* to a two-fold simple rotation axis.

An axis of symmetry, whether of the simple rotation or inversion-rotation type, may or may not be a crystallographic axis, but is always in the direction of a possible edge and at right angles to a possible face of the crystal.

A crystal in which every face is accompanied by a similar parallel face, so that a line passed through the centre passes through exactly equivalent points on each side of the crystal, is said to be *centro-symmetrical* and to possess a *centre of symmetry*. Centro-symmetry results when the operation of rotation by 180° is followed by reflection across a plane of symmetry normal to the rotation axis. This is equivalent to inversion through the centre. Thus, if the case of the centro-symmetrical octahedron of the cubic system is taken (Fig. 1.15 *a*, p. 18), the upper right front face (111), may be turned through 180° around the vertical axis, and then reflected across a horizontal plane of symmetry to give its opposite lower left back face ($\bar{1}\bar{1}\bar{1}$).

On the basis of the number and kinds of elements of external symmetry which they may possess, crystals are found to fall into 32

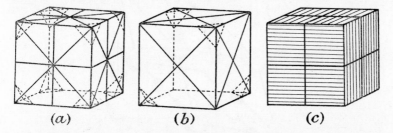

(a)   *(b)*   *(c)*

Fig. 1.12. Symmetry planes in the cubic system. The planes are shown by their traces on the faces which would be visible if the figures were solid.

different *symmetry classes*. Particulars of these classes and of their distribution among the seven crystal systems will be given later in this chapter, but for the moment we shall consider some general points in connection with them.

A statement of the symmetry elements possessed by a crystal is a convenient way of expressing the manner in which its similar parts are spatially related, the term 'similar parts' being taken to mean not merely outward similarity of form, but also *likeness of orientation with respect to the internal structure*. A law which governs crystal growth states that *similar parts of a crystal are similarly modified*. These statements may be illustrated by reference to Fig. 1.12 *a* and *b*, in which two cubic crystals are shown, the first (*a*) possessing all the planes of symmetry of the class of highest symmetry in this system, namely nine, and the other (*b*) having only diagonal planes of symmetry. Should one corner of the crystal in *a* be modified by the growth of a face parallel to the octahedron, then every other corner must be similarly modified to satisfy the symmetry; reflection across the planes of symmetry requires this. In (*b*), however, modification of any corner in the same way would only mean modification of *four* similar corners as shown, giving a combination of the cube and tetrahedron. Thus the eight corners of such a cubic crystal must be made up of two dissimilar groups of four. Actual examples of these two cases are discussed in the next paragraph. In contrast to them, a cube of pyrite

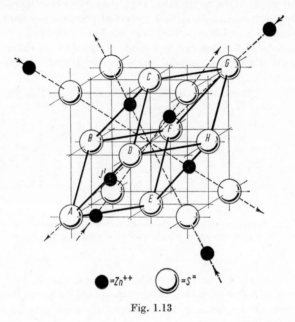

$$\bullet = Zn^{++} \qquad \bigcirc = S^{=}$$

Fig. 1.13

FeS_2 (Fig. 1.12 *c*) has only vertical and horizontal planes of symmetry. a fact which is revealed by the directions of the striations upon its faces, these striations reflecting, as it were, the 'grain' of the internal structure.

The fundamental reason why crystals belonging to the same system may belong to different symmetry classes lies in the fact that the building units of a crystal have their own characteristic symmetry which influences that of the structure as a whole, and which may be quite different from that of the building units in another crystal based on a similar lattice. The following example will illustrate this. Fig. 1.13 shows the structure of the cubic modification of zinc sulphide (zinc blende). This consists of equal numbers of zinc and sulphide ions, each arranged on a face-centred cubic lattice, which is therefore the lattice of the structure as a whole. The system and lattice are the same as those of sodium chloride shown in Fig. 1.3 (p. 4). but the relative positions of the positive and negative ions in the two cases are different. The zinc blende structure may be imagined to be derived from that of sodium chloride by shifting in parallel directions all the positive ions halfway along diagonals of the smaller cubes into which the structures are divided by the thin continuous lines in the figures. Thus if the shift is imagined to be from the back top right corner of each of these cubes towards the front bottom left corner, the central ion J in Fig. 1.3 becomes J′ in Fig. 1.13. If now we select as the units of pattern the similar and similarly oriented parallelepipeds ABCDEFGH in the two cases, we see that in sodium chloride the included positive ion J is centrally placed, whereas in zinc blende the corresponding ion J′ lies towards one end of the unit along the diagonal AG. In other words, the unit in sodium chloride has a centre of symmetry, whereas that in zinc blende has not. AG is a diagonal of the Bravais face-centred cell in the two structures, and along this direction and those of the other diagonals of the cell (shown as broken lines in the figures) there is an important difference in the spacings of the ions in the two cases. In sodium chloride, the positive and negative ions alternate at equal intervals, thus

$$-Cl-Na-Cl-Na-Cl-,$$

but in zinc blende the zinc and sulphide ions are associated in pairs, all pointing the same way, with wider spacings between, so

$$-S-Zn\underline{\quad\quad}S-Zn\underline{\quad\quad}S-Zn-.$$

These directions are therefore non-polar axes in sodium chloride, and parallel faces formed across opposite ends of each of these axes are 'similar' in the sense used above. Moreoever since all four directions are structurally equivalent, all faces formed across these axes and having the same indices (except for sign) will be similar, and the symmetry of the crystal is therefore that shown by the example in Fig. 1.12 *a*. In zinc blende, however, the directions of the cell diagonals are polar axes, and parallel faces formed across opposite ends of an axis are not similar, since at one end the Zn—S pairs are pointing outwards and at the other end inwards, as shown by the arrow heads in Fig. 1.13. At the corners of the Bravais cell, outward-pointing pairs and inward-pointing pairs each have a tetrahedral distribution, and so the symmetry of the crystal is that shown in Fig. 1.12 *b*.

Nomenclature of Crystal Symmetry. Before discussing in greater detail the relationships of the crystal classes it is convenient here to describe the symbols by which the various symmetry operations are referred to, and to show how by combining them the various crystal classes may be defined unambiguously.

Various systems have been proposed by different authors but that of Hermann and Mauguin is most convenient for our purpose since the essential symmetry of each crystal class is at once apparent.

A plane of symmetry is referred to by the letter *m*, and simple rotation axes by the numbers 2, 3, 4 or 6, according to whether they

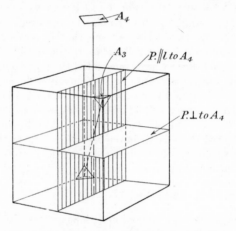

Fig. 1.14. Illustration of crystal class 4/*m*3*m*.

are two-, three-, four-, or six-fold. Inversion axes are of three-, four- or six-fold character and are symbolised by $\bar{3}$, $\bar{4}$ and $\bar{6}$ respectively. A centre of symmetry (i.e. a 360° rotation with subsequent inversion) is denoted by $\bar{1}$ and asymmetry by the figure 1, that is, a complete rotation of a point around a centre, which brings it back to its original position. The symbols are combined in the following manner. The symbol denoting the symmetry of the principal axis is given first. For example in the hexagonal system, 6 or $\bar{6}$; in the trigonal system 3 or $\bar{3}$; and in the tetragonal system by 4 or $\bar{4}$. If the principal axis is normal to a plane of symmetry, the fact is indicated by placing the symbol *m* after the axis symbol with a stroke between as follows: 4/*m*.

The symbols for secondary axes follow, and lastly the remaining symmetry planes if they exist, placing those parallel to the principal axis first. Only sufficient symbols are used rigidly to define the crystal class; the other elements of symmetry follow from those designated in the symbol. For example, in the holohedral class (i.e. class of highest symmetry) of the cubic system, represented most simply by a cube, the symbol may be built up on the lines given above. The vertical axis is four-fold and is normal to a symmetry plane. There are four three-fold axes, but only one is necessary in the symbol as it will be repeated by the four-fold vertical axis. A vertical plane of symmetry comes next, and so the symbol becomes $4/m3m$, or more simply still, $m3m$. A little experimenting with a diagram such as that shown in Fig. 1.14, will demonstrate that all the other symmetry elements proper to this crystal class are implied by this symbol.

Forms. From the discussion on symmetry it will be seen that owing to the operation of the symmetry elements the faces occurring in a crystal group themselves into sets, in each of which the members are similarly orientated to the crystal axes. Each of these sets of crystallographically similar faces, having the same Millerian indices (except as regards sign), is known as a *form*. Three kinds of forms occur in crystals as follows:

Forms consisting simply of two parallel faces cutting only one axis are known as *pinacoids*.

Forms consisting of 3, 4, 6 or more faces parallel to the vertical axis are known as *prisms*.

Forms parallel to a horizontal axis, and cutting the other two, are known as *domes*. (These are really non-vertical prisms.)

Forms cutting three axes are known as *pyramids*. Pyramids may produce solid figures, or *closed forms*, by themselves, but prisms, domes, and pinacoids require the presence of other forms with which to complete the crystal; they are therefore known as *open forms*. The number of possible faces belonging to a form varies according to the system and class to which the crystal belongs. For example, in the triclinic system the highest number of faces in a form is two, in the orthorhombic system eight, and in the cubic system forty-eight. Forms are conveniently referred to by taking the indices of the positive face, if one occurs, and enclosing it in braces thus: {111}. The cube is therefore {100}, and the octahedron {111}.

In systems of low symmetry, forms are named, where necessary, after axes to which they are parallel, or in some other distinguishing way. Thus in the orthorhombic system, the form {100} is parallel to the *macro-* (longer) horizontal axis, *b* and is therefore called the *macro-pinacoid*; the form {010} is parallel to the *brachy-* (shorter) horizontal axis, *a* and is therefore called the *brachy-pinacoid*. The form {001} which intersects the vertical axis, *c*, is termed the *basal pinacoid*. The same terms are used in the triclinic system.

In the monoclinic system, the axes other than *c* are the *clino-* (or *a* axis) and *ortho-* (or *b* axis). The pinacoid {010} is thus named the *clino-pinacoid* and the {100} the *ortho-pinacoid*.

In each system, one class exhibits the maximum symmetry possible in that system and is called the *holohedral* or *holosymmetric* class.

A general term for a class of lower than holosymmetric symmetry is *merosymmetric*, and some crystals within these classes show forms in

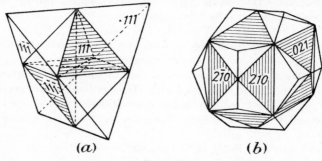

(*a*)   (*b*)

Fig. 1.15

which only one-half or one-quarter of the faces of the corresponding holohedral forms are developed. Such forms have been termed *hemi-hedral* and *tetartohedral* respectively. An example is furnished by the two cubes shown in Figs. 1.12 *a* and *b*. In the first, the highest sym-metry of the cubic system is exhibited and in particular the form composed of faces which truncate the corners affects all eight corners; in other words, the form consists of eight faces. In the second cube, however, the corresponding form consists of four faces only, and is therefore hemihedral.

In further illustration of the above, Fig. 1.15 *a* and *b* shows the relation of the octahedron and the tetrahexahedron to the tetrahedron and the pyritohedron respectively. The faces of the holohedral form developed in the hemihedral crystal are shaded. It will be noticed that the vertical simple four-fold axis in each case becomes a digonal one ($= \bar{4}$ in Fig. 1.15 *a*), in the form of lower symmetry, and that to each holohedral form there correspond two hemihedral forms termed positive and negative, which taken together present the form of the holohedral crystal.

The lower symmetry which gives rise to these hemihedral forms is often masked in the crystal either by the non-appearance of the form indicative of the lower symmetry—only 'holohedral' forms being present—or because both positive and negative forms, equally developed, occur together. For instance, in the cubic system the forms {100} and {110} may occur alone in all the merosymmetric classes, the true symmetry of which is thereby masked, and methods other than

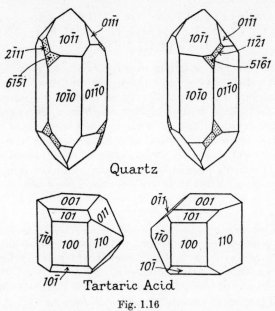

Quartz

Tartaric Acid

Fig. 1.16

morphological measurements are needed for their determination (see p. 37).

In certain classes crystals occur which are terminated differently at opposite ends of an axis which is both one of symmetry and a crystallographic axis. These crystals may be designated *poles* or *hemimorphic*. Examples are tartaric acid, $(CH.OH.COOH)_2$, monoclinic, class 2; hemimorphite, $Zn_4(OH)_2Si_2O_7,H_2O$, orthorhombic, class 2mm; and strontium antimonyl tartate, $Sr(SbO)_2(C_4H_4O_6)_2$, class 6. These and other examples showing this property are figured on pp. 23–31. In the crystal classes which possess only axes of symmetry *enantiomorphous* forms may occur. This means that two types of each crystal species are possible, a right-handed or *dextro-* variety and a left-handed or *lœvo-* variety. A complete crystal of one sort is the mirror image of the other, and neither can be turned about so as to occupy the same position in space as the other. Fig. 1.16 shows crystals of right-handed and left-handed quartz and tartaric acid. Enantiomorphous crystals have the property of rotating the plane of polarisation of light, the *dextro-* and *lævo-* varieties acting in opposite directions in this respect. This property will be dealt with more fully in subsequent chapters.

THE CLASSIFICATION OF CRYSTALS. THE 32 CRYSTAL CLASSES (POINT GROUPS) AND THE CRYSTAL SYSTEMS

Crystals are classified according to the number and kinds of elements of symmetry they possess. As has been shown these elements operate by repeating building units of the crystal (and hence external features like faces and edges) around a point which may be regarded as the centre of the crystal. Each such combination of elements (or, as it is also called, *point group*) of which only 32 are possible, corresponds to one of the crystal classes. A broad survey of these classes shows that one class (1) actually possesses no symmetry at all and is known as the asymmetric class. Then there are ten classes possessing only axes of symmetry, the so-called *holoaxial* classes (classes 2, 22, 4, 42, 3, 32, 6, 62, 23 and 24), in which enantiomorphous forms may occur owing to the absence of planes of symmetry. Next come seventeen classes in which planes of symmetry occur, among which is the monoclinic class *m*, having no axis of symmetry. Lastly there are four classes ($\bar{1}$, $\bar{4}$, $\bar{3}$ and $\bar{6}$) having only inversion axes of symmetry.

As already stated, the 32 classes of crystals thus broadly outlined are divided into seven system (by some authors into six, by combining the hexagonal and trigonal systems). The classes within each system have some common element of symmetry or may be described with reference to the same arrangement of crystal axes. For example all cubic classes display four three-fold diagonal axes and all hexagonal crystals show either a six-fold or an inversion six-fold axis $\bar{6}$, while the three classes of the monoclinic system may be described by reference to three unequal crystal axes, two of which are at right angles, the third being at an angle not a right angle and lying normal to the plane containing the other two.

Triclinic, or Anorthic System. *Referred to three unequal axes at unequal angles, α, β and γ, other than 90° to one another. Any one of these axes may be taken as the vertical one, c, and of the other two, b, the longer and lateral one, is called the* macro-axis, *and* a, *the shorter, the* brachy-axis (Fig. 1.17). *Characterised by no symmetry or only centrosymmetry.*

Two classes occur in this system:

CLASS 1. No symmetry.

Example: Calcium thiosulphate, $CaS_2O_3,6H_2O$ (Fig. 1.19).

CLASS Ī. A centre of symmetry, C.*

Example: Copper sulphate, $CuSO_4,5H_2O$ (Fig. 1.20).

Under the microscope, no ortho- or right-angle shapes will be seen with crystals of this system.

Triclinic System.

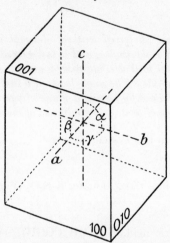

Fig. 1.17. Triclinic axes and three pinacoids.

$$\alpha \neq \beta \neq \gamma.$$

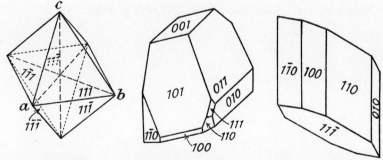

Fig. 1.18. Triclinic pyramid.

Fig. 1.19. Calcium Thiosulphate (after Tutton). Class 1. Each face comprises one *form*.

Fig. 1.20. Copper sulphate. Class Ī. Each face accompanied by a parallel face.

* In the description of each crystal class, the point group symbol is followed by a short summary of the complete symmetry. A, followed by II, III, IV, or VI indicates an axis of digonal, trigonal, tetragonal, or hexagonal symmetry respectively. Ā indicates an inversion axis. P indicates a plane of symmetry, and C a centre of symmetry.

Monoclinic System. *Referred to three unequal axes, a, b and c, of which b and c are at right angles, and a is inclined to c at an angle not 90° in a plane normal to that containing b and c. a is called the* clino-axis *and b the* ortho-axis. *The angle between a and c is referred to as β* (Fig. 1.21). *Characterised by having a plane of symmetry with a digonal axis of symmetry normal to it, or by only one of these elements.*

Three classes occur in this system:

CLASS m. 1 P.

Example: Potassium tetrathionate, $K_2S_4O_6$ (Fig. 1.24).

CLASS 2. 1 AII, polar.

Example: Tartaric acid, $(CH.OH.COOH)_2$, enantiomorphous, in two forms, *dextro-* and *lœvo-* (Fig. 1.25).

CLASS $2/m$ 1 AII at right angles to P; C.

Example: Ferrous sulphate, $FeSO_4,7H_2O$ (Fig. 1.26).

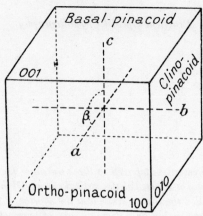

Fig. 1.21. Monoclinic axes and three pinacoids.

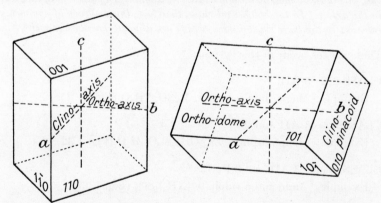

Fig. 1.22. Combination of monoclinic unit prism and basal pinacoid.

Fig. 1.23. Combination of monoclinic
ortho-dome and clino-pinacoid.

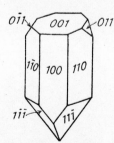

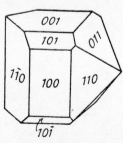

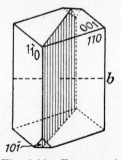

Fig. 1.24. Crystal of
potassium tetrathion-
ate, class *m*.

Fig. 1.25. Tartaric acid
(*dextro*-variety), Class 2.
Compare Fig. 1.16.

Fig. 1.26. Ferrous sul-
phate.
Class 2/m. Showing sym-
metry plane and the
digonal axis of symmetry.

Orthorhombic System. *Referred to three unequal axes at right angles, of which any one may be selected as the vertical one, c. Of the horizontal axes, the longer, b, is called the* macro-axis, *and the shorter, a, the* brachy-axis. *Characterised by possessing only digonal axes of symmetry, of which c is one, and a and b may be the other two. Two symmetry planes may intersect in the axis c. In the holohedral class, therefore, three planes of symmetry intersect in the three crystal axes, which are digonal axes of symmetry.*

Three classes occur in this system:

CLASS 222. 3 AII.

Example: Magnesium sulphate, $MgSO_4,7H_2O$ (Fig. 1.31).

CLASS *mm*. 1 AII and 2 P.

Example: Hemimorphite, $Zn_4(OH)_2Si_2O_7,H_2O$ (Fig. 1.32).

CLASS *mmm*. 3 AII and 3 P; C.

Example: Ammonium sulphate $(NH_4)_2SO_4$ (Fig. 1.33).

Orthorhombic System.

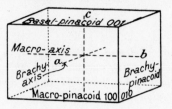

Fig. 1.27. Orthorhombic axes and three pinacoids.

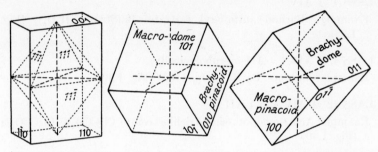

Fig. 1.28. Rhombic unit prism and bipyramid.	Fig. 1.29. Combination of macro-dome and brachy-pinacoid.	Fig. 1.30. Combination of macro-pinacoid and brachy-dome.

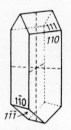
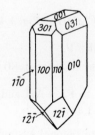
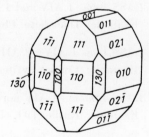

Fig. 1.31. Epsomite (magnesium sulphate), $MgSO_4,7H_2O$, Class 222.	Fig. 1.32. Hemimorphite (zinc silicate) $Zn_4(OH)_2Si_2O_7,H_2O$, Class mm.	Fig. 1.33. Ammonium sulphate (after Tutton). Class mmm. Combination of pinacoids, brachy-domes, prisms and pyramid.

25

Tetragonal System. *Referred to three axes a_1, a_2 and c, all at right angles, the vertical axis, c, being unequal to the other two, which are equal in length. Characterised by one four-fold axis of symmetry parallel to c, or by a four-fold inversion axis.*

There are seven classes in this system:

CLASS 4. 1 AIV.
Example: Barium antimonyl tartrate, $Ba(SbO)_2(C_4H_4O_6)_2$ (Fig. 1.38).

CLASS $\bar{4}$. 1 $\bar{A}$IV (= AII morphologically).
Example: Cahnite, $Ca_4B_2As_2O_{12}.4H_2O$ (Fig. 1.39).

CLASS 42. 1 AIV and 4 AII.
Example: Acid monopotassium trichloracetate, $Cl_3CCO_2K.Cl_3CCO_2H$ (Fig. 1.40).

CLASS $4/m$. 1 AIV normal to P; C.
Example: Scapolite, $n(CaCO_3,3CaAl_2Si_2O_8)$
$m(NaCl,3NaAlSi_3O_8)$ (Fig. 1.41).

CLASS $4mm$. 1 AIV and 4 P.
Example: Diaboleite, $Pb_2CuCl_2(OH)_4$ (Fig. 1.42).

CLASS $\bar{4}2m$. 1 $\bar{A}$IV; 2 AII and 2 P.
Example: Copper Pyrites, $CuFeS_2$ (Fig. 1.43).

CLASS $4/mmm$. 1 AIV normal to P; 4 AII and 4 P; C.
Example: Rutile, TiO_2 (Fig. 1.44).

The indices of a face in the tetragonal system refer to the axes a_1, a_2 and c in that order. In drawings, the a_2 axis occupies the same position as the b axis in drawings of crystals of the triclinic, monoclinic, and orthorhombic systems, namely, pointing to the right.

Tetragonal System.

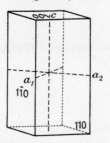

Fig. 1.34. Tetragonal prism and basal pinacoid.

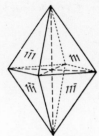

Fig. 1.35.
Tetragonal
bipyramid.

Fig. 1.36.
Combination of
two pyramids
and a prism.

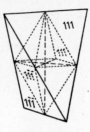

Fig. 1.37.
Tetragonal
sphenoid.

Fig. 1.38
Barium antimonyl
tartrate
Ba(SbO)$_2$(C$_4$H$_4$O$_6$)$_2$.
Class 4.

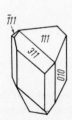

Fig. 1.39. Cahnite,
Ca$_4$B$_2$As$_2$O$_{12}$,4H$_2$O.
Class $\bar{4}$.

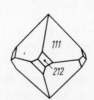

Fig. 1.40. Acid monopotassium
chloracetate
Cl$_3$CCO$_2$K,Cl$_3$CCO$_2$H
Class 42.

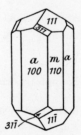

Fig. 1.41. Scapolite,
n(CaCO$_3$,3CaAl$_2$Si$_2$O$_8$)
m(NaCl,3NaAlSi$_3$O$_8$)
Class 4/m.

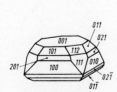

Fig. 1.42.
Diaboleite,
Pb$_2$CuCl$_2$(OH)$_4$.
Class 4mm.

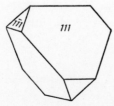

Fig. 1.43. Copper pyrites,
CuFeS$_2$.
Class $\bar{4}$2m.

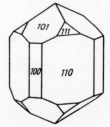

Fig. 1.44. Rutile. TiO$_2$,
Class 4/mmm.

27

Trigonal, or Rhombohedral System. *Referred by some authors to three axes of equal length, a_1, a_2 and a_3, meeting at equal angles other than 90° and by others to four axes, three horizontal, a_1, a_2 and a_3, at angles of 120° and a vertical axis, c, of different length from the others. Characterised by the possession of a vertical trigonal axis of symmetry.*

There are five classes in this system:

CLASS 3. AIII.
    Example: Sodium periodate, $NaIO_4,3H_2O$ (Fig. 1.47).

CLASS $\bar{3}$. 1 AIII and C.
    Example: Dioptase, CuH_2SiO_4 (Fig. 1.48).

CLASS 32. 1 AIII normal to 3 AII.
    Example: Cinnabar, HgS (Fig. 1.49).

CLASS 3*m*. 1 AIII and 3 P.
    Example: Tourmaline (Fig. 1.50).

CLASS $\bar{3}$*m*. 1 AIII normal to 3 AII; 3 P; C.
    Example: Corundum, Al_2O_3 (Fig. 1.51).

In the first system of axes (above), the indices of a face refer to the axes a_1, a_2 and a_3 in that order. In the second system (Bravais-Miller), the indices of a face refer to the axes a_1, a_2 a_3 and c in that order. In drawings, the a_1 axis points to the left front, the a_2 axis to the right and the a_3 axis to the left rear. The negative portion of the a_3 axis is therefore in the front the drawing. This system is used in the figures on p. 29.

Trigonal System.

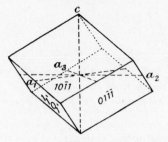

Fig. 1.45. A rhombohedron and trigonal axes.

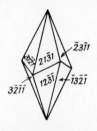

Fig. 1.46. Scaleno-
hedron.

Fig. 1.47.
Sodium periodate
$NaIO_4,3H_2O$.
Class 3.

Fig. 1.48.
Dioptase.
Class $\bar{3}$.

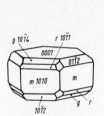

Fig. 1.49.
Cinnabar, HgS.
Class 32

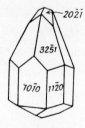

Fig. 1.50.
Tourmaline.
Class $3m$.

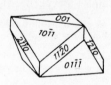

Fig. 1.51.
Corundum, Al_2O_3.
Class $\bar{3}m$.

Hexagonal System. *Referred to four axes, three horizontal ones, a_1, a_2 and a_3, of equal length, inclined to one another at 120° and a vertical axis, c, different in length from the others, and at right angles to them. Characterised by a vertical axis of hexagonal symmetry or by a hexagonal inversion axis.*

There are seven classes in this system:

CLASS 6. 1 AVI.

Example: Strontium antimonyl tartrate, $Sr(SbO)_2(C_4H_4O_6)_2$* (Fig. 1.54).

CLASS $\bar{6}$. 1 $\bar{A}$VI (= morphological 3-fold axis normal to P).

Example: None known.

CLASS 62. 1 AVI normal to 6 AII.

Example: Double salt of barium antimonyl tartrate and potassium nitrate, $Ba(SbO)_2(C_4H_4O_6)_2,KNO_3$* (Fig. 1.55).

CLASS 6/m. 1 AVI normal to P; C.

Example: Apatite, $(CaF)Ca_4(PO_4)_3$ (Fig. 1.56).

CLASS 6mm. Dihexagonal-pyramidal class. 1 AVI and 6 P.

Example: Greenockite, CdS (Fig. 1.57).

CLASS $\bar{6}$2m. 1 $\bar{A}$VI (= 3-fold axis normal to P); 3 AII and 3 P.

Example: Benitoite, $BaTiSi_3O_9$ (Fig. 1.58).

CLASS 6/mmm. 1 AVI normal to P; 6 AII and 6 P; C.

Example: Beryl, $Be_3Al_2Si_6O_{18}$ (Fig. 1.59).

* These substances are placed in the classes 6 and 62 on grounds other than morphology since morphological forms typical of these classes have not been seen. Thus the true symmetry of strontium antimonyl tartrate is revealed by etch figures as in Fig. 1.54. Class 62 is not illustrated by drawing of an actual example but by a conventional hexagonal traphezohedron (Fig. 1.55), which has this symmetry.

Hexagonal System.

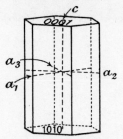

Fig. 1.52. Hexagonal prism with
basal pinacoid showing axes.

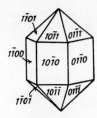

Fig. 1.53.
Combination of
hexagonal pyra-
mid and prism.

Fig. 1.54.
Strontium antimonyl
tartrate, $Sr(SbO)_2(C_4H_4O_6)_2$.
Class 6. Class shown by etch figures.

Fig. 1.55.
Hexagonal trapezohedron.
Class 62.

Fig. 1.56. Apatite,
$(CaF)Ca_4(PO_4)_3$,
Class $6/m$.

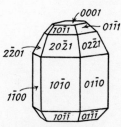

Fig. 1.57.
Greenockite, CdS,
Class $6mm$.

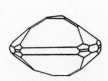

Fig. 1.58. Beni-
toite, $BaTiSi_3O_9$,
Class $\bar{6}2m$.

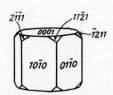

Fig. 1.59. Beryl,
$Be_3Al_2Si_6O_{18}$.
Class $6/mmm$.

31

Cubic System. *Referred to three equal axes,* a_1, a_2 *and* a_3, *all at right angles.* (*In drawings, these axes are orientated respectively like the a, b and c axes in the orthorhombic system.*) *Characterised by possessing four trigonal axes of symmetry, and three rectangular axes of symmetry which may be tetragonal or digonal* (= $\bar{4}$ *in class* $\bar{4}3m$).

There are five classes in this system:

CLASS 23. 4 AIII and 3 AII.

    Example: Sodium chlorate, $NaClO_3$ (Fig. 1.66).

CLASS 43. 4 AIII, 3 AIV and 6 AII.

    Example: No undoubted example.

CLASS $m3$. 4 AIII, 3 AII, 3 P, and C.

    Example: Pyrite FeS_2 (Fig. 1.67).

CLASS $\bar{4}3m$. 4 AIII, 3AII and 6 P.

    Example: Tetrahedrite, Cu_3SbS_3 (Fig. 1.68).

CLASS $m3m$. 4 AIII, 3 AIV, 6 AII, 9 P and C.

    Example: Garnet, $(Ca,Mg,Fe^{..},Mn^{..})_3(Al,Fe^{...},Cr)_2(SiO_4)_3$.

Cubic System.

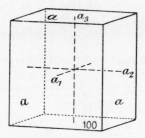

Fig. 1.60. Cube and cubic axes.

Fig. 1.61.
Octahedron.

Fig. 1.62.
Rhombic
dodecahedron.

Fig. 1.63.
Tetrahexahedron.

Fig. 1.64.
Icositetrahedron.

Fig. 1.65.
Hexakis-
octahedron.

Fig. 1.66. Sodium
chlorate, NaClO₃.
Class 23

Fig. 1.67.
Combination of
cube and pyritohedron
Class m3,
e.g. pyrite, FeS₂.

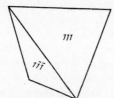

Fig. 1.68.
Tetrahedron.
Class 4̄3m, e.g.
tetrahedrite, Cu₃SbS₃.

Fig. 1.69.
Combination of
icositetrahedron
and dodecahedron.
Class m3m,
e.g. garnet,
(Ca,Mg,Fe··,Mn··)₃
(Al,Fe···,Cr)₂(SiO₄)₃.

33

Habit and Habit Variation. All the crystals considered hitherto have been described as bounded by plane faces and the illustrations of them have been so constructed as to give the faces of a given *form* (p. 17)

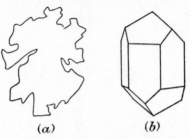

(a)   *(b)*

Fig. 1.70. Anhedral and euhedral quartz crystals.

(a) Section of anhedral crystal from granite.
(b) Euhedral crystal.

equal shapes and sizes. In practice, the student may be confused because, for a number of reasons, actual crystals do not always look like this. First, crystal growth may be impeded by adjacent crystals growing simultaneously and the development of plane faces may be inhibited. Such crystals are to be seen in cast metals, or in igneous rocks where similar conditions may obtain, or where a given substance, crystallising late, may be constrained to occupy only the spaces left between substances already crystallised. Such irregularly shaped crystals are described as *anhedral* or *allotriomorphic*, the terms being synonymous, while those bounded by plane faces are termed *euhedral* or *idiomorphic* (see Fig. 1.70). That anhedral crystals have a regular arrangement of the building units may be proved by X-ray analysis or by the fact that they have the same optical properties as have idiomorphic crystals of the same substance.

Naturally occurring minerals or crops of crystals of the same substance may exhibit an astonishing variety of outward shapes. For example, the mineral calcite, $CaCO_3$, which crystallises in the trigonal system shows a large number of different shapes as a result of the combination of different forms. Each combination of forms is called a *habit*. The four drawings in Fig. 1.71 illustrate the diversity of appearance that is possible in crystals of this substance. Each one belongs not only to the same system but to the same crystal class ($\bar{3}m$, p. 28), and is developed upon the same internal structure.*

* Differences of habit such as this must be carefully distinguished from differences of shape due to the compound's existing in more than one crystalline modification (*polymorphism*). Thus $CaCO_3$ exists also as an orthorhombic modification (aragonite) based on a different structure from calcite.

While it is known that the internal structure plays an important part in determining the frequency with which certain forms tend to be developed (planes with higher reticular density of atoms being more commonly represented by faces), it is also true that the environment of

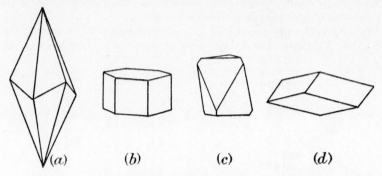

Fig. 1.71. Habits of calcite.

the growing crystal plays a most important part in the determination of habit. The nature and degree of saturation of the solvent, the presence of impurities, and the rate of crystallisation all have an influence in determining the actual forms that will be developed and their relative importance.

Again, crystals showing the same habit may appear very different superficially. The three crystals represented in Fig. 1.72 are all

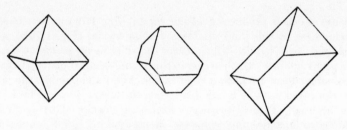

Fig. 1.72. Unevenly developed octahedra of magnetite.

octahedra of the cubic system. This form {111} is a closed form of eight faces, no other being present, but the uneven development of faces masks the regular symmetry, and shapes may be produced looking more like trigonal or tetragonal forms. Measurement of the interfacial angles would reveal the true symmetry. It may be emphasised here that measurement of angles is the only morphological basis for crystal classification. Distortion of crystals is due to fortuitious features of the environment. During growth crystals are usually resting on a face, which is thereby prevented from receiving molecules from the solution except at its edges. Convection currents also may contribute material from certain directions in preference to others.

It is convenient to notice here a number of general terms descriptive of habit. The moderate development of a pair of parallel faces at the

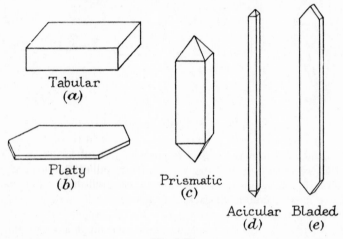

Tabular
(*a*)

Platy
(*b*)

Prismatic
(*c*)

Acicular   Bladed
(*d*)   (*e*)

Fig. 1.73

expense of others produces a *tabular* crystal (Fig. 1.73 *a*). An excessive development of this kind produces a *platy* crystal (Fig. 1.73 *b*), as in mica and lead iodide, which occur in thin hexagonal plates, and potassium chlorate, which occurs in thin rhomb-shaped plates. Crystals of columnar form are known as *prismatic* (Fig. 1.73 *c*), unless the prism is so elongated as to be needle-like, when the term *acicular* (Fig. 1.73 *d*) may be used. Typical prismatic forms are developed by potassium dithionate, magnesium sulphate heptahydrate, and ammonium dihydrogen phosphate, whilst acicular forms are given by the unstable monoclinic modification of sulphur, by potassium permanganate, potassium nitrate, and by most oxalates and tartrates. Flattened needles may be termed *bladed* crystals (Fig. 1.73 *e*).

The various habits of calcite, mentioned above (Fig. 1.71), are the result of the development of an entirely different set of faces in each case, but crystals like those shown in Fig. 1.73 *c* and *d*, only differ in the relative development of the same set of faces. In this case the only difference in the crystallographic description would be in the use of one of the descriptive terms already mentioned.

Habit and Point Group Symmetry. It sometimes happens that the true symmetry of a crystal is masked by the habit. For example, crystals of calcite, class $\bar{3}m$, may outwardly appear like those of class $6/mmm$ (Fig. 1.52), the holohedral class of the hexagonal system, because the only forms developed are a six-sided prism in combination with the basal pinacoid. The mineral quartz, SiO_2, class 32, may, by the development of a similar prism and the two rhombohedra $(10\bar{1}1)$ and $(01\bar{1}1)$ of the same size, give the impression that it belongs also to class $6/mmm$ (Fig. 1.53). A positive tetrahedron of the cubic system may be combined with a negative one equally developed, giving the appearance of a holohedral octahedron, class $m3m$. Sometimes two crystals of low symmetry may be combined in a penetration twin (p. 43) giving a habit outwardly of higher symmetry. The forms of the holohedral classes, being developed along planes of higher reticular densities have a tendency to occur with greater frequency to the exclusion of those faces that are characteristic of the lower symmetry.

In such cases, the true symmetry may be revealed by methods other than those of goniometry. The optical properties are symmetrically related to the crystal systems, and may be used in certain cases to resolve doubts. For example, crystals which exhibit optical activity (p. 97) cannot be holohedral, nor belong to classes of symmetry having planes of symmetry. Multiple twinning (p. 44) of crystals of low symmetry may simulate higher symmetry, but microscopic examination will generally reveal the composite nature of the crystal.

Polar crystals (p. 19) may develop electrical charges of different sign at opposite ends of the polar axis on suffering a change of temperature (pyro-electricity), and this may be detected by appropriate means. For example, the mineral tourmaline (Fig. 1.50, p. 29) shows this property which may be demonstrated by blowing a mixture of finely divided red lead and sulphur through a muslin screen (whereby the particles are charged positively and negatively respectively), when the two substances attach themselves respectively to opposite ends of the tourmaline crystal. Obviously such crystals cannot possess a centre of symmetry.

The relative rates of the growth of crystals in different directions are influenced by their symmetry, and so is their dissolution in solvents. A very convenient method, therefore, for revealing the true symmetry is by the application of solvents to the various faces of the crystal.

When an appropriate solvent is applied for a short time, the face becomes covered with small depressions of characteristic shape, the outline being determined by the rate of dissolution in different directions. Every face of the same form will have similar etch pits (etch figures) which will conform to the point group symmetry normal to the face in question. For example, if a plane of symmetry passes through the face, the symmetry of the etch figure will reflect this.

In Fig. 1.74 three examples are given in illustration. The shapes of the crystals are outwardly holohedral, but their true symmetry is

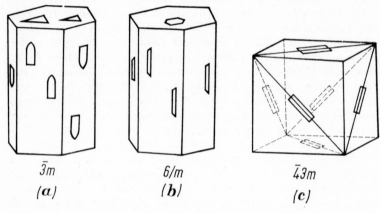

$\bar{3}m$ $6/m$ $\bar{4}3m$

(a)   *(b)*   *(c)*

Fig. 1.74

actually lower. Fig. 1.75 a shows calcite, $CaCO_3$, class $\bar{3}m$. The etch figures on the base are triangular showing a three-fold symmetry, but those on the prism faces are in two sets, each alternate face having the pits oriented in opposite directions. The pits are symmetrical about a vertical line which marks the trace of a plane of symmetry of which there must be three parallel to the vertical axis. The faces of the prism are obviously related to one another by a three-fold rotation followed by an inversion. Fig. 1.74 b illustrates etch figures like those made by acid on a crystal of apatite, $(CaF)Ca_4(PO_4)_3$. The edges of the hexagonal pits on the (0001) plane are not parallel to the faces of the prism, and therefore there are no vertical planes of symmetry. The etch pits on the prism faces are similar to one another but are symmetrical to a horizontal plane of symmetry. The class must therefore be $6/m$.

Fig. 1.74 c represents the type of etch figure which might occur on the faces of a cube which masks the symmetry of the tetrahedron,

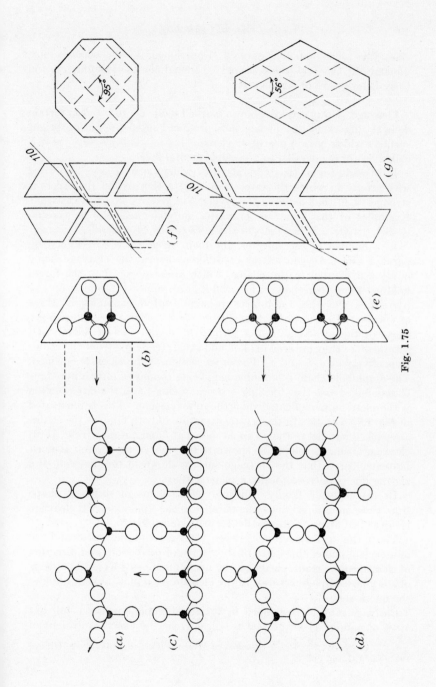

Fig. 1.75

class $\bar{4}3m$. The four-fold axes of the holohedral cube become morphologically two-fold, there are only diagonal planes of symmetry, and there is no centre of symmetry.

Cleavage. Many crystals show a marked tendency to break in certain definite directions, the planes thus produced often presenting bright surfaces which have a pearly or vitreous lustre. This *cleavage*, as it is called, is always parallel to a possible crystal face.

It is readily seen that crystals with widely spaced layers crowded with atoms, in which the inter-atomic attraction within the layers is stronger than that between the layers, will give rise to good cleavage. Examples of this type are graphite, molybdenite, (MoS_2), gypsum ($CaSO_4,2H_2O$), and members of the mica family of minerals.

In a number of the silicates, the main structure is determined by parallel silicon-oxygen chains of different types, the cleavage being developed parallel to the chains, which are stronger than the forces holding them together. The well-known mineral families of the pyroxenes and the amphiboles provide typical examples of these structures. In Fig. 1.75 the silicon-oxygen chains are illustrated, those of the pyroxenes being formed of single rows of linked SiO_4 tetrahedra. They are seen in plan, and in side (end) and front elevations respectively at *a*, *b* and *c*. The cross-section of the chain is outlined. The amphibole chain is a double one, being composed of two pyroxene chains linked together forming a series of rings, and the cross-section is therefore more elongated than the pyroxene one. This is illustrated in Fig. 1.75 *d* and *e*. In the crystal structure of both families the chains are packed parallel to the *c* axis as shown at *f* and *g* respectively, {110} cleavages being developed as shown to the right of the figure. It must be remembered that the cleavage surface shown in the diagram as a zig-zag line is microscopically a plane surface.

In the feldspar family, silicon-oxygen chains of different shape from those mentioned above lie parallel to the *clino*-axis, and cleavage is developed along them parallel to {010} and {001}.*

The intimate connection between cleavage and the outward form of a crystal makes the study of the degree of perfection, and direction of cleavage important, cleavage fragments often being as useful objects of study as complete crystals in the identification of a substance under the microscope.

Cleavage may be developed in various directions in a crystal, but a set of parallel cleavage planes will only be the exact equivalent of

---

* See Bragg, W. L., *Atomic Structure of Minerals* (Cornell Univ. Press, Ithaca, 1937) pp. 197 and 232.

another set if both are developed parallel to crystallographically similar faces. For example, fluorite, CaF_2 (cubic), may be cleaved parallel to the octahedron, {111}, and therefore has four directions of equivalent cleavage. Galena, PbS, and sodium chloride (both cubic) cleave

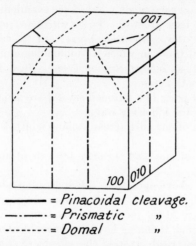

——— = *Pinacoidal cleavage.*
—·——·· = *Prismatic* „
------- = *Domal* „

Fig. 1.76. Some types of orthorhombic cleavage.

parallel to the cube faces, {100}, and therefore possess three equivalent cleavage directions.

Fig. 1.76 shows an orthorhombic crystal with some possible equivalent cleavage directions distinguished by similar types of line.

Cleavage is defined in terms of *direction* (i.e. the face or form to which it is parallel—cubic, octahedral, prismatic, pinacoidal, basal, etc.), and *quality* (i.e. *perfect* with lustrous surfaces, *imperfect, difficult*, etc.).

Different types of *fracture* surfaces may be developed upon crystals with or without cleavage. Fracture is termed *conchoidal* when it is curved like a shell, e.g. as in quartz or glass; *splintery* when it is like that of wood or other fibrous substances; or simply *uneven* when it has neither of the foregoing characteristics.

Twinned Crystals. Crystals are often found joined together in groups of various kinds. These may vary from irregular matted complexes with a random arrangement through the more regular *parallel growths*, in which each crystal is orientated similarly, to groups of two or more crystals in which the individuals grow together symmetrically so that they share a common plane, or appear to occupy a common volume, while being orientated differently. Crystals of the last kind are known as *twinned crystals* and are usually to be recognised by the presence of re-entrant angles or by having elbow or cruciform shapes. Where the units of the twin are very small, microscopic examination may be necessary to reveal the true structure. Twins which are joined on a common plane, known as the *composition plane*, are called *juxtaposition* or *contact* twins, and those in which a volume common to both parts is shared are known as *interpenetration* twins. Figs. 1.77 to 1.79 show typical twins of both types.

The component parts of a twinned crystal are usually related to one another in one of the following ways:

1. by reflection of one part across a plane which is common to both parts, or

2. by rotation of one part through 180° about an axis common to both parts, or

3. by both the above operations taken simultaneously.

The terms reflection and rotation used above refer only to the spatial relationships of the members of the twinned crystal and not to the method by which twinning has been brought about.

In centro-symmetrical crystals the effects of reflection of a part across a plane and rotation about an axis at right angles to that plane are equivalent, but in crystals which are not centro-symmetrical, these two operations produce different results.

The plane across which reflection is imagined to have taken place, or the plane normal to the axis of rotation, is called the *twinning plane*, and the axis, the *twinning axis*. No symmetry plane of the untwinned crystal can become a twinning plane, nor can an axis of even symmetry (i.e. digonal, tetragonal, or hexagonal) become a twinning axis, but a symmetry plane of a higher class may be the twinning plane of a crystal belonging to a class of lower symmetry, which does not possess the plane of symmetry in question. A twinning axis is always a possible crystal line, i.e. a crystal axis, or the normal to a possible crystal face, and the twinning plane is most often parallel to a fundamental crystal face which is not a symmetry plane, as stated above. The composition plane is often the same as the twinning plane, but not necessarily so, and, when not coincident, they are often at right angles to one another.

Fig. 1.77 shows a regular octahedron twinned on a plane parallel to the octahedron face (111), and in Fig. 1.78 a gypsum crystal is shown twinned on a plane parallel to (100). In each case the position of the parts can be described by imagining one part to have been rotated 180° about an axis normal to the twinning plane, or by supposing that one part is the mirror image of the other across the twinning plane, which now becomes a symmetry plane of the twinned crystal. It will be noticed that both the twinning plane and the twinning axis bear the same relation to both parts of the twin.

When interpenetrant twinning takes place, the parts obey the same laws as apply in contact twins, some common axis of rotation or common

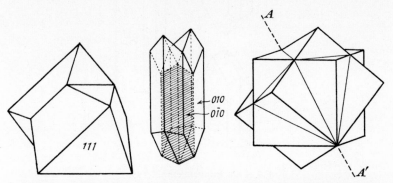

Fig. 1.77. 'Spinel twin' octahedron twinned on (111).

Fig. 1.78. Arrow head twin of gypsum.

Fig. 1.79. Interpenetration twin of fluorite.

reflection plane existing as in the cases described above. This fact can often be seen more clearly if it is imagined that the two parts are entirely separated, while retaining the appropriate orientation. The interpenetrant cubes of Fig. 1.79 are related by reflection across an octahedral plane, or by rotation about the axis AA'.

Twinning might sometimes be described as an attempt to attain a higher degree of symmetry than the separate individuals of the twin possess, for further planes and axes of symmetry are thereby introduced. When two individuals having less than holohedral symmetry interpenetrate so as to produce a crystal having outwardly the holosymmetry of the system to which the individuals belong, the twinning is called *supplementary twinning*. An example is furnished by the orthorhombic mineral hemimorphite, $Zn_4(OH)_2Si_2O_7,H_2O$ belonging to Class *mm* (Fig. 1.80). When twinned on (001) and completely interpenetrant, outwardly the full orthorhombic holohedral symmetry is exhibited. Left- and right-handed enantiomorphous forms may also be twinned by interpenetration, giving apparent holosymmetry.

Multiple Twinning and Mimetic Twins. Twins are often formed
having three or more members. When the composition plane is parallel
to a pinacoid, every alternate member of the series is similarly orientated

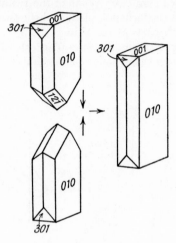

Fig. 1.80. Supplementary twinning in hemimorphite.

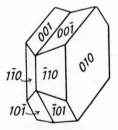

Fig. 1.81. Simple twin
of albite.

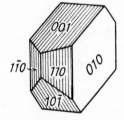

Fig. 1.82. Multiple twin
of albite.

but where the twinning plane is parallel to a prism or a pyramid face,
a cyclical grouping results like two or more elbow twins in series. When
many individuals make up the twin it is described as a *multiple twin*.
This type is excellently displayed by the triclinic plagioclase feldspars
which are a series of mixed crystals of albite, $NaAlSi_3O_8$, and anorthite,
$CaAl_2Si_2O_8$. These minerals display many different modes of twinning
but perhaps the one most frequently met with it that illustrated in

Figs. 1.81 and 1.82. The face (010) is both twin and composition plane. Fig. 1.81 shows a simple twin of albite with the re-entrant angle between (001) and (00$\bar{1}$). Fig. 1.82 shows a crystal made up of many thin lamellae of microscopic thickness, so that the re-entrant angle on the base is not seen macroscopically and the crystal outwardly simulates monoclinic symmetry. Twinning of this kind which has the result of

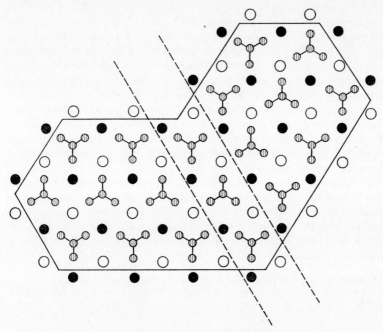

Fig. 1.83. Aragonite twin (after Bragg).

imitating symmetry of a higher rank is called *mimetic* twinning. Such mimetic twins have the physical properties of the forms of lower symmetry of which they are composed. Their optical properties readily differentiate them from possible polymorphs of the same composition which may have higher symmetry. Among artificial chemical substances good multiple twinning is shown by the stable γ- form of o-nitroaniline, and a good example of mimetic twinning is shown by isopropyl-ammonium chloroplatinate, $(C_3H_7NH_3)_2PtCl_6$, which is outwardly orthorhombic, but on microscopic examination is seen to be composed of monoclinic lamellae twinned on (100). Above 32°C. the crystals change to a truly orthorhombic form.

Many questions as to the mechanics of twin formation are still unanswered. While it is known that a twin structure may be induced by pressure (as in calcite), it is evident that the bulk of the twins found in nature or in the laboratory must have grown initially as twins, the parts of adjacent twins being so orientated as to bring similar portions of the structure together so as to make a 'fit'. Bragg* has described the interesting example of the twinning of aragonite. Fig. 1.83 shows a section of the mineral perpendicular to the *c* axis. The *a* axis of the left-hand crystal runs from left to right and the *b* axis at right angles to this. The structure is projected on to the (001) face, and the twin plane is (110). The faces (110) and (010) are drawn in, and the two dashed lines which mark the junction area are parallel to the (110) face. The structure is shown to be pseudohexagonal, the calcium atoms being arranged approximately in hexagonal close packing, a CO_3 group being placed between each group of six calcium atoms. If the alignment of the various atoms is studied it will be seen that those CO_3 groups which fall between the dashed lines could belong to the structures of either of the two members of the twin.

All junctions are not as straightforward nor so simple as the example just described. Bragg† has shown that in orthoclase the twins of Carlsbad type are related by a rotation of the structural chains round the twin axis by 180° which brings the oxygen atoms of adjacent parts of the twin only into near coincidence, but near enough to effect a satisfactory linkage.

* Bragg, W. L., *The Crystalline State*, Vol. 1, Bell, London, 1933, 177.

† Bragg, W. L., *Atomic Structure of Minerals* (Cornell Univ. Press, Ithaca, 1937) p. 245.

2 THE OPTICAL PROPERTIES OF CRYSTALS

Crystals of most substances permit at least some light to pass through them, but we must distinguish between cases in which (a) the crystal is *transparent*, i.e. allows the light to pass without appreciable loss in intensity, and (b) the crystal *absorbs* part of the light and so reduces its intensity. This is not wholly a classification of substances, but rather of their behaviour towards light of different colours. Thus crystals of some substances are transparent to light of all colours, while others are transparent only to a part or parts of the spectrum and show varying degrees of absorption over the rest. (Substances which show strong absorption over the whole spectrum, such as the metals, cannot be studied optically by the methods described in this book, but only by reflected light.)

We shall first confine our attention to transparent crystals (by which we mean crystals in the spectral regions in which they are transparent), but we may note at once that much of what will be said about these applies with only minor modifications to cases in which there is weak absorption. Transparent crystals are classified optically as follows.

1. *Cubic crystals.* These, like gases, liquids, and glasses (if free from strain) are *isotropic* with respect to the propagation of light, which means that light of a given colour (*monochromatic light*) travels through them with the same velocity in all directions. They are *singly-refracting*, i.e. they bend, or *refract*, an obliquely incident ray of monochromatic light along one direction only.

2. *Non-cubic crystals.* These are *anisotropic*. For general directions of propagation they divide an entering ray of monochromatic light into two polarised rays (see later), which pursue slightly different paths and travel with different velocities, one of which at least is also dependent on the direction of propagation of the ray. Such crystals are therefore *doubly-refracting*, or *birefringent*. There are, however, certain directions of propagation through these crystals along which double refraction does not occur. These directions are called *optic axes*. *Tetragonal*, *trigonal*, and *hexagonal crystals* have one optic axis

47

(co-directional with the *c* axis), and are termed *uniaxial*. *Orthorhombic monoclinic*, and *triclinic crystals* have two, and so are termed *biaxial*.

Materials in which there is some degree of preferred molecular orientation, short of that existing in a true crystal, are also birefringent. Examples are natural fibres, fibres and films of high polymers which have been 'drawn' (i.e. pulled out in one direction) in manufacture, and many biological structures, such as the cell walls of plants.

THE WAVE PROPERTIES OF LIGHT

Wave Motion. Many phenomena associated with the passage of light, including those with which we are concerned in studying the optical

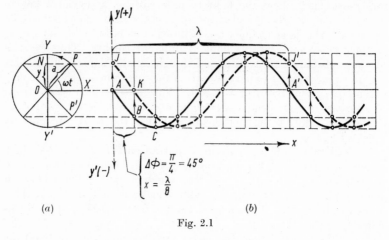

$$\Delta\phi = \frac{\pi}{4} = 45°$$
$$x = \frac{\lambda}{8}$$

(*a*)   (*b*)

Fig. 2.1

properties of crystals, may be explained on the assumption that the light travels as *waves* having mathematically similar properties to those transmitted along a horizontal stretched rope or cord when one end is oscillated transversely with a *simple harmonic motion*.

Simple harmonic motion is defined as follows. In the circle YXY′ in Fig. 2.1 *a* let the radius vector OP rotate in an anticlockwise direction with a uniform angular velocity of ω radians per second, angles being measured from the horizontal radius OX which also represents the position of the rotating radius at zero time. Then at any subsequent time t, the angle swept out by OP will be ωt; or, if OP has made more than one complete revolution $(2n\pi + \omega)t$, where n is an integer. Let N be the foot of the perpendicular dropped from P on to the vertical diameter YOY′. As OP rotates with uniform velocity, N moves to and fro between Y and Y′ with what is termed simple harmonic motion.

Its velocity is obviously not uniform, being at a maximum when it passes through O and becoming zero at Y and Y′ where its direction of movement is reversed. The equation for the motion of N, i.e. the equation which gives its displacement from O as a function of time is

$$ON = OP . \sin NPO = OP . \sin XOP = OP . \sin \omega t,$$

or, denoting ON by y and OP by a.

$$y = a . \sin \omega t \qquad . \qquad . \qquad . \qquad 2.1$$

A familiar example of simple harmonic motion is afforded by the bob of a pendulum swinging through a small arc. In general, it is the motion performed by any particle or small body oscillating under the influence of a *restoring force* which is directly proportional to the displacement from the central position of equilibrium, the adjective 'restoring' meaning that the force acts in the opposite direction to the displacement. In the case of a pendulum the restoring force is a component of gravity.

Referring again to Fig. 2.1 a we see that a complete oscillation or vibration of a particle represented by N corresponds to a complete rotation of OP around the circle, i.e through 2π radians, or 360°. If the particle starts at O (OP coincident with OX), it moves out to Y, back through O to Y′, and from there to O again. The time taken for this whole journey is termed the *period* (T) of the vibration. The reciprocal of this, $1/T$, is termed the *frequency* (ν) of the vibration. The point which the particle has reached at any instant is expressed by the angle ωt, which is called the *phase*, or *phase angle*, of the vibration at that instant, and it will often be convenient to denote this by the single symbol ϕ. The maximum displacement of the particle from its central position, i.e. OY or OY′ in the figure, is called the *amplitude* of the vibration, and so is given by the radius (a) of the circle. Thus we may rewrite Eqn. 2.1.

$$y = a . \sin \phi . \qquad . \qquad . \qquad . \qquad 2.2$$

The *energy* of the vibrating particle *is proportional to the square of the amplitude*, as will now be shown. The restoring force (see above), which we will denote by G, is equal to $-ky$, where k is a constant and the minus sign arises because G acts in the opposite direction to y. The energy of the particle is constant, and is partly potential and partly kinetic except at the position of maximum displacement ($y = a$), where it is all potential, since the particle is momentarily at rest. This limiting value of the potential energy is thus the same as the total energy and is equal to the work required to displace the particle from its equilibrium position by the distance a, which is given by

$$\int_0^a -G.dy = \int_0^a ky.dy = \tfrac{1}{2}ka^2 \qquad . \qquad . \qquad . \ 2.3$$

Returning now to the propagation of waves along a stretched rope, let A in Fig. 2.1 *b* be the end which is oscillated transversely with simple harmonic motion (i.e. the *source* of the waves) and let the amplitude be that defined by Fig. 2.1 *a*. (We will suppose that the other end is very far away, so that we need not consider complications arising from the fact that the waves are reflected back along the rope when they get to that end.) The movements of A set up simple harmonic oscillations of the same frequency at all points along the rope, i.e. the energy of the oscillations is handed on from point to point, but owing to the flexibility of the rope the phase of the oscillation at any point lags behind that at the source by an amount which is proportional to the distance from the source. Thus, when A is at the central position and moving towards its upper limit in the figure, the point B, for example, is $\pi/4$ or $45°$ behind, while C is $\pi/2$ or $90°$ behind, and so on. The curve passing through all such points gives the wave form at this instant, thus ABC . . . A'. The distance in the x direction separating two successive points occupying similar positions on the curve, such as A and A', is termed the *wave-length*, and is usually denoted by λ.*

To make clear the nature of the propagation of the waves, consider an instant when all displacements have advanced in phase by $45°$, say, from those represented by the curve ABC . . . A', i.e. by $45/360$ $= 1/8$ of a complete vibration. This gives the curve traced by a broken line, JK . . . J', which has exactly the same shape as ABC . . . A', but is situated $\lambda/8$ to the right of it in the x direction, i.e. the direction of propagation. (The shift is measured, for example, by AK, and this is $1/8$ of AA'.) Thus we see that the propagation of the waves consists in the bodily translation of the wave form in the direction of propagation, and that an advance of one wave-length past any point takes place in the time required to complete one vibration at that point, i.e. in the period T. In considering the wave propagation process as a whole, the period is in fact usually defined as the time taken for one complete wave to pass a given point, and similarly the frequency $1/T$ is defined as the number of waves passing a given point per second.

---

* Since the angle ωt is the same at A and A' it would in many contexts be permissible to say that they are in the same phase. But if we are to consider the progress of the waves mathematically, as we shall be doing in a moment, we must regard their phases as differing by 2π radians, or $360°$.

The *velocity of propagation* of the waves (v) is given by the product of the frequency and the wave-length, thus

$$v = \lambda/T = \lambda\nu \qquad . \qquad . \qquad . \qquad 2.4$$

An equation for the wave form may be found as follows. At a given time t let ϕ_0 be the phase at the source (e.g. that corresponding to the displacement AJ in the figure) and ϕ_x the phase at a distance x from the source. Then

$$\phi_0 - \phi_x = k . x \qquad . \qquad . \qquad . \qquad 2.5*$$

where k is a constant. When $\phi_0 - \phi_x = 2\pi$, i.e. when ϕ_x refers to a point on the wave which is separated by one wave-length from the point of origin, as J′ is from J in the figure, we have

$$2\pi = k . x = k . \lambda,$$

so that $k = 2\pi/\lambda$. Substituting in Equation. 2.5 we obtain

$$\phi_x = \phi_0 - \frac{2\pi x}{\lambda}.$$

But $\phi_0 = \dfrac{2\pi t}{T}$, and so

$$\phi_x = 2\pi\left(\frac{t}{T} - \frac{x}{\lambda}\right) \qquad . \qquad . \qquad . \qquad 2.6$$

We now substitute this expression for the phase at distance x from the source into Equation 2.2 to give

$$y = a . \sin 2\pi\left(\frac{t}{T} - \frac{x}{\lambda}\right) \qquad . \qquad . \qquad . \qquad 2.7$$

This gives the value of the displacement y (positive values upwards and negative ones downwards in Fig. 2.1 *b*) at a given time t and distance x in terms of the period and the wave-length. The equation can be put into other forms by introducing the frequency, $\nu = 1/T$, or the velocity of propagation of the waves, $v = \lambda\nu$. It is assumed that the amplitude a remains constant along the wave train, a condition which presupposes the complete absence of frictional forces in the system, and is therefore not realisable in practice, though a sufficient approximation to this condition holds over short lengths of the train.

* $\phi_0 - \phi_x$ is positive because the phases of successive points along the rope decline in the x direction.

Since the displacement is proportional to the sine of the phase angle, which itself is proportional to the distance from the source, the wave form follows what is termed a *sine curve*, or *sinusoid*.

The Nature of Light Waves. At the beginning of the nineteenth century Thomas Young demonstrated that the beams of light spreading from two pinholes in a screen, illuminated by the same small source (see later) interact, or *interfere*, in part destructively.* This can only be explained satisfactorily by attributing wave properties to the light, the destructive effect being produced wherever the wave crests of one beam coincide with the wave troughs of the other. Young supposed that the vibrations giving rise to the waves were *longitudinal*, i.e. occurred in the direction of propagation as is the case in sound waves. Waves of this kind, could not, however, account for the fact that when ordinary light is reflected obliquely from a surface, or passed through a doubly refracting crystal, it becomes *polarised*, i.e. its properties around its direction of propagation are no longer wholly symmetrical.

A few years later Augustin Fresnel showed that both interference and polarisation phenomena could be quantitatively explained in terms of *transverse* waves described by the same equations as those derived above for the case of a stretched rope. On this model, polarised light was simply that in which the transverse vibrations were confined to a particular plane (*plane-polarised* light), or were restricted orientationally in some other way. Fresnel's experiments, extending those of Young, established beyond all doubt the wave nature of light, while his numerous mathematical studies in this field laid a firm foundation for the wave theory.

Light travels freely, in fact most rapidly, through a vacuum, and Fresnel and Young, as well as many of their predecessors, assumed that it was conveyed by a hypothetical medium, the *ether*, which was supposed to pervade all space. Fresnel pictured the ether as having the properties of an elastic solid, and the transverse vibrations of the light to consist of displacements of the ether particles from their positions of equilibrium. Although this idea was extremely fruitful in leading to logical explanations of a wide range of optical phenomena, it was open to the objection that elastic solids can transmit longitudinal as well as transverse waves, whereas the fact that light can be

---

* Light normally travels in straight lines, but when it grazes the edge of an obstacle, or passes through a small aperture, it always spreads to some extent into the regions outside the path of direct illumination. This spreading is termed *diffraction*, and is in itself evidence of the wave nature of light. Analogous effects with water waves may be readily observed.

completely plane-polarised shows that its vibrations are exclusively transverse.

In 1865 Clerk Maxwell put forward the *electromagnetic theory of light*, the central idea of which was that light waves are pulses of electromagnetic strain energy, and not of mechanical energy as pictured by Fresnel. This theory did not demand an 'elastic solid' ether, though it was generally held that some form of all-pervading medium was still required to account for the propagation of the waves through a vacuum. Starting with four fundamental equations giving the relations in time and space between the strength of a moving electric field and that of the associated magnetic field, Maxwell showed that electromagnetic waves having exclusively transverse vibrations would be produced whenever an electric charge was accelerated or put into periodic motion. It also followed from the equations that the velocity of these waves in a vacuum would be the same for all wave-lengths, and equal to the ratio of the two fundamental units in terms of which electric current may be expressed, namely that of the electromagnetic unit to the electrostatic unit.

In terms of Maxwell's theory a plane-polarised ray* of monochromatic light travelling through a vacuum consists of electric and magnetic fields oscillating in strength at right angles to one another and to the direction of propagation, and in phase with one another. The oscillations are simple harmonic, and at any instant the ends of the vectors defining the directions and strengths of the fields trace out sinusoidal wave forms as shown in Fig. 2.2, in which OE is the *electric vector* and OH the *magnetic vector* for the point O.

Experimental support for the theory was obtained in 1887 by Hertz, who produced waves of undoubted electromagnetic character, though of much longer wave-length than those of visible light, by means of an oscillating electric discharge, and found that their velocity was equal within the accuracy of his determinations to the known velocity of light, namely about 3×10^{10} cm./sec.† The waves could be reflected and refracted like light waves, and they exhibited similar interference and polarisation phenomena. Further support came from determinations of the ratio of the electromagnetic and electrostatic units of

---

* As strictly defined, a ray is simply a line representing the rectilinear path along which the energy of the light is transmitted in any direction from a point on the light source. It is also convenient, however, to think of it as an infinitely narrow pencil of light, i.e. a longitudinal element of a beam of light of finite width, such as we have to deal with in practice, and it is in that sense that we shall use the term in this book.

† All determinations of the velocity of light up to that period had been of the velocity *in air*, but this is practically the same as the velocity in a vacuum.

current by various investigators (Weber and Kohlrausch, Lord Kelvin, Ayrton and Perry) which had been made by that time, and all of which gave values near to 3×10^{10} cm./sec.

All subsequent work has combined to confirm the electromagnetic nature of light waves as described by the Maxwell equations, and it is now known that visible light occupies only a very small section of a

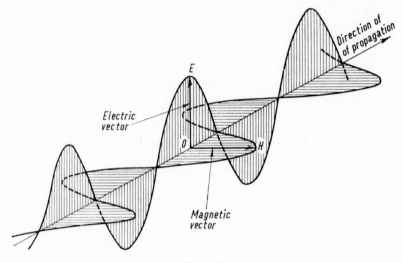

Fig. 2.2

vast range of electromagnetic radiations, extending from the γ-rays emitted in radioactive disintegrations, with wave-lengths of the orders 10^{-10} to 10^{-8} cm., to the radio waves which have wave-lengths of up to many miles. The wave-lengths for visible light range from about 4×10^{-5} cm. (violet) to $7 \cdot 5 \times 10^{-5}$ cm. (dark red), or 4000 to 7500 Ångstrom units (symbol Å, or simply A), where $1 \text{Å} = 10^{-8}$ cm.

As already mentioned, the velocity of light in a material medium is less than that in a vacuum. Briefly the explanation of this is that the alternating electric field of the waves incident on the atoms of the medium produces oscillations of their electron clouds with respect to their nuclei, and these oscillations in turn generate secondary waves. Interference effects between the two sets of waves result in a reduction of the velocity of the light as a whole. The magnitude of the effect depends on the frequency of the incident light.

If all space is pervaded by a luminiferous ether, it is likely that the

earth is moving in relation to it, and that therefore the velocity of light
as measured on the earth will be different in different directions.
Michelson and Morley in a series of classical experiments (1881–7)
failed, however, to find any such difference. This failure later formed
the basis of Einstein's original theory of relativity (1905) which,
without directly denying that an ether exists, asserts that no experiment can ever be devised which will *prove* that it does. Since Einstein's
theory has been confirmed in various ways, the modern attitude is to
accept this situation, however difficult it may be to conceive of energy
being relayed through 'nothingness'. It is best to think of light waves
simply as periodic variations in the strengths of associated electric
and magnetic fields along the direction of propagation, and the wavy
lines in drawings such as Fig. 2.2 as graphs of these variations, without
concerning ourselves with the attributes of a hypothetical vehicle, the
existence of which, it seems, we have no chance of proving or disproving.

Experiments by Wiener in 1890 showed that it is the electric vector
of light and not the magnetic vector which affects a photographic plate.
From this it is assumed that the electric vector is responsible for other
observed optical effects. In future, therefore, we shall simplify the
representation of a plane-polarised ray by taking account only of the
plane containing the electric vector, which we shall call the *plane of
vibration*, while the direction of the vector at any point we shall call the
vibration direction.

Combination of Wave Motions. We shall now consider what happens
according to wave theory when two polarised rays are caused to travel
along the same path. We shall deal only with two sets of conditions,
which are important in the study of the optical properties of crystals.

1. *The rays are plane-polarised, have the same wave-length, and vibrate
in the same plane.* This is a case to which the term *interference* is usually
applied. Examples are shown in Fig. 2.3 *a*, *b* and *c*. The waves associated with the two rays are shown as full lines, and those for the
resultant ray by a broken line. The rule for finding the resultant waves
is very simple: their displacement (y in Equation 2.2) at any point is
the algebraic sum of the displacements of the component vibrations.
Thus in Fig. 2.3 *a*, $OY_r = OY_1 + OY_2$ (*constructive interference*), while
in *b*, $OY_r = OY_2 - OY_1$ (*destructive interference*). In the latter
example, if the amplitudes of the component vibrations had been
equal, the light would have been completely suppressed (*complete
destructive interference*). It should be apparent that the same principle
of algebraic addition determines the resultant wave form in Fig. 2.3 *c*.
Thus $OY_r = OY_1 + OY_2$, and $OY_r' = OY_2' - OY_1'$.

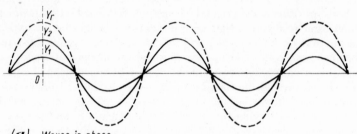

(a) Waves in phase

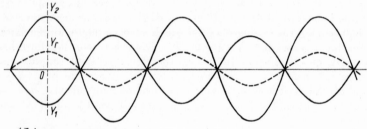

(b) Waves 180° out of phase

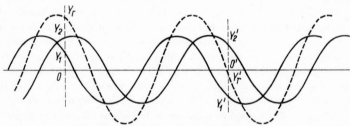

(c) Waves out of phase by an arbitrary amount

Fig. 2.3. Interference of light waves.

A more generalised treatment is shown in Fig. 2.4. The relative phases and amplitudes of the two component rays are represented by means of a vector diagram like Fig. 2.1 *a*. At a given instant let OP_1 be the radius vector defining the phase angle, ωt, and the displacement, OY_1, of the one component and OP_2 be that defining the phase angle, $(\omega t + \delta)$, and the displacement, OY_2, of the other, where δ is the *phase difference* between the two. Then by the principles of vector addition the phase and displacement of the resultant are defined by OP_r, the

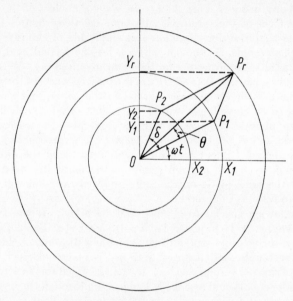

Fig. 2.4

diagonal lying between OP_1 and OP_2 of the parallelogram $P_1OP_2P_r$, i.e. the phase angle is X_1OP_r, or $(\omega t + \theta)$, and the displacement OY_r. As time advances the parallelogram rotates bodily in an anticlockwise direction (since by definition the frequencies of the component vibrations are the same (i.e. OP_1 and OP_2 rotate at the same rate ω), and thus the resultant vibration is also simple harmonic, and of the same frequency as that of the components.

2. *The rays are plane-polarised, have the same wave-length, and vibrate in planes at right angles to one another.* In these conditions the recti-linear vibrations of the two components at any point along the joint path combine to give a resultant vibration which is in general elliptical,

3

i.e. is described by a rotating electric vector the end of which follows
an elliptical path. The resultant ray is said to be *elliptically polarised*.
The equation for the ellipse is

$$\sin^2 \delta = \frac{y^2}{a^2} + \frac{z^2}{b^2} - \frac{2yz}{ab} \cos \delta \qquad . \qquad . \qquad . \ 2.8$$

where δ is the phase difference between the component vibrations as
before, a and b their amplitudes, and y and z their electrical displacements at any instant. Figs. 2.5 *i* to *ix*, show the effect of the value of
δ on the form of the resultant vibration. In these figures OS (= a)
represents the vibration direction and amplitude of the ray with the
smaller phase angle, i.e. the one which is lagging behind, and OF (=b)
represents the same properties for the more advanced ray. With respect
to the above equation, OS and OF are the positive parts of the reference
axes. The ray direction is the normal to the paper, and the light is
supposed to be travelling towards the reader. Under each figure are
given the phase difference in degrees, and also the corresponding
relative retardation, or *optical path difference* (R), expressed as a fraction
of a wave-length. R is the distance measured along the direction of
propagation by which a given phase on the more advanced ray lies
ahead of the same phase on the more retarded ray, and will be dealt
with more fully in Chapter 4.

The following special cases may first be noted. If the two com-
ponents happen to be in phase, i.e. $\delta = 0°$, $360°$, etc. (Fig. 2.5 *i* and *ix*),
the ellipse shrinks to a straight line, which is a diagonal of the circumscribing rectangle, and the resultant ray is plane-polarised. In this
case, since $\sin \delta = 0$ and $\cos \delta = 1$, the equation reduces to $y = (a/b).z$,
which is the equation of a straight line passing through the origin, with
a slope of a/b and with y and z of the same sign. Thus the vibration
direction is the 'positive' diagonal of the rectangle as shown. When
$\delta = 180°$ the resultant ray is again plane-polarised (Fig. 2.5 *v*), but
since $\cos \delta = -1$, the equation reduces to $y = -(a/b).z$, and the
vibration direction is the other diagonal of the rectangle. In the cases
$\delta = 90°$, $\delta = 270°$ (*iii* and *vii*), the equation reduces to $y^2/a^2 + z^2/b^2 =$
1, which is the equation for an ellipse with principal semi-axis a and b,
i.e. an ellipse standing upright in the circumscribing rectangle. If the
amplitudes of the two components are equal ($a = b$), the ellipse in
these cases becomes a circle, and the resultant ray is said to be *circularly
polarised*.

In the general cases represented by Fig. 2.5 *ii*, *iv*, *vi* and *viii*, the
ellipse occupies an inclined position in the rectangle. The principal
axes of the ellipse are not coincident with either of the diagonals of the

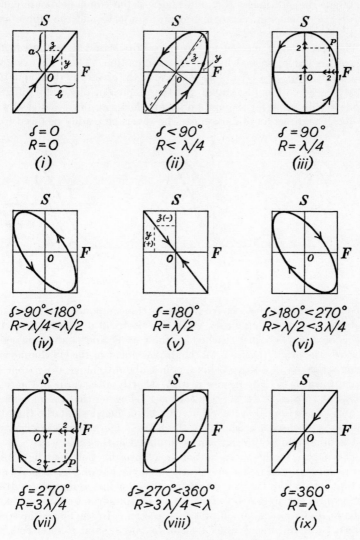

Fig. 2.5. Elliptically polarised light.

rectangle (see *ii*), unless the amplitudes of the components are equal, i.e. $a = b$, when the rectangle becomes a square and the ellipse axes and diagonals coincide.

The direction of motion in the ellipse (indicated by arrows in the figures) is not expressed by the ellipse equation. Thus, for example, the ellipses in cases *iii* and *vii* are both given by the equation $y^2/a^2 + z^2/b^2 = 1$ as just stated, but they represent physically different kinds of vibration, for the motion is anti-clockwise in *iii* and clockwise in *vii*. The direction of motion can, however, be readily deduced from

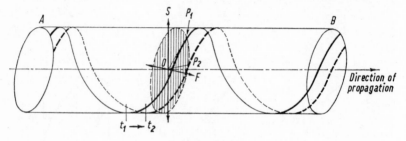

Fig. 2.6. Elliptically polarised light.

a consideration of the relative phases of the components at successive instants of time. Thus in *iii*, when the electrical displacement in the OF component has just reached its limit at F, and is about to move towards the origin (position 1), the displacement in the OS component, being a quarter of a wave behind, is just about to move away from the origin towards S. The resultant is F. Shortly afterwards in the same vibration (positions 2), the resultant is P, showing that the movement is anti-clockwise. In case *vii* it can be deduced similarly that the motion is clockwise, as shown in the figure. The directions of motion in the other elliptical forms can be obtained in the same way.

The nature of the wave motion in elliptically polarised light may perhaps be appreciated more clearly with the aid of Fig. 2.6. At any instant the ends of the electric vectors for all points along the ray trace out a spiral curve (the wave form) lying on the surface of an imaginary cylinder (AB) having an elliptic cross section. In the figure the spiral shown by a full line is that for the instant t_1, and it intersects the elliptic section P_1P_2 at P_1 (vector = OP_1). At a later instant t_2 the spiral has moved bodily to the right (broken line), and the point of intersection on P_1P_2 has moved to P_2 (vector = OP_2). OS and OF are the vibration directions and amplitudes of the two component rays as in Fig. 2.5. It is clear that continued movement of the spiral to the right will result in a clockwise rotation of the point of intersection around the ellipse, and we have in fact the case represented otherwise in Fig. 2.5. *viii*.

Monochromatic Light. Light of a given colour is commonly defined quantitatively by its wave-length, as has been implied above. The figure stated is the wave-length in a vacuum or, as a very close approximation to this, in air, because it is not a constant quantity irrespective of the medium through which the light travels. The velocity of light of any colour is less in a material medium than in a vacuum, and it follows from equation 2.4 that the wave-length or the frequency (or possibly both) must also be less in the medium. There is, however, no reason to suppose that the frequency changes when the light enters a medium from a vacuum, or passes from one medium to another, because its vibrations are excited and forced by those which it was executing before it crossed the boundary. Therefore it is the wave-length that alters, being always less than that in a vacuum, and varying from medium to medium in proportion to the velocity of the light in each. We see from this that the frequency really offers a more fundamental definition of colour than does the wave-length.

Rewriting equation 2.4 we have for any given colour,

(*a*) in a vacuum $\lambda_0 \nu = c$, where λ_0 is the vacuum wave-length, and *c* the velocity which is the same for all wave-lengths (see above), and

(*b*) in a medium $\lambda_m \nu = v_m$, where λ_m is the wave-length and v_m the velocity in the medium. Dividing we obtain

$$\lambda_0/\lambda_m = c/v_m = n \qquad . \qquad . \qquad . \qquad . \quad 2.9$$

where *n* is the *refractive index* of the medium for this colour. For transparent media *n* increases with increase in the frequency, i.e. with decrease in the wave-length (*normal dispersion*). If absorption occurs over any range or ranges of the spectrum, however, this rule breaks down in the region of the wave-lengths absorbed (*anomalous dispersion; see later*).

Light of definite frequencies is emitted by single atoms in the gaseous state at high temperatures or when subjected to an electric discharge, a familiar example being the yellow light emitted by sodium atoms, e.g. when a sodium salt undergoes dissociation on being introduced into a bunsen flame. This is explained by the *quantum theory* (Planck, Bohr, and others) as follows. The electrons in the atoms can occupy only certain discrete levels of energy, and under the above conditions some of them are continually being raised from lower to higher levels and then dropping back. Each transition from a higher to a lower level is accompanied by the emission of a 'particle', or *quantum*, of radiation (also called a *photon*), the frequency of which is proportional only to the energy change in the transition, and thus for a transition between two given levels is constant.*

The above explanation introduces us to a phenomenon with which wave theory is not adequate to deal, and to the difficult idea that light behaves as a train of waves in some situations, and as a stream of particles in others. This dual nature is also possessed by particles which we normally think of as 'matter', e.g. electrons, beams of which can be diffracted like light, and must therefore have a wave character as well as a particle character. This is not the place to discuss this matter further and, since most of the phenomena with which we shall be concerned are those in which the wave nature of light is predominant, we shall use the wave model exclusively.

Light from Real Sources. So far in our theoretical treatment we have dealt only with rays of light which were assumed to be mono-chromatic and plane-polarised with a constant plane of vibration, or with the results of combining such rays. According to wave theory a ray of this kind is to be represented by a sinusoid of indefinite length. Light from real sources is, however, *unpolarised*, i.e. its vibrations are executed in all planes parallel to its direction of propagation, and its emission, considered over successive very small intervals of time, is not perfectly steady. In particular, sudden changes of phase occur at intervals of the order of 10^{-8} sec. If the source emits monochromatic light, therefore, we must picture the sinusoid of wave theory as broken up into a series of sections or separate wave trains, each of which has no definite phase relation with the ones which precede and follow it, and we may explain the fact that the light is unpolarised by supposing that these trains have different planes of vibration, all planes being equally represented.

White light, as is emitted by the sun or an incandescent solid, such as a lamp filament, presents a much more complicated problem to wave theory but, as is well known, it can be separated, or analysed, into a continuous spectrum, in which all wave-lengths are represented, by means of a prism or a diffraction grating, and for our present purposes

* Actually the light obtained is never strictly monochromatic, partly because the atoms are in rapid random motion relative to the observer (resulting in the Doppler effect, analogous to the rise and fall in the note of a vehicle passing at high speed), and partly because the emission is attended by sudden changes of phase, which are equivalent to momentary changes of frequency (see next section). The resulting spread of wave-lengths is, however, extremely small, and for most practical purposes it may be ignored.

it will be sufficient to regard it as simply a mixture of lights of all wave-lengths.

The series of wave trains from two separate sources, or from different points on the same extended source, can have no constant phase or vibration plane relationship to one another, and so if they are superposed no macroscopic interference effects will be observed. Such effects can be obtained only by combining rays derived originally from the same small source, so that their phases and vibration planes keep 'in step'. Thus in Young's original experiment (p. 52) the source was a pinhole in a screen illuminated by sunlight, and this illuminated two other pinholes in a screen some distance away, interference effects being produced between the rays spreading from these. In optical crystallography we are concerned with interference effects between rays resulting from the double refraction of the rays incident on the crystal, and therefore once again derived from the same source. Rays or beams of light which have a constant phase and vibration plane relationship to one another through being derived from the same original source are said to be *coherent*, and the effective sources of them, such as the two pinholes in the second screen in Young's experiment, are termed *coherent* sources.

Coherence between two rays will be destroyed if the optical path difference between them is made so large that corresponding wave trains no longer overlap. Except in this extreme condition, which does not arise in the routine study of crystals under the polarising microscope, we may continue to represent rays from the same source by unbroken sinusoids since the phase *difference* between them, on which their interaction depends, is not affected by their phase discontinuities.

Wave Fronts. In Fig. 2.7 let O be a point source of monochromatic light inside a transparent isotropic medium. The light travels with the same velocity in all directions, and at any instant after the source begins to radiate the ends of the rays lie on the surface of a sphere, of which R_1S_1 represents a section. All points on this surface are in the same phase and it is therefore termed the *wave front* of the whole disturbance, though the term may also be applied to any other surface in the disturbance, which passes through points in the same phase, such as that represented by the section R_2S_2. However, unless the context shows otherwise, we shall use the term to mean the leading front, e.g. R_1S_1, in this or other systems of light waves.

The waves in Fig. 2.7 are three-dimensional, and their vibrations may be thought of as a combination of those occurring along every ray direction. Thus, for example, at the instant to which the figure refers, the electric field around the whole section R_2S_2 is directed clockwise and has reached its maximum strength (since the wavy lines lie clockwise of the rays and their peaks coincide with the section), and the vibrations at other points on this surface will be in harmony. The waves are said to be *spherical* from the shape of their wave front. The tangent plane at any point on the front (as at R_1) is the wave front associated with the ray which meets the surface at that point, and is at right angles to the ray. In a parallel beam this plane is the same for

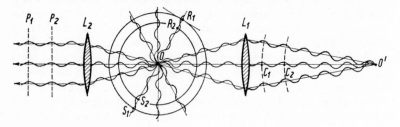

Fig. 2.7. Wave fronts in singly refracting media.

all the rays, and defines the wave front of the beam, as will presently appear.

Now let a convex lens L_1, having a refractive index greater than that of the medium surrounding O and free from spherical aberration (see Chapter 3), be placed as shown in the figure at a distance from O which is greater than its focal length. Rays travelling beyond R_1S_1 and entering the lens will be brought to a focus at O′, and it can be shown that they will arrive in phase. The waves in the beam converging on O′ are also spherical, and C_1 and C_2 are examples of their wave fronts.

L_2 is a lens like L_1 but placed at a distance from O equal to its focal length. Rays emerging from it are therefore parallel and form a beam with plane wave fronts, e.g. P_1 and P_2, i.e. consisting of *plane waves*. It will be evident that spherical (diverging) waves approximate more and more nearly to plane waves over restricted areas of the wave front as the distance from the source increases.

On p. 49 it was shown that the energy associated with a simple harmonic motion is proportional to the square of the amplitude. It follows that in a light wave the intensity, i.e. the amount of energy passing through unit area in unit time, is also proportional to the square of the amplitude. Now when light is radiated from a point source, as from O above, the intensity along any ray direction must decrease with increasing distance from the source, because the energy (which we may assume is being generated by the source at a constant rate) is being spread over an increasing area. It is clear that the intensity at any point is inversely proportional to the area of the whole wave front on which the point lies, i.e. to the square of the distance from the source, and so the amplitude must be inversely proportional to the first power of the distance. This decrease in amplitude is shown in the figure, as well as the reverse effect in the beam of light converging on O′, which is due to the fact that the intensity is increasing with distance in this case. In the parallel beam produced by the lens L_2 there is no change of amplitude because the area of the wave front is constant.

Wave Surfaces. The geometrical figure formed by the wave front of monochromatic light emitted from a point source is termed in a more general sense the *wave surface*, or *wave surface figure* of the medium for that wave-length. (By some the term *ray surface* is preferred, since the surface is the focus of points attained by rays). When drawn on a scale representing the velocity of the light, it summarises graphically the optical properties of the medium, and it is also used in certain constructions, as will presently appear. As we have seen, isotropic media have spherical wave surfaces. In dealing with birefringent crystals we shall encounter wave surfaces of other shapes.

UNIAXIAL CRYSTALS

The first recorded observation of the phenomenon of double refraction was made by Erasmus Bartolinius in 1669 on the transparent variety of calcite known as Iceland spar. The phenomenon was studied by Huygens (1690), who was successful in accounting for all but that part of it requiring a knowledge of polarisation.

If a small black spot marked on a piece of white paper is covered with a cleavage rhombohedron of Iceland spar, half an inch thick or more, two virtual images of the spot are seen through the spar. One of the images is due to rays which obey the ordinary laws of refraction, and are therefore called *ordinary* rays. When the line of vision is normal to the paper this image appears immediately above the spot itself, and remains stationary when the crystal is rotated in a horizontal plane. The other image is due to rays which do not obey the ordinary laws of refraction, and are therefore called *extraordinary* rays. When the line of vision is normal to the paper, this image appears to one side of the actual spot, and rotates with the crystal when the latter is turned in a horizontal plane. The paths of the two sets of rays (indicated for simplicity by single lines) are shown in Fig. 2.8 *a*, in which

A is the spot, B the ordinary image (that is the image due to the ordinary rays), and C the extraordinary image. B is higher than C because in calcite the extraordinary rays travel more rapidly than the ordinary rays.

This division of the light into two rays is observed no matter what face of the rhombohedron be laid on the paper. But if a plate of the crystal cut perpendicular to the *c* axis were used, only one image of

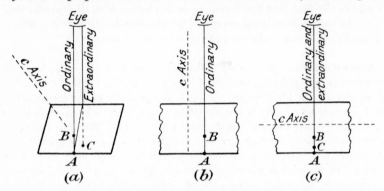

Fig. 2.8. Passage of light through calcite.

A is the black spot, B the ordinary image, and C the extraordinary image.

the spot would appear if the line of vision were normal to the paper, and this image would be above the spot, and would remain stationary during rotation of the plate in a horizontal plane (Fig. 2.8 *b*). For oblique lines of vision, however, two images would be seen. Finally, if a plate of the crystal cut parallel to the *c* axis were used, a normal line of vision would yield, apparently, a single image, which, however, could be shown by a suitable focussing device to consist of two images immediately above one another (Fig. 2.8 *c*).

Calcite belongs to the trigonal system. Results similar to the above are theoretically obtainable with any trigonal, tetragonal, or hexagonal crystal, but it is rare to find transparent crystals, other than those of calcite, which are sufficiently thick and birefringent to show a clear separation of the two images.

Wave Surfaces of Uniaxial Crystals. Huygens' explanation of these results, which has been fully confirmed by later work, was as follows. If a point source of monochromatic light be imagined to exist anywhere inside the crystal, the light will be propagated as two independent sets of rays. One set (ordinary rays) travel with the same velocity in all directions, as they would in an isotropic medium, and so their wave surface is a sphere (Fig. 2.7). The wave surface of the other set (extraordinary rays) is an *ellipsoid of rotation*, which touches the spherical wave surface, corresponding to the same instant of time, at the two points where the axis of rotation emerges. The axis of rotation is the optic axis (which, as already mentioned, has the same direction as the *c* crystallographic axis), and in this direction light travels with a single velocity and does not suffer double refraction.

The ellipsoid may lie either inside or outside the sphere. Figs. 2.9 and 2.10, which depict *principal sections* of the wave surfaces, i.e.

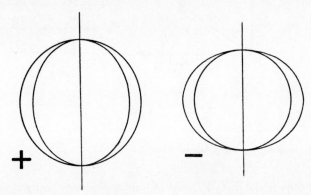

Fig. 2.9. Wave surfaces of   Fig. 2.10. Wave surfaces of
a positive uniaxial crystal.   a negative uniaxial crystal.

sections containing the optic axis, illustrate these two possibilities respectively. In calcite, since the extraordinary rays are faster than the ordinary rays (except along the optic axis where the distinction between the two vanishes), the wave surfaces are related as in Fig. 2.10. Such crystals are said to have *negative* birefringence. Those with wave surfaces related as in Fig. 2.9, for example quartz, are said to have *positive* birefringence.

Ray Velocity and Wave Velocity. We have already noted that when the wave surface is spherical, the wave front at any point is perpendicular to the ray which meets the surface at that point (Fig. 2.7). The same is not true in general for extraordinary rays. Thus in Fig. 2.11, which shows a principal section of an extraordinary wave surface, the tangent plane PRP′ is not perpendicular to the ray ORR′, so that the direction in which the wave front corresponding to this ray is to be regarded as travelling, i.e. the direction normal to itself, is different from the ray direction, but is given by ON, the normal to PRP′. ON is called the *wave-front direction, wave direction,* or *wave normal.* The significance of this will perhaps be clearer if we consider a parallel beam of extraordinary rays as in Fig. 2.12. The three-dimensional waves in this have plane wave fronts, but these fronts are not normal to the ray directions, OT_2, $O'T_2'$, $O''T_2''$, etc. If $T_1T_1'T_1''$ is the leading wave

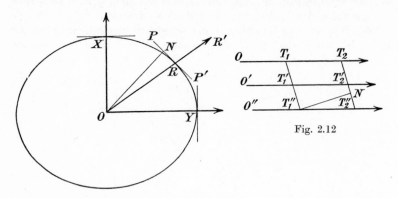

Fig. 2.12

Fig. 2.11. Wave fronts of extraordinary rays.

front at time t_1 and $T_2T_2'T_2''$ that at time t_2, the *ray velocity* is proportional to the distance between the wave fronts measured along the ray directions, i.e. is equal to

$$\frac{T_1T_2}{t_2 - t_1},$$

while the *wave-front velocity,* or *wave velocity* is proportional to the perpendicular distance between the wave fronts, i.e. is equal to

$$\frac{T_1''N}{t_2 - t_1}.$$

In Fig. 2.11 these two velocities are proportional respectively to OR and ON.

This difference between wave direction and ray direction and the associated velocities disappears when the rays travel along either of the principal axes of the elliptic section, e.g. along OX or OY, since in these cases the wave front is perpendicular to the ray, as for ordinary rays.

Huygens' Construction. Once the orientation and form of the wave surfaces in a crystal are known, the directions into which light will be refracted on entering any face or artificial plate of the crystal can be easily determined by means of a geometrical construction due to Huygens, and based on an important principle, enunciated by him, that all points on a wave front can be regarded as sources of secondary

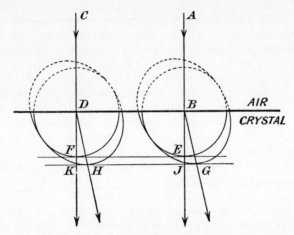

Fig. 2.13

waves, the combinations of which determine the fronts of the waves lying ahead.

Consider first the case of a parallel monochromatic beam, ABCD in Fig. 2.13, incident normally on a plane surface of a uniaxial crystal. BD in the figure is the wave front of the beam at the instant when it reaches the crystal.* According to Huygens' principle we may imagine that secondary waves spread from all points on BD, with velocities in different directions given by the wave surfaces, and that these secondary waves combine to give the wave fronts in the crystal. These wave fronts are simply the tangent planes that are common to the wave surface figures, which we may think of as being constructed around all points on BD.

* For simplicity we are representing here what is actually a three-dimensional problem by means of a plane diagram, and shall continue to do so in giving other examples of Huygens' construction. Since, however, the crystal surface and the wave fronts of the light will always be normal to the plane of the diagram, and so will appear as rectilinear traces, this should cause no confusion.

The figures corresponding to a given instant will be of the same size for, since all the incident rays entered the crystal together, the light will penetrate to the same depth in a given time from all points of entry. The wave fronts in the crystal are therefore parallel to the crystal surface, and in order to find them we need only construct wave surface figures about the two limiting points B and D, as shown in Fig. 2.13. FE, the tangent plane to the spheres, is the wave front of the ordinary beam and HG, the tangent plane to the ellipsoids, the wave front of the extraordinary beam. It goes without saying that the wave surface figures must have the correct orientation with respect to the crystal surface in this construction. In the case shown in the figure the optic axis is inclined at about 45° to the surface, and so the orientation is approximately the same as that shown in Fig. 2.8 *a* for calcite. BEFD is the ordinary refracted beam, and BGDH the extraordinary one. The ray directions in the beams are the same as those of the beams themselves, i.e. parallel to DF or BE for the ordinary rays, and to DH or BG for the extraordinary ones. At first sight this statement appears to be at variance with our picture of rays spreading in all directions into the crystal from all points on BD, but this is not so because it can be shown that rays other than *those travelling along the directions of the beams*, will be destroyed by mutual interference.

It will be noted that the ordinary refracted rays travel in the same direction as the incident rays, as they would do in an isotropic medium, while the extraordinary rays deviate from this direction. *Both wave fronts, ordinary and extraordinary, travel in the same direction, however, i.e. normally to the crystal surface*, since they are parallel to one another and to the crystal surface, and this is the same as the direction of the incident, and ordinary refracted, rays. The velocity of the ordinary refracted rays is proportional to DF or BE, and is the same as that of their wave front. The velocity of the extraordinary rays is proportional to DH or BG, while that of their wave front is proportional to DK or BJ.

There are two cases of perpendicular incidence in uniaxial crystals which should receive special consideration. In the first, Fig. 2.14 *a*, the crystal surface is perpendicular to the optic axis. Here, it is clear, there is no double refraction whatever, and all rays pass through the crystal with the same velocity. In the second, Fig. 2.14 *b*, the crystal surface contains the optic axis. The directions of the extraordinary and ordinary rays coincide and neither deviates from the course of the incident light. The light, however, travels through the crystal as two distinct sets of rays having different velocities, and gives rise to two images of any object viewed in this direction, the one image being immediately above the other. For calcite these two cases were discussed in a different way on p. 66, Fig. 2.8 *b* and *c*.

In Fig. 2.15 a parallel beam ABDC of monochromatic light enters a uniaxial crystal obliquely. More precisely, ABDC represents any longitudinal section of the beam which is perpendicular to the crystal

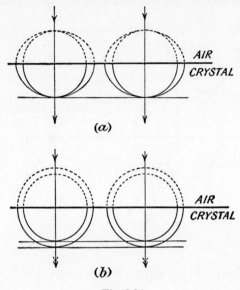

(*a*)

(*b*)

Fig. 2.14

surface. Such sections are said to be in a *plane of incidence* (or, since all such sections are optically equivalent, simply 'in *the* plane of incidence').

The construction for finding the directions of the refracted beams in this case has to take account of the fact that the rays in the incident beam enter the crystal at different times, CD arriving first and AB last. This is done as follows. Let DE be the wave front of the incident beam at the instant when the ray CD reaches the crystal surface. With D as centre describe the wave surfaces in their correct orientation, and on such a scale that they bear the same relation to the velocities of the light in the crystal as BE does to its velocity in air. Let BF and BG represent the planes passing through B, which are perpendicular to ABDC and tangent to the sphere and ellipsoid at F and G respectively. Then DF and DG are, respectively, the directions of the ordinary and extraordinary beams, and BF and BG their wave fronts at the instant when the ray AB is just about to enter the crystal. The construction depends on the fact that the two components of the light travel from D through the distances given by the wave surface figure in the same time as the light travels from E to B in the air.

Consider first the refraction of the ordinary rays. It is clear that this is governed by the same principle as that which determines refraction in an isotropic medium, since in both cases the wave surface is a sphere.

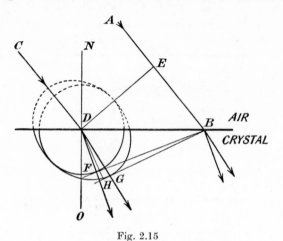

Fig. 2.15

If NO is the normal to the surface of the crystal at D, it may easily be proved that

$$\frac{\sin \text{NDC}}{\sin \text{FDO}} = \frac{\text{BE}}{\text{DF}} = \frac{v}{v'} \qquad . \qquad . \qquad . \qquad . \ 2.10$$

where v is the velocity of the light in air, and v' that of the ordinary rays in the crystal. This may be compared with Equation 2.9 (p. 61), and since v is very nearly equal to c ($c/v = 1{\cdot}00029$ for the sodium D line), we see that *the sine of the angle of incidence* (NDC) *divided by the sine of the angle of refraction* (FDO) *is very nearly equal to the refractive index of the crystal (for ordinary rays)* for light of the particular wavelength in question. Or we may say that this sine ratio is equal to the refractive index *with respect to air*, this being almost the same as the *absolute* refractive index, i.e. the index with respect to a vacuum, as defined by Equation 2.9. For most practical purposes the distinction between the two is of no consequence. We may further note that since the wave surface is a sphere, this sine ratio will be independent of the direction of propagation of the light through the crystal. For isotropic media this constant relationship was first discovered by Snell about 1621, though not actually expressed by him in trigonometrical terms.

The refraction of the extraordinary rays shows important differences in general from that of the ordinary rays. Firstly, the extraordinary rays are not necessarily in the plane of incidence (produced), unlike the ordinary ones, which must always lie in this plane because their wave surface is a sphere. Thus DF in Fig. 2.15 is in the same plane as ABDC. It happens that in this figure the optic axis, and thus a principal section of the ellipsoidal wave surface, lies in the plane of incidence, and in this particular case the extraordinary rays, e.g. DG, do also lie in this plane, but in general the 'bulge' of the ellipsoid might be either in front of or behind the plane of the diagram, in which cases the point of tangency, G, would be similarly displaced from the position shown.

The extraordinary rays also deviate from the law of sines, and in two respects. Not only does the refractive index depend on the direction of the rays, but the sine of the angle of incidence divided by the sine of the angle of refraction is not, in general, equal to the reciprocal of the velocity of the rays in the crystal with respect to that in air, Thus in Fig. 2.15

$$\frac{\sin \text{NDC}}{\sin \text{GDO}} \neq \frac{\text{BE}}{\text{DG}}$$

If, however, instead of considering the ray direction, we consider the *wave normal*, DH, where DH is perpendicular to the plane BG, then it may easily be proved that

$$\frac{\sin \text{NDC}}{\sin \text{HDO}} = \frac{\text{BE}}{\text{DH}}$$

Thus for an extraordinary ray, the sine of the angle of incidence divided by the sine of the angle of refraction of the wave front is equal to the velocity of the ray in air divided by the velocity of its wave front in the crystal. This sine ratio is the extraordinary refractive index of the crystal (strictly, in air) for the particular direction through it, along which the ray travels.

It should be pointed out that this definition of refractive index holds for all rays, whether ordinary or extraordinary. For with ordinary rays the wave-front direction and ray direction coincide, so that it is immaterial which term is used.

The wave normal of an extraordinary ray always lies in the plane of incidence, irrespective of the ray direction, because the wave front is always perpendicular to this plane. Thus in the figure, DH is in the same plane as ABDC (like the ordinary ray DF).

When an extraordinary ray reaches the opposite side of the crystal, its refraction on entering the air is governed by the same principles as those which determined the refraction of the incident rays. Accordingly after passing through a parallel-sided crystal plate, it regains the original direction of the incident light, just like ordinary rays do. It is also important to realise that it loses its 'extraordinary' character, i.e. its wave front becomes perpendicular to the ray direction, because it is now travelling in an isotropic medium, though for labelling purposes in certain problems it is convenient to continue to refer to it as 'the extraordinary ray'.

The Polarisation of Light by Crystals. If the rays emerging from a crystal of Iceland spar be allowed to enter another crystal of the spar, they will, in general, undergo a second double refraction, so that an object viewed through the two crystals will give four images. For certain positions of the two crystals relative to one another, however (not including those in which the rays pass along the optic axes), this does not occur, and only two images, as with a single crystal, are seen. This shows that the rays which emerge from the first crystal are of a different nature from rays of ordinary light, for otherwise they would undergo double refraction at all positions of the second crystal. These facts were known to Huygens, but he was not able to explain them, and the problem remained unsolved until an accidental observation by Malus in 1808 gave the clue. Happening to examine the sunlight reflected from a window through a doubly-refracting crystal, Malus found that when he rotated the crystal about the direction of the light, the two images of the sun disappeared alternately every 90°. This observation may be said to mark the discovery of polarised light, the theory of which was subsequently developed by Fresnel and others. The explanation of Malus's observation is given below.

When light strikes the surface of a transparent isotropic medium such as glass obliquely, it is partly reflected and partly refracted. In general, both the reflected and refracted rays are partially polarised, the former having a maximum amplitude of vibration in the plane perpendicular to the plane of incidence, and the latter a maximum amplitude in the plane of incidence. Brewster (1811) discovered, however, that when the angle between the reflected and refracted rays is 90°, the reflected rays are completely plane-polarised, though the refracted ones are still only partially polarised. This condition is shown in Fig. 2.16 in which the directions of vibration of the reflected and refracted rays are represented by dots (vibrations in and out of the paper), and strokes (vibrations in the plane of the paper) respectively.

If i_p is this particular *polarising angle* of incidence, and r_p the corresponding angle of refraction, it can be shown by simple trigonometry that $\sin i_p/\sin r_p = n$ (the refractive index of the glass) $= \tan i_p$ (Brewster's Law). For ordinary glass, i_p is $ca.57°$.

When ordinary unpolarised light enters a doubly-refracting crystal, the two components into which it is divided (except when it travels along an optic axis) are *plane-polarised* and *have vibration planes which are at right angles to one another.* This behaviour is predicted by the electromagnetic theory, as applied to anisotropic media. When the light is incident normally, the vibration planes of the two components make traces on the crystal surface which are at right angles to one another. These traces define the vibration directions, since the vibrations of extra-

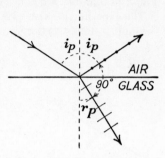

Fig. 2.16. Brewster's Law.

ordinary rays are believed to be parallel to the wave front like those of ordinary rays, and both wave fronts are parallel to the crystal surface (see Fig. 2.13). The amplitudes of the two components are the same.

When, however, the entering light is itself plane-polarised, the result depends on the orientation of its vibration direction with respect to those permitted by the crystal. Fig. 2.17 shows three possibilities. COD and EOF are the vibration directions within the crystal, and AOB is that of the incident light, OA (or OB) representing its amplitude. The light waves are supposed to be travelling normally to the paper. In *b*, AOB makes some arbitrary angle with COD and EOF, and the light is then resolved along the two crystal directions according to the same principle as that underlying the parallelogram of forces. OC′ (or OD′) is the amplitude of the component vibrating along COD, and OE′ (or OF′) that of the component vibrating along EOF. In *a*, AOB is coincident with EOF, and there is no component along COD; the light is transmitted with a single vibration direction, and with the same amplitude, OA, as that of the incident light. In *c*, the situation is similar, except that all the light is transmitted with its vibrations along COD.

It will be noted that in *b* the two components, where they overlap, will combine to give elliptically polarised light according to the principles given on pp. 57–61. It is, however, sometimes convenient to disregard this combination and treat problems in which this situation arises

simply in terms of the two component vibrations, as will appear later.
Malus's observation may now be explained. The light must have been
reflected from the window at, or near, the polarising angle, so that it
was essentially plane-polarised. The disappearance of the two images
alternately would occur at positions of the crystal corresponding to
Fig. 2.17 *a* and *c*, which are 90° apart.

The experiments with two crystals of Iceland spar, mentioned at the
beginning of this section are explained as follows. If the two crystals

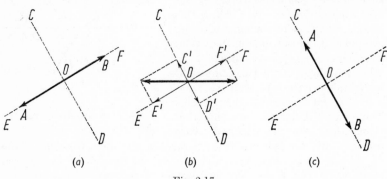

(a)   (b)   (c)

Fig. 2.17

have different orientations, each component emerging from the first
will encounter the second as in Fig. 2.17 *b*, and will undergo a second
double refraction, so that four images will be seen. (It is understood
that we are dealing with highly birefringent crystals which are thick
enough to ensure complete separation of the emergent ordinary and
extraordinary beams.) On the other hand, if the crystals have the same
orientation, the vibration directions of the beams emerging from the
first will be parallel to those permitted by the second, so that there
will be no further resolution, and the effect will be simply the same as
that of passing the light through a single crystal of thickness equal to
the sum of those of the two.

Vibration Directions in Uniaxial Crystals. The vibration directions
in uniaxial crystals are given by the following simple rules:

1. *an extraordinary ray always vibrates in the plane containing the
ray and the optic axis, i.e. in a principal section of the ellipsoid of revolution,*
and

2. *an ordinary ray always vibrates at right angles to the plane containing
the ray and the optic axis.*

As already stated, the vibration direction is parallel to the wave front for both kinds of rays.

These rules are illustrated in Fig. 2.18, which shows a principal section of a negative uniaxial wave surface figure. (There is no need to show also a positive wave surface figure, since the only difference is that the ellipsoid is inside the sphere in that case.)

OR is an extraordinary ray travelling in an arbitrary direction. The vibrations are in the plane ROX, where OX is the optic axis, and are parallel to the wave front RN. This is denoted by the strokes across

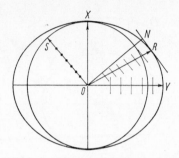

Fig. 2.18. Vibration directions in negative uniaxial crystal.

OR, which are parallel to RN and at right angles to the wave normal ON. OY is an extraordinary ray travelling in the equatorial circular section of the wave surface. Here ray and wave directions coincide, and the vibration direction is at right angles to the ray.

OS is an ordinary ray travelling in an arbitrary direction. The vibration direction is at right angles to the plane SOX, and at right angles to the ray, as with all ordinary rays. This is denoted by the dots on OS.

A ray travelling along OX (the optic axis) can vibrate in any plane parallel to OX, as if it were in an isotropic medium.

If the radii of the figure represent velocities of the light with respect to its velocity in a vacuum (or, as a near approximation, in air), the refractive indices are given by the reciprocals of the lengths of the lines representing the wave normals. Thus, for example, the extraordinary refractive index for light travelling along the ray direction OR with wave direction ON is 1/ON.

The Indicatrix. In the preceding section we have seen that the wave surface figure for a uniaxial crystal, in conjunction with the rules giving the vibration directions, affords a complete description of its optical properties for light of the wave-length concerned, when we remember also that the optic axis has the same direction as the *c* crystallographic axis. The optical properties can, however, be more conveniently represented by means of a single-surfaced figure, the *optical indicatrix*, which was derived in 1891 by L. Fletcher* from the extraordinary wave surface. The essential difference between the wave surface figure and the indicatrix is that in the former the radii represent directions of

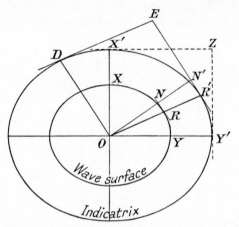

Fig. 2.19. Derivation of indicatrix from wave surface.

propagation, along any one of which (except the optic axis) two components with different velocities can travel, while in the latter the radii are directions of *vibration*, with any one of which one refractive index, and one only, is associated.

In Fig. 2.19 let XRY be the extraordinary wave surface (shown for simplicity in principal section as an ellipse), the radii of which represent actual velocities of the light with respect to that in a vacuum. Let OX be the semi-axis of rotation (optic axis), and OY a radius of the circular section. Let the radius OR be an extraordinary ray travelling in any other direction.

On the axes OX and OY produced, construct another ellipsoid of rotation, X'R'Y' (shown in the figure in principal section), with OX' as the axis of rotation, and with axial lengths OX' = 1/OY and OY' = 1/OX. This is Fletcher's indicatrix, which from its construction, is concentric with, and geometrically similar to, the extraordinary wave surface.

* *Min. Mag.*, 1891, **9**, 278.

Produce the ray OR to meet the indicatrix at R'. Draw the radius OD in the same principal section of the indicatrix as OR' and conjugate* to it. Complete the parallelogram R'ODE. Draw the wave normal ON of the ray OR and produce it to meet R'E at N'.

Now since the parallelogram R'ODE is formed by conjugate radii, its area is equal to that of the rectangle OX'ZY' (where X'Z and Y'Z are the tangents to the section of the indicatrix at X' and Y' respectively), for OX' and OY' are also conjugate radii:

i.e. area of R'ODE = ON'.OD = OX'.OY',

or
$$OD = \frac{OX'.OY'}{ON'}.$$

But since the wave surface and indicatrix are similar,

$$\frac{ON'}{ON} = \frac{OY'}{OY},$$

or
$$ON' = \frac{OY'.ON.}{OY}.$$

Substituting in preceding equations

$$OD = \frac{OX'.OY}{ON} = \frac{1}{ON}\left(\text{since } OX' = \frac{1}{OY}\right).$$

But 1/ON is the refractive index of the crystal for the ray OR. It follows therefore that the refractive index for any extraordinary ray, the direction of which is represented by a radius of the indicatrix, is given by the length of the conjugate radius lying in the same principal section. In the case under consideration, a ray travelling in the direction OR' has a refractive index equal to OD, the conjugate radius to OR' in the same principal section. It also follows that the refractive index of a wave front travelling in any direction through the centre of the indicatrix is equal to the radius of the indicatrix which is perpendicular to, and in the same principal section as, the line of direction. In the present case, the refractive index of the wave front travelling along ON' is OD, the angle N'OD being a right angle, and OD being in the same principal section of the indicatrix as ON'. Further, the line OD, besides giving by its length the above information, gives by its direction the vibration direction of the ray OR', and of the wave front

* Conjugate radii are such that the tangents to the ellipse at the extremities of the radii form a parallelogram with them. For a given ellipse, this parallelogram has a constant area.

travelling along ON′, for, as already stated, an extraordinary ray vibrates in the plane of the principal section of the wave surface in which it lies, and this section occupies the same plane as the principal section of the indicatrix in which the ray lies.

Consider now how the indicatrix expresses the vibration direction and refractive index of an ordinary ray. It has been shown that the refractive index of such rays is independent of their direction, and

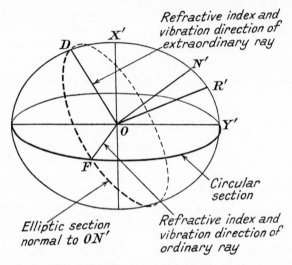

Fig. 2.20. Negative uniaxial indicatrix.

in the present case is equal to 1/OX. This in turn is equal to OY′, which is a radius of the circular section of the indicatrix. The vibration plane, as already stated, is normal to the principal section in which the ray lies, and the vibration direction may therefore be represented by any line drawn from the ray and perpendicular to this principal section. Such a line is either of the two radii of the circular section, which are perpendicular to the ray, and the choice of either of these has the advantage that its length represents the refractive index of the ray. Thus in the case of an ordinary ray (or wave front) travelling along ON′ in Fig. 2.19, its refractive index and vibration direction are represented by a line drawn from O normal to the plane of the paper, and of length equal to OY′. This is the line OF in Fig. 2.20, in which the indicatrix is drawn in perspective. The other letters in this figure have the same significance as in Fig. 2.19.

We have seen that the properties of the extraordinary wave front travelling along ON' are represented by OD, those of the ordinary wave front travelling in the same direction by OF. Now it may be shown that OD and OF are the semi-axes (i.e. smallest and greatest radii) of the elliptic section* of the indicatrix which is normal to ON' and passes through O. Since ON' represents any direction, it follows that *the refractive indices and vibration directions of the two wave fronts (ordinary and extraordinary) which can travel along any direction in the crystal, are given by the semi-axes of the elliptic section of the indicatrix which passes through its centre, and to which the direction in question is normal.* The one semi-axis is always a radius of the circular section, and this is the one which refers to the ordinary ray.

There are two special cases to be considered. The first is that in which the wave fronts travel along OX'. This is the optic axial direction, and the section of the indicatrix normal to this is a circle, which of course has no smallest and greatest radii. This represents the fact that the light can vibrate in any direction, and does not suffer double refraction. The second case is that in which the wave fronts travel along OY' (or any other radius of the circular section). The elliptic section of the indicatrix normal to this direction has the special feature that it is that section in which the difference between the semi-axes is a maximum—the semi-axes being in fact those of the indicatrix itself, namely OX' and OY'. In this case, then, the crystal shows its maximum double refraction. These are the two cases which were considered from the standpoint of Huygens' construction in Fig. 2.14 *a* and *b*, p. 71.

The refractive indices corresponding to OX' and OY' are conventionally denoted by ε and ω. Thus ω is the refractive index of the ordinary ray, and ε is the extreme value of the refractive index of the extraordinary ray, i.e. the value which differs most widely from ω. In negative crystals $\varepsilon < \omega$, whilst in positive crystals $\varepsilon > \omega$ (cf. Figs. 2.9 and 2.10, p. 67). The sign of the double refraction is thus given by $\varepsilon - \omega$.

In Fig. 2.13, p. 69, the fact is illustrated that when a ray of light enters a plane crystal surface perpendicularly, the two wave fronts travel through the crystal in the same direction as the incident ray, although the two *rays* in the crystal pursue, in general, different paths. In practice, crystals are usually examined under such, or nearly such conditions, and it is for this reason that attention has been mainly drawn to this case in the above treatment of the indicatrix. When,

* All sections of an ellipsoid of rotation which pass through its centre are ellipses, with the exception of the circular section at right angles to the axis of rotation.

however, the incident ray is not perpendicular to the crystal surface, neither the two rays formed from it inside the crystal, nor their wave fronts, travel in the same direction as each other (see Fig. 2.15, p. 72). Nevertheless they are always polarised in planes at right angles to one another.

BIAXIAL CRYSTALS

As already stated on p. 48, crystals of the orthorhombic, monoclinic, and triclinic systems are *biaxial,* i.e. possess two directions which correspond very closely to the optic axis in uniaxial crystals. In general, when a ray of monochromatic light enters a biaxial crystal, it is divided into two rays polarised in planes at right angles to one another, but neither of these rays obeys the ordinary laws of refraction; in other words, two extraordinary rays are formed. Passing through any point in the crystal, however, there are three planes at right angles to one another, each of which is characterised by the fact that one of the two rays which can travel in any direction in it has a constant refractive index. These three planes are defined by three mutually perpendicular axes which are, respectively, the vibration directions of rays having the maximum, the minimum, and a particular intermediate refractive index.

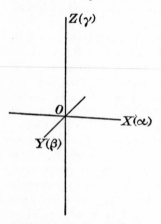

Fig. 2.21. Principal vibration directions of a biaxial crystal.

Let these three axes for a given crystal and a defined wave-length of light be represented by OX, OY, and OZ in Fig. 2.21, OX being the vibration direction for rays having the smallest refractive index in the crystal, OZ the vibration direction for rays having the greatest refractive index, and OY the vibration direction perpendicular to OX and OZ, and corresponding therefore to a particular intermediate refractive index. These three indices are usually referred to as α, γ and β* respectively, and these symbols have been included in Fig. 2.21 adjacent to the axes to which they refer.

* The N_p, N_g, N_m of some American authors. The subscripts mean 'petty', 'greatest', and 'mean' respectively. More recently the symbols N_x, N_z, and N_y have come into use.

Consider now rays travelling in the plane XOY through O. In any such direction, two rays can travel, and one of them vibrates along OZ (i.e. normal to the plane), and has the constant refractive index γ, whilst the other vibrates in the plane, and its refractive index depends on its direction as follows: when it is travelling along OY, it vibrates along OX and its refractive index is α; when it is travelling along OX, it vibrates along OY and its refractive index is β; for all other directions of travel its vibration direction is intermediate between OX and OY, and its refractive index is intermediate between α and β.

The behaviour of rays passing through O in the planes YOZ and XOZ is exactly analogous to the above. In YOZ one ray always vibrates

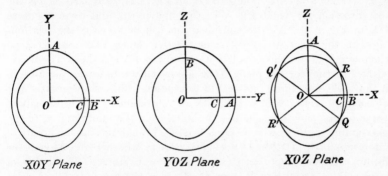

XOY Plane   YOZ Plane   XOZ Plane

Fig. 2.22. Principal sections of biaxial wave surfaces.

along OX with refractive index α, whilst the index of the other varies between β and γ, being β when it is travelling along OZ and vibrating along OY, and γ when it is travelling along OY and vibrating along OZ. In the plane XOZ, one ray always vibrates along OY with refractive index β, and that of the other varies between α and γ, being α when it is travelling along OZ and vibrating along OX, and γ when it is travelling along OX and vibrating along OZ.

In each of these three planes, then, one ray behaves as an ordinary ray. Its wave direction is the same as its own direction, and the section of its wave surface made by the plane is a circle. The corresponding wave-surface section for the other ray is an ellipse, the semi-axes of which coincide with the two axes defining the plane (e.g. OY and OX in the case of the plane XOY). For this ray, the wavefront direction is coincident with the ray direction when, and only when, it is travelling along these axes.

Fig. 2.22 gives the wave-surface sections made by these three planes.

OA, OB and OC represent the velocities of rays travelling along the three axes of Fig. 2.21 with refractive indices α, β and γ respectively. Therefore OA $= 1/\alpha$, OB $= 1/\beta$ and OC $= 1/\gamma$, and OA $>$ OB $>$ OC. The positions of the three axes of Fig. 2.21 with respect to the wave-surface sections are indicated by broken lines in Fig. 2.22. In the section made by the plane XOY, the circle lies entirely inside the ellipse, for the ray which travels with constant refractive index, and therefore constant velocity, has the largest index (γ), and therefore the smallest velocity (OC), offered by the crystal. OC is therefore the radius of the circle, and the major and minor semi-axes of the ellipse are OA and OB respectively. OA is the ray direction for which the refractive index is α; it therefore corresponds to OY in Fig. 2.21. Similarly OB is the ray direction for which the refractive index is β, and corresponds to OX in Fig. 2.21. A little consideration will make clear the relations between the wave-surface sections for the planes YOZ and XOZ on the one hand, and the axes OX, OY and OZ on the other. The wave-surface section for the plane XOZ is especially interesting, because in it the circle and ellipse intersect at four points. This is because the ray of constant velocity has the index of refraction β, the intermediate value, whilst the other changes its index from the minimum, α, to the maximum, γ. Rays which travel from O through any of the points of intersection (e.g. OR) have the same velocity whether they have wave fronts corresponding to the circle or to the ellipse. The point of intersection opposite to R, namely R', is in the same straight line as OR, and similarly QOQ' is a straight line, where Q and Q' are the other two points of intersection. There are thus two directions, ROR' and QOQ', through the crystal along which all rays travel with the same velocity. These two directions are known variously as *secondary optic axes*, *lines of single ray velocity*, or *optic biradials*.

The complete wave-surface figure is shown in Fig. 2.23. For the present purpose it is sufficient to note that it has three planes of symmetry, which are the three sections shown in Fig. 2.22, and that, as can in a general way be gathered from these sections, it is a double-surfaced figure, the surfaces meeting one another at the four points R, R', Q and Q', where the secondary optic axes emerge. These points form the bottoms of four funnel-shaped depressions on the outer shell of the figure. In consequence of this, there are innumerable planes tangent to the figure at each of these points. Thus, for example, taking the XOZ section at R (Fig. 2.24), there is the plane UW, tangent and normal to the circle, and another, ST, tangent and normal to the ellipse. These planes are the wave fronts of the two rays travelling along OR, which belong respectively to the circular and elliptical parts

of the XOZ section. They are normal to the section because the latter
is a plane of symmetry of the wave-surface figure. For any other
section of the figure containing OR, there is a corresponding pair of
planes tangent to the two sides of the depression, and these planes are
the wave fronts of the two rays which travel in the section along OR.

It follows that a ray which travels along OR can have a wave front
corresponding to any one of these tangent planes, the actual one in

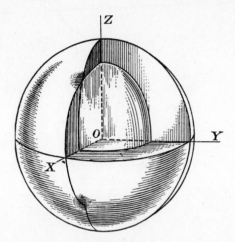

Fig. 2.23

any particular case being determined by the respective inclinations of
the incident ray and OR to the crystal surface. If, for any given inclination of OR to the crystal surface, *all* the incident rays which are
refracted along OR are considered, it is found that they lie on the
surface of a converging cone; consequently they emerge on the other
side of the crystal as a diverging hollow cone. This emergent cone is
represented by MRL in Fig. 2.24. The ray RL is that which, in the
crystal, had the wave front UW. It therefore belongs to the circular
part of the XOZ section (see above), and like all other rays in this
part, vibrates at right angles to the section. The ray RM, diametrically
opposite to RL on the cone, is that which, in the crystal, had the wave
front ST. It therefore belongs to the elliptical part of the XOZ section,
and so vibrates in the plane of the section. The vibration directions
of these two rays are represented respectively by dots and strokes in
the figure.

The other rays in the cone are also polarised, but each ray has a different vibration direction, this property varying continuously as we pass round the cone, and all possible vibration directions being represented. Light which travels along a secondary optic axis, then, may vibrate in any plane.

The phenomenon just considered is known as *external conical refraction*. Actually the cone is not observed in practice, for it must be

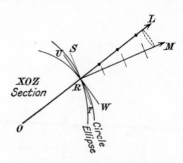

Fig. 2.24. External conical refraction.

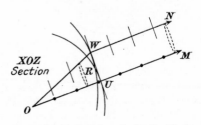

Fig. 2.25. Internal conical refraction.

remembered that the secondary optic axis is indeed a *direction*, and not a single line through the crystal, so that when a real beam of light is passed in this direction, the light emerging is the result of the overlapping of innumerable cones.

Consider again the XOZ section at one of the points of intersection of the circle and ellipse, R (Fig. 2.25). Let UW be the common tangent to the circle (at U) and to the ellipse (at W). Now the form of the complete wave-surface figure is such that the plane which contains UW, and which is normal to the XOZ section, is tangent to the wave surface all round R, the line of tangency being a circle, and U and W being two opposite points on this circle. It follows therefore that all members of the hollow cone of rays travelling from O to points on this circular ring of tangency have the same wave front, i.e. their wave-front velocities and, therefore, their refractive indices are identical. The direction in which this common wave front travels is that of the ray OU, for this ray is perpendicular to the wave front. OU is therefore called a *direction of single wave velocity*. OU is also perpendicular to the tangent plane covering the depression in the wave surface opposite to R, namely R′ in Fig. 2.22, and similarly there is a direction which is perpendicular to the tangent planes covering the two depressions Q and Q′ (Fig. 2.22), so that there are two directions of single wave velocity in the crystal. These two directions are also known as *primary optic axes, optic binormals*, or, simply (and usually), *optic axes*.

The ray OU (Fig. 2.25) belongs to the circular part of the XOZ section, and consequently vibrates in a direction perpendicular to the section. On the opposite side of the cone of rays having the same wave velocity as OU, there is the ray OW which belongs to the elliptical part of the XOZ section, and therefore vibrates in the plane of the section. These vibration directions are shown in the figure by dots and strokes respectively. The other rays in the cone are also polarised, but each ray vibrates in a different direction which varies continuously as we pass round the cone, just as in the case of the cone of rays which emerge from a secondary optic axis.

If a parallel beam of unpolarised light enters a crystal plate at perpendicular incidence, the surface of the plate being perpendicular to a primary optic axis, Huygens' construction shows (Fig. 2.26) that each ray as it enters the crystal is refracted into a hollow cone of rays, which, on emerging on the opposite side of the crystal, forms a hollow cylinder. All the rays travelling through the crystal have the same wave velocity and therefore the same refractive index. Thus in the figure the rays AB and A′B′ form the cones BDE and B′D′E′ inside the crystal, and the cylinders DEHG and D′E′H′G′ outside the crystal, respectively. In similar circumstances, the cone UOW in Fig. 2.25 would form the cylinder MUWN. Light emerges from the crystal vibrating in all directions, as it was before it entered the crystal, but having undergone what is termed *internal conical* refraction.

If the light is polarised before it enters the crystal, the other circumstances being the same as in the preceding paragraph, the vibration direction of the light is not altered by its passage through the crystal, but its ray direction in the crystal is determined by its vibration direction. Thus in Fig. 2.26, if the ray AB is vibrating in the plane of the paper, i.e. in the plane of the XOZ section, it will travel through the crystal in the direction BE. If, on the other hand, it is vibrating in the plane perpendicular to the paper, it will travel along BD, i.e. without deviation. For other vibration planes it will travel along the appropriate side of the cone BDE, between BE and BD.

The properties shown by the single optic axis in uniaxial crystals are thus divided between two sets of directions in biaxial crystals. The primary optic axes possess the property of single wave velocity,

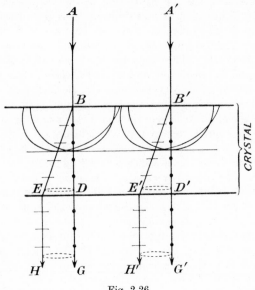

Fig. 2.26

the secondary optic axes that of single ray velocity. For practical purposes, however, it is only the primary optic axes which are of importance, and it is these directions which behave similarly to the optic axis of uniaxial crystals in ordinary interference phenomena (see, however, p. 182). To illustrate the truth of this statement, let us compare the case considered in Fig. 2.26 with that in which parallel light at normal incidence enters a crystal cut normal to a secondary optic axis (Fig. 2.27). Huygens' construction shows that in the latter case two beams polarised in planes at right angles to one another are produced. In other words, the light behaves no differently from the general case of light entering an anisotropic medium.

The angular difference between the primary and secondary optic axes increases with the birefringence of the crystal (i.e. the value of

$\gamma - \alpha$), and with the value of the acute angle between the secondary optic axes. In most inorganic crystals it is considerably less than 1°, an exceptional case being that of orthorhombic sulphur ($\gamma - \alpha = 0 \cdot 29$) in which it is more than 3°. In the preceding diagrams it has

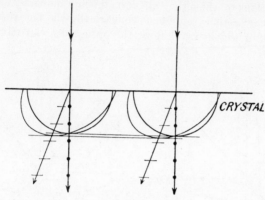

Fig. 2.27

been much exaggerated for the sake of clearness, and, consequently, so have the cones of inner and outer conical refraction.

The Biaxial Indicatrix. This is a triaxial ellipsoid, constructed on the three axes OX, OY and OZ of Fig. 2.21, their lengths, for this purpose, being such that they represent the refractive indices to which they respectively refer, when regarded as directions of vibration. Thus, $OX = \alpha$, $OY = \beta$ and $OZ = \gamma$. Fig. 2.28 shows such an indicatrix. All sections of the indicatrix passing through its centre are, with two exceptions shortly to be dealt with, ellipses, and, just as in the case of the uniaxial indicatrix, *the semi-axes of any such elliptic section give the vibration directions and refractive indices of the two wave fronts which can travel in a direction normal to the section.* Thus in Fig. 2.28, let ON represent a given direction, and let OL and OM be the semi-axes of the elliptic section (shown by a broken line) which is normal to ON. Then OL and OM represent the vibration directions and refractive indices of the two wave fronts which can travel along ON.

Consider now all sections of the indicatrix which have OY as a common semi-axis. The value of the other semi-axis in these sections varies from OX to OZ, and somewhere between these limits it must be equal to OY, since OY is intermediate in length between OX and OZ. In this case, then, the two 'semi-axes' of the section are equal, and it is in fact a circle. There are two such circular sections, equally inclined to OZ. The two directions normal to these two sections are the primary optic axes, or optic axes, with which we have already dealt. They are represented by UOU' and VOV' in Fig. 2.29, the circular sections to which they are normal being shown by broken lines. These circular sections represent geometrically the fact that rays, the wave fronts of which travel along the optic axes, can vibrate in any

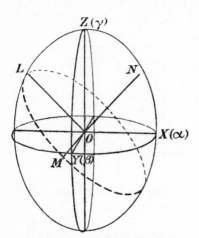

Fig. 2.28. Biaxial indicatrix.

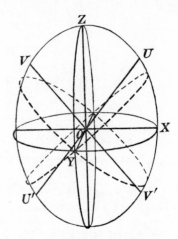

Fig. 2.29. Biaxial indicatrix showing circular sections and optic axes.

plane, and that they all have the same refractive index, which, since OY is the radius of the circles, is β.

From the above it will be seen that the optic axes necessarily lie in the XOZ, or $\alpha\gamma$ section of the indicatrix, which is therefore called the *optic axial plane*. The angles between the optic axes are bisected by the indicatrix axes OX (α) and OZ (γ), the one which bisects the acute angle (commonly called the *optic axial angle* and denoted by 2V) being termed the *acute bisectrix*, or *first median line* (Bx$_a$), and the other the *obtuse bisectrix*, or *second median line* (Bx$_o$). When γ is the acute bisectrix the crystal is said to be *positive*, and when α is the acute bisectrix the crystal is said to be *negative*. These two cases are distinguished in Fig. 2.30, which shows XOZ sections of positive and negative indicatrices.

It is helpful to remember that, *except when* 2V *is near to* 90°, β is (i) nearer to α than to γ in a positive crystal, and (ii) nearer to γ than to α

in a negative crystal. The exact relation between α, β, γ and 2V will be given in Chapter 5 (p. 234).

The negative *uniaxial* indicatrix (see p. 80) can be regarded as a negative biaxial indicatrix in which the optic axial angle is zero. The former is thus the limiting case of the latter in the direction of decreasing

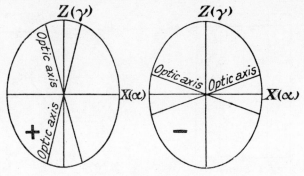

Fig. 2.30

optic axial angle. Similarly the positive uniaxial indicatrix may be regarded as the limiting case of a positive biaxial indicatrix.

ORIENTATION AND DISPERSION OF THE INDICATRIX

The orientation and dispersion of the indicatrix are governed by the cardinal principle that the symmetry of the crystal determines the symmetry of the optical, and other physical properties. It should be noted that as far as optical properties are concerned, it is the symmetry of the holohedral class of the system to which the crystal belongs which is determinative, or in other words, the symmetry of the Bravais lattice. This is necessarily so because a beam of light cannot be unsymmetrical about its direction of propagation, so that if, for example, the crystal belongs to a class in which a given plane is not one of symmetry, whereas it is so in the holohedral class, the optical properties will still be symmetrical about this plane. Thus if we construct the indicatrix about the origin of the crystallographic axes, its orientation for the different crystal systems is as follows:

In uniaxial crystals (tetragonal, trigonal, and hexagonal) the optic axis for light of all wave-lengths coincides with the c crystallographic axis.

In orthorhombic crystals the three axes of the indicatrix coincide with the three crystallographic axes, whatever the wave-length.

In monoclinic crystals one axis of the indicatrix, but any one, coincides with the b crystallographic axis, no matter what the wave-length. The other two indicatrix axes therefore lie in the

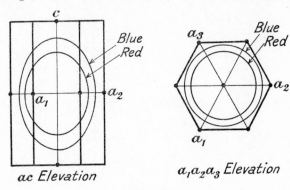

ac Elevation $a_1 a_2 a_3$ *Elevation*

Tetragonal.

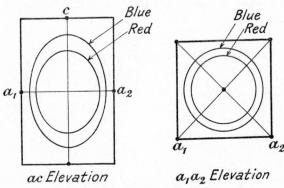

ac Elevation $a_1 a_2$ *Elevation*

Trigonal and Hexagonal.

Fig. 2.31. Orientation and dispersion of the indicatrix in uniaxial crystals.

ac plane (i.e. the symmetry plane in the holohedral class), but anywhere in that plane, their positions depending on the wave-length.

In triclinic crystals the orientation and dispersion may be in any direction whatever.

The above facts are presented graphically in Figs. 2.31 and 2.32, in which the crystals of the various systems are represented by simple prism and pinacoid forms. Normal dispersion (p. 61) over the whole spectrum is assumed, so that the indicatrix for blue light is shown as being larger than that for red light.

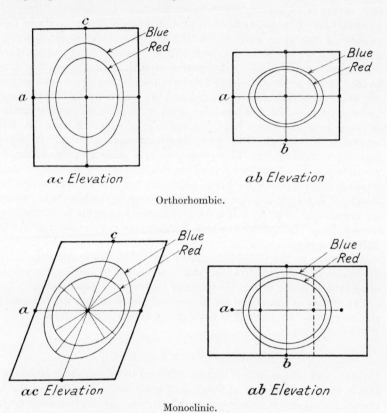

Fig. 2.32. Orientation and dispersion of the indicatrix in biaxial crystals.

(A diagram for the triclinic case is not given because of the completely unsymmetrical orientation of the indicatrix in crystals of this system.)

From the foregoing it will be seen that the dispersion of any anisotropic crystal is made up of one or more of the following elements of dispersion:

(a) Dispersion of each principal index;
(b) Dispersion of the birefringence, i.e. of $(\gamma - \alpha)$ or $(\varepsilon - \omega)$;
(c) Dispersion of the directions of the indicatrix axes.

For the whole range of the visible spectrum, (a) and (b) commonly affect only the second decimal place (at least in inorganic crystals; but see p. 181), and (b) is usually much smaller than (a), whilst (c) only occurs in monoclinic and triclinic crystals. In all biaxial crystals, however, the disproportionate dispersion of α, β and γ leads to dispersion of the optic axes which, though often very small, amounts in some cases to large angles, and even to a change in the orientation of the optic axial plane, quite apart from any shift of this plane due to (c). Thus the orthorhombic mineral brookite has optic axial angles which are considerable in both red and blue light, but the optic axial plane is (001) in the first case and (010) in the second. For an intermediate yellowish-green light the optic axial angle is zero, i.e. the crystal is uniaxial for this wave-length, though it is still morphologically orthorhombic. This phenomenon is known as *crossed-axial-plane dispersion*. Another effect of dispersion observed in some crystals is *change in the optical sign*. For example, the uniaxial mineral torbernite (air-dried to $8H_2O$), is positive in red light, negative in blue light, whilst for green light (5150 Å) it is isotropic Another example is afforded by *trans*-stilbene (monoclinic), which is positive for wave-lengths above 4070 Å and negative for shorter wave-lengths.

Alteration in the temperature of a crystal is also accompanied by dispersion of the indicatrix, but this is too small to affect microscopic observations made within the range of laboratory temperatures.

The effects of dispersion on the optical phenomena observed under the microscope are treated in more detail in Chapters 4 and 5.

ABSORBING CRYSTALS

Crystals and glasses which appear coloured by transmitted light owe this to the fact that they absorb one or more bands of wave-lengths in the visible spectrum to an appreciable degree. Absorption consists in a progressive decline in the amplitude, and therefore the intensity, of the light as it penetrates more and more deeply into the medium, the energy thus lost being in most cases converted into heat. The fundamental reason for this phenomenon is given later (p. 102).

In anisotropic crystals the absorption depends on the vibration direction of the light. Thus the two polarised components into which a ray of monochromatic light is resolved on entry suffer in general different degrees of absorption, and when white light is used the transmission colours for the two components may therefore differ considerably. This phenomenon is known as *pleochroism*, and observations on this constitute the most important practical application of absorption in the study of crystals under the polarising microscope. It is dealt with in more detail in Chapter 4. In coloured cubic crystals and glasses the absorption is the same for all directions of propagation, this being merely another manifestation of their optical isotropy.

For any given wave-length the absorption in a cubic crystal or a glass, or for a particular direction of vibration in an anisotropic crystal, follows *Lambert's Law*, namely

$$I_x = I_0 e^{-\kappa x} \quad . \quad . \quad . \quad . \quad . \quad 2.11$$

where I_0 is the intensity of the light entering the medium, I_x its intensity after passing through a thickness x, and κ is a constant called the *absorption coefficient*,* or *absorption modulus*, which has the meaning that for each unit of thickness ($x = 1$) the fractional reduction in intensity, I_x/I_0, is equal to $e^{-\kappa}$, or $1/e^\kappa$. The significance of this may be illustrated by an example. Suppose that x is measured in microns (10^{-3} mm.) and that for a thickness of 1 micron ($x = 1$) the intensity is reduced to one half, i.e. $I_x/I_0 = e^{-\kappa} = 0.5$. (This corresponds to a value of κ of 0.69.) For a thickness of 20 microns (0.02 mm.), which is a typical value for crystals of a size suitable for study under the microscope, I_x/I_0 would be $(0.5)^{20} = ca.\ 10^{-6}$, which is so small that the material would be practically opaque. If, however, I_x/I_0 for 1 micron were 0.9, it would be reduced only to $(0.9)^{20} = ca.\ 10^{-1}$ for 20 microns, and this degree of transmission would be clearly apparent to the eye, unless the incident intensity were extremely weak.

If white light is passed through an absorbing crystal or glass and is then analysed by means of a spectrometer, an *absorption spectrum* is obtained. This may be described as the spectrum of white light with a part or parts blacked out, corresponding to the band or bands of wave-lengths absorbed. As we pass across an absorption band the absorption coefficient rises to a maximum and then declines as the other limit of the band is approached. As judged by eye alone the width of an absorption band increases with increase in the thickness of the specimen, and its edges shade off. This is because of the large effect of thickness on the apparent opacity, when the absorption is considerable, as demonstrated by the above example.

* An alternative form of Lambert's Law which is more convenient to use in certain theoretical treatments is

$$I_x = I_0 e^{-\frac{4\pi}{\lambda_0} kx},$$

where λ_0 is the wave-length *in vacuo*, and k is a constant having the meaning that when $x = \lambda_0$, the fractional reduction in intensity is $1/e^{4\pi k}$. The term 'coefficient of absorption' is applied to this constant by many writers, and there is no general agreement on this point of nomenclature.

An absorption band may be situated at the blue, or the red, end of the spectrum and overlap into the ultra-violet or infra-red regions respectively. All substances have absorption bands somewhere in the range of electromagnetic radiations (p. 54), whether they have any in the visible region or not.

Anomalous Dispersion. As mentioned on p. 61 the refractive index (n) of a transparent medium increases with decrease in the wave-length.

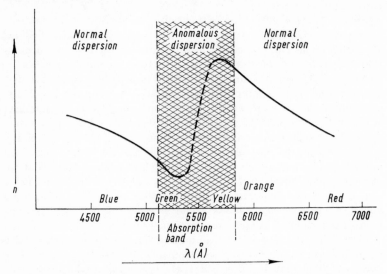

Fig. 2.33. Anomalous dispersion at an absorption band.

This relationship (*normal dispersion*) follow very nearly *Cauchy's equation*, $n = A + B/\lambda^2$, where A and B are constants.* The change of refractive index in passing through an absorption band is, however, quite different, and is illustrated in Fig. 2.33 by a hypothetical case in which there is absorption in the green-yellow region of the spectrum. With increasing wave-length, n passes through a minimum and then rises to a maximum before entering another range of normal dispersion. In the case shown, this results in the index for orange light being greater than that for blue. The curve is shown as a broken line over the middle part of the band, because it is not usually possible to determine the index in this region owing to the strong absorption.

* A more exact form of the equation is $n = A + B/\lambda^2 + C/\lambda^4$, where C is another constant.

This behaviour is known as *anomalous dispersion*, a description dating from the original discovery of the phenomenon, and now rather unsatisfactory, since the theoretical reasons for it are well understood. The reader who is interested in these may refer to one of the advanced works cited at the end of the book.

The Indicatrix for Absorbing Crystals. The optical properties of an absorbing crystal for a given wave-length are described by surfaces corresponding to the wave surfaces and indicatrix of a transparent crystal, with the addition of another surface giving the absorption coefficient in different directions. These surfaces are not ellipsoids and the ones for biaxial crystals cannot be represented geometrically since they are defined in terms of complex numbers, though they do make geometrically representable traces on the optical symmetry planes, i.e. the planes corresponding to XOY, YOZ, and XOZ in Figs. 2.22 and 2.23. (The relationship between optical and morphological symmetry is the same as for transparent crystals; see p. 92.) For general directions of propagation in biaxial crystals an entering ray of light is resolved into two elliptically polarised components of equal ellipticity, with the major axes of the ellipses at right angles to one another, but rays travelling in the optical symmetry planes or in uniaxial crystals are plane-polarised as in transparent crystals. Further information about the optical properties of absorbing crystals will be found in the relevant works cited at the end of the book.

Having said all this we may go on to point out that the light which contributes to the *visible* microscopic image of a coloured crystal of a thickness suitable for study in this way (say 0·01 to 0·03 mm.) will contain only wave-lengths for which the crystal is transparent, or its absorption coefficient comparatively small. For these latter wave-lengths the optical surfaces will approximate very closely to those for transparent crystals (i.e. ellipsoids), and the elliptically polarised components in biaxial crystals to plane-polarised ones. If therefore observations on absorption phenomena are confined to qualitative descriptions of pleochroism, as is usual in routine work, we may disregard the special optics of absorbing crystals.

OPTICAL ACTIVITY

In the preceding pages of this chapter, no account has been taken of the so-called *optically active* substances, which *rotate* the plane of vibration of polarised light. As already stated in Chapter 1 (p. 20) crystals of these substances belong to the ten enantiomorphous symmetry classes, in which planes of symmetry are absent. Not all substances crystallising in these classes are optically active, however (for example, barium nitrate, class 23, is not), for in addition to the point group symmetry elements, a necessary condition is that the crystal structure must possess parallel axes around which the atoms are arranged spirally and in the same sense. The spirals may be right-handed or left-handed, and this accounts for the existence of two forms of the crystal, one rotating the plane of vibration to the right and the other to the left.*

In optically active cubic crystals the rotational effect is the same for all directions of propagation, but in most optically active crystals of other systems it is clearly shown only when the light is travelling along, or nearly along, an optic axis. For most other directions the effects of optical rotation and double refraction are superposed, that of the latter being generally predominant, while for certain directions the rotational contribution is zero.

Optical rotation is illustrated in Fig. 2.34. OR is a plane-polarised ray of monochromatic light passing through the crystal in the direction of an optic axis (or in any direction if it is a cubic one). The vibration direction on entry is OT and this then undergoes progressive rotation to become RU on exit, or in other words the vibration plane which the light would have if the crystal were not optically active, i.e. ORST, is twisted into the helicoidal surface ORUT. The rotation angle $\phi = $ SRU is directly proportional to the thickness d traversed, and when $d = 1$ mm. is known as the *specific rotation* of the crystal. Reference to the footnote below will show that the case illustrated in the figure is one of *lævo*-rotation.

In transparent crystals the specific rotation, like the refractive index n, increases with decrease in the wave-length, and the theoretical connection between these two dispersions is sufficiently close for them to follow the same form of equation. Thus $\phi \approx A' + B'/\lambda^2$, which is analogous to the simplified Cauchy equation (p. 96), A' and B' being constants as in that case. At an absorption band, however, the dispersion of ϕ, like that of n, becomes 'anomalous'.

* Right-handed (or *dextro*-) rotation is usually taken to mean that if the observer is facing the oncoming light, the plane of vibration is rotated in a clockwise direction, while left-handed (*lævo*-) rotation means that this plane is rotated anti-clockwise. This is the same convention that we adopted on p. 59 to express the direction of rotation of the electric vector in circularly and elliptically polarised light. It may be noted that this convention has the somewhat unsatisfactory feature that the stated sense of the rotation is opposite to the sense of the screw traced out by the vibration along the direction of propagation, i.e. *dextro*-rotation corresponds to a left-hand screw, and *lævo*-rotation to a right-hand screw.

Optically active substances are of two types, namely (*i*) those which are active in the fused or dissolved state as well as in the crystalline state; (*ii*) those which are active in the crystalline state only. In substances of type (*i*) the molecules are themselves devoid of planes of symmetry, and can therefore exist in two different forms that are mirror images of one another. To this property of the molecules is attributed the existence of *dextro*- and *lævo*-rotatory forms of the

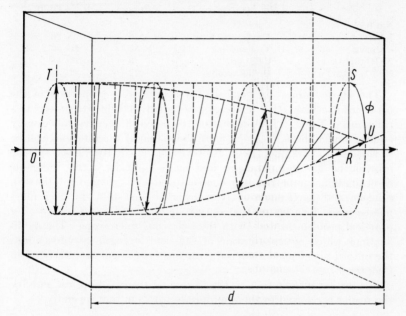

Fig. 2.34. Optical activity.

substance in the liquid state and in solution. Such molecules form spiral arrangements in the crystal structure, and so in the crystalline state the substance will have a rotatory power which is the resultant of that due to the molecules and that due to the spiral arrangement. An interesting example is afforded by the naturally occurring substance cane sugar (sucrose). This is known only in one enantiomorphous form which is *dextro*-rotatory in solution, but its monoclinic crystals have specific rotations of 2° 12′ (*dextro*-) and 6° 24′ (*lævo*-) in sodium light for sections normal to the two optic axes respectively. The reason why the values are different is that the optic axes are parallel to (010), and so pursue structurally different directions.

In substances of type (*ii*), the structural units have not the symmetry limitations possessed by those of substances of type (*i*), and do not of themselves give rise to optical activity. Accordingly as soon as the crystal structure is destroyed by fusion or solution, the activity disappears. Some of the better known examples of this type are given in the following table:

	SYSTEM	CLASS	SPECIFIC ROTATION IN Na LIGHT
$NaClO_3$ . . .	Cubic	23	3° 8′
$KLiSO_4$ . . .	Hexagonal	6	3° 26′
α-Quartz . .	Trigonal	32	21° 43′
$NaIO_4,3H_2O$.	Trigonal	3	23° 18′
$MgSO_4,7H_2O$.	Orthorhombic	222	2° 36′

The above values are typical of a considerable proportion of the rotations in crystals that have been measured, and since they refer to a rhickness of 1 mm. it is clear that on the much thinner crystals usually studied under the microscope (0·01 to 0·03 mm.) the rotations will be so small as to pass unnoticed. However, cinnabar, HgS, has a specific rotation of 325° for red light, and many optically active inorganic co-ordination compounds are known to have very large rotations in solution, and therefore probably in the crystalline state too. So it must not be taken for granted that optical activity will never constitute a practical problem in work with the polarising microscope. The modifications which optical rotation of sufficient strength introduces into the optical phenomena observed with this instrument are described in Chapter 5.

For further information on the cause and theory of optical activity the reader is referred to the appropriate works in the Appendix.

OPTICAL SECTIONS UNDER THE MICROSCOPE

As the reader will have seen so far, the optical properties of crystals have been described mainly with reference to the passage of light at perpendicular incidence through parallel-sided crystal plates. These conditions commonly prevail when well-formed crystals are examined under the microscope, because each crystal tends to lie upon a broad face, which is usually opposed by a similar parallel face. Frequently, however, crystalline particles of quite irregular shape have to be examined. It might appear at first as though observations on such material would be valueless, because the light would be deviated irregularly on entering the particles, and the observed phenomena would therefore correspond to no one section of the indicatrix. This situation is avoided, however, by mounting the particles in a liquid whose refractive index matches their mean refractive index, so that the light passes through them with but little deviation, no matter what their shape. The optical properties of any crystal or crystal fragment mounted in this way may thus be taken as corresponding to the section of its indicatrix which is normal to the path of the light.

In the sequel, when a crystal under the microscope is stated to be, or to present, a certain section, its section normal to the optical axis of the microscope is referred to. The statement does not necessarily imply that the crystal is in the form of a plate parallel to the section named.

RELATION BETWEEN OPTICAL PROPERTIES, CHEMICAL NATURE, AND CRYSTAL STRUCTURE

Crystalline substances may be broadly divided into those which are (a) non-conductors of electricity, or *dielectrics*, and (b) conductors of electricity. The main representatives of group (b) are the metals. The essential difference is that in (a) all the electrons are bound to individual atoms or molecules, whereas in (b) a certain proportion are 'free', i.e. belong not to particular atoms or molecules but to the structure as a whole. Under the influence of an electrical potential, these free electrons drift towards the positive pole, and this is the mechanism of metallic conduction.

The interactions between light and the ultimate particles of matter can only be explained quantitatively by means of the quantum theory (p. 61), but for our present purpose a simpler explanation in terms of classical wave theory will suffice.

When a beam of light passes through a dielectric the centres of gravity of the electron clouds of its atoms are displaced in relation to the positively charged nuclei by the electric field of the waves, i.e. the atoms become electric dipoles, or, as is said, are *polarised* by the waves.* The field is, however, alternating in direction with the frequency of the light used, and so the orientation of the atomic dipoles oscillates in sympathy with the electric vector of the light (though somewhat retarded in phase in relation to it) or, in other words, the electron clouds are caused to vibrate.

The electron clouds of single atoms, or the combined electron clouds of the atoms in a molecule, have certain natural frequencies of vibration like any system bound by elastic forces. If the frequency of the light

---

* It is unfortunate that the same term is used to describe the vectorial properties of light vibrations, but the context will always show the sense in which it is used.

does not agree with any of these natural frequencies, the clouds are put into forced vibrations of low amplitude, little energy is lost by the light, and the medium is said to be transparent. If, however, the frequency of the light matches one of the natural frequencies, a phenomenon analogous to resonance in sound occurs. Free vibrations of large amplitude are induced in the clouds, and much or most of the energy of the light is absorbed. If the atoms in the medium are widely separated from one another, as in a monatomic gas at low or medium pressure, the natural frequencies of their electron clouds are sharply defined, being in fact the same as those of the characteristic radiation *emitted* when the atoms are excited by high temperatures or an electric discharge (p. 61). The absorption spectrum of such a gas therefore consists of sharply defined dark lines occurring at the same wave-lengths as the lines in the emission spectrum. When atoms or molecules are close together, however, as in a liquid or a crystal, they modify each other's natural frequencies in such a way that absorption is spread over a *band*, or bands, of wave-lengths (p. 95). A further consequence of this close proximity is that the strong vibrations produced by the light are quickly damped by friction-type forces, and the energy absorbed thus appears finally as heat. In a gas, the atoms or molecules get rid of their excess energy by emitting their characteristic radiation.

In a conductor such as a metal the free electrons have no natural frequencies, since they are not bound to individual atoms or molecules by elastic forces. Light of any wave-length therefore puts these electrons into motion, the energy of the light being absorbed in the process. These moving electrons constitute electric currents, which dissipate their energy as heat in the usual way.

Polarisability of Atoms. The polarisation of an atom in a transparent medium by a light wave may be expressed quantitatively by the moment of the dipole produced by the electric field of the wave, i.e. by the product sq, where s is the distance separating the charges $+q$ and $-q$ at the two poles. This moment is proportional to the field strength E, and also increases with the frequency of the light. It may also be affected by the dipoles of neighbouring atoms in the medium. If, however, we assume that this last effect is absent, either because the other atoms are too far away or because they are so arranged that they cancel one another's effects, we may write for a given frequency:

$$sq = \alpha E \qquad . \qquad . \qquad . \qquad . \qquad 2.12$$

where α is a constant characteristic of the atom in the particular state of combination in which it occurs in the medium, and called its *polaris-ability*. Inspection of the equation shows that α has the dimensions of a volume, and that it is numerically equal to the moment of the dipole produced by a field of unit strength.

Polarisability is a property which varies widely for atoms of different elements. As a rough generalisation it may be said to increase with increase in the size and looseness of binding of the electron cloud. Further, atoms of the same element in different states of combination have different polarisabilities, since the state of combination influences the strength of binding of the electron cloud. For example the chloride ion (I), as in sodium chloride (p. 4), is more polarisable than the chlorine atom in gaseous hydrogen chloride (II) in which the hydrogen-chlorine linkage is mainly covalent.

$$:\overset{..}{\underset{..}{Cl}}:^{-} \qquad\qquad H:\overset{..}{\underset{..}{Cl}}:$$

$$\text{(I)} \qquad\qquad\qquad \text{(II)}$$

In (I) the nucleus of the atom has to hold an additional electron (as compared with the neutral atom) and this results in a general loosening of the electron system. In (II), which may be regarded as the result of a combination of (I) with a proton (hydrogen nucleus), the effect of the extra electron has been largely neutralised by the proton, and the electron system is therefore more tightly bound and less polarisable.

Polarisability and Refractive Index. The simplest case is that of a monatomic element (e.g. neon) in the liquid or gaseous state, i.e. a medium in which single atoms all of the same kind are distributed at random. It may be shown that owing to this random arrangement, the average effect of neighbouring dipoles on the dipole of any atom in the medium is zero for all directions of the electric vector. The relation between the atomic polarisability α and the refractive index n for a given wave-length is given by the *Lorentz-Lorenz equation:*

$$\frac{n^2 - 1}{n^2 + 2} \cdot \frac{A}{D} = \frac{4}{3} \pi N_0 \alpha = [R_A] \qquad . \qquad . \qquad . \; 2.13\,a$$

where A is the atomic weight, D the density of the medium, N_0 the Avogadro number (number of molecules in a gram molecule, or of atoms in a gram atom), and $[R_A]$ is known as the *atomic refractivity*. For the derivation of this equation the reader must consult more advanced works.

Now suppose that the liquid or gas consists of molecules composed of two or more atoms. In general each molecule will have a polarisability which varies with the direction of the electric vector for reasons which are given below, but since the molecules are distributed and oriented at random, we may, when treating the medium as a whole, regard them as having a mean polarisability $\bar{\alpha}_M$ which is an additive function of the atomic polarisabilities, and apply the Lorentz-Lorenz equation as follows:

$$\frac{n^2 - 1}{n^2 + 2} \cdot \frac{M}{D} = \frac{4}{3}\pi N_0 \bar{\alpha}_M = [R_M] \ . \qquad . \qquad . \ 2.13\,b$$

where M is now the molecular weight, and $[R_M]$ the *molecular refractivity*. The equation shows that if we were to compare a series of compounds having similar values of M/D, those with the greater values of $\bar{\alpha}_M$ would have the greater refractive indices (since an increase in the quotient $(n^2 - 1)/(n^2 + 2)$ corresponds to a greater value of n).

Polarisability and Birefringence. In a crystal the atoms have a particular spatial relationship to one another, and in general the effect of neighbouring dipoles on the polarisation of any atom varies with the direction of the electric vector, as shown below. However, this effect falls off very rapidly with the distance between the atoms concerned—in fact as the third power of this distance—and in a qualitative treatment of the problem it is sufficient to regard it as operating only between atoms which are linked by chemical bonds, i.e. between atoms which are in the closest proximity to one another.

Consider the simple case (Fig. 2.35) of two atoms which are chemically linked, and more widely separated from other atoms in the crystal. In (a) the electric vector of the light is parallel to the line joining the atomic centres, and the dipoles are in line, thus $- + - +$. Such an arrangement of the charges results in the moments of the dipoles being increased by induction above the value (or values, if the atoms are different) which they would have if the effects of their immediate neighbours cancelled out, i.e. if their polarisabilities had the 'normal' or 'isotropic' values for the particular state of combination in which they happen to be. In (b) the electric vector is at right angles to the line joining the atomic centres, charges of like sign are adjacent, and by induction the dipole moments are reduced from the values corresponding to the normal polarisabilities.

The polarisability of such an atom pair as a whole for different directions of the electric vector (assuming that it is unaffected by its neighbours) may be represented by the radius vectors of an ellipsoid of revolution, as in Fig. 2.35 c, in which the principal semi-axes, α_1' and α_2', correspond to the polarisabilities in cases (a) and (b) respectively, so that $\alpha_1' > \alpha_2'$.

Crystals built up of similarly oriented molecules have refractive indices which reflect the directional polarisabilities of the molecules. Thus if diatomic molecules, as in Fig. 2.35, were arranged parallel or nearly parallel to one another the crystal would have a larger refractive

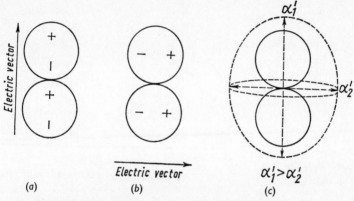

Fig. 2.35. Polarisability of elongated (rod-like) atom group.

index for light vibrating in the direction of the long axes of the molecules than for light vibrating transversely thereto, and the same would be true for any crystal built up of similarly oriented molecules having a pronounced elongation in one direction, i.e. rod-shaped molecules. Whether the crystal was uniaxial or biaxial would depend on the side-to-side packing of the rods, but in either case the optical sign of the crystal would be *positive*. The same principle can be extended to salts having monatomic cations, and rod-like anions arranged parallel to one another. The cations can contribute little to the birefringence, which arises mainly from the shape and arrangement of the anions.

Examples of such positive crystals are afforded by (*i*) paraffins, aliphatic alcohols and acids; (*ii*) natural fibres, e.g. silk, consisting of long molecules approximately parallel to the fibre axis; (*iii*) selenium (parallel spiral chains of Se atoms); (*iv*) sodium azide (parallel linear N_3^- ions).

Fig. 2.36 *a* shows a chemically linked group of three atoms situated at the corners of a triangle with a smaller atom at the centre. Examples are the anions $CO_3^=$ and NO_3^-. Such a group is essentially flattened or plate-like, and has a greater polarisability for any direction of the electric vector which lies in the plane of the atomic centres than for the direction normal to this plane. If the three larger atoms are identical, as in the examples above, the polarisation figure is an oblate ellipsoid of revolution as shown in the figure, with $\alpha_1' < \alpha_2'$. Crystals in which

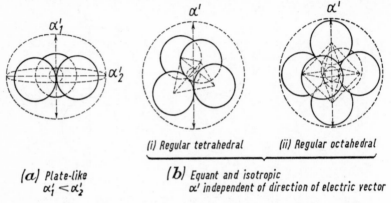

(i) Regular tetrahedral   (ii) Regular octahedral

(a) Plate-like   (b) Equant and isotropic
$\alpha_1' < \alpha_2'$ α' independent of direction of electric vector

Fig. 2.36. Polarisability of (a) plate-like, and (b) equant, atom groups.

such groups are similarly oriented, such as calcite, $CaCO_3$, and sodium nitrate, $NaNO_3$, and many other carbonates and nitrates, are *negatively* birefringent with larger refractive indices for light vibrating parallel to the planes of the plates (corresponding to α_2' in the polarisation ellipsoid) than for light vibrating normally to these planes (corresponding to α_1'). Other examples of plate-like atom groups are the aromatic rings of organic chemistry. Crystals of hexamethyl benzene, $C_6(CH_3)_6$, and naphthalene, $C_{10}H_8$, for example, have their plate-like molecules arranged approximately parallel to one another, and have a strongly negative birefringence. Similarly, the parallel layers of atoms in the micas result in negative birefringence.

Figs. 2.36 *b,i* and *b,ii* show respectively a group of four similar atoms arranged at the corners of a regular tetrahedron around a smaller atom (examples: $SO_4^=$, ClO_4^-, SiO_4^{4-}), and a group of six similar atoms arranged at the corners of a regular octahedron around a smaller atom (examples: $PtCl_6^=$, $CdCl_6^{4-}$). Such 'equant' groups have a spherical polarisation figure, i.e. are equally polarisable for all directions of the electric vector. Crystals based on these, unless they contain other groups which are strongly anisotropic, are therefore *isotropic* or *weakly birefringent*. For example, all anhydrous sulphates of monatomic cations, such as K_2SO_4, have very low birefringences. The various forms of silica, which are networks of SiO_4 tetrahedra, are also weakly birefringent or, in the case of cristobalite, cubic.

The above cases do not exhaust the possibilities. Some crystals have rod-like atom groups inclined in different directions but lying in parallel planes. This is so for the linear N_3^- ions in potassium azide. Such an arrangement is equivalent to a structure based on parallel plate-like groups, and so results in negative birefringence. Another type of structure is based on plate-like groups which are all parallel to a single direction but not to one another. This is equivalent to a system of parallel rods, and so leads to positive birefringence. Examples are rhombic sulphur (S_8 rings parallel to the c axis, but in two sets with their planes approximately at right angles to one another), and crystalline benzene (C_6H_6 rings arranged in a somewhat similar manner to the S_8 rings in rhombic sulphur). Yet another type of structure is based on strongly anisotropic atom groups, which are, however, arranged in such a way as to cancel or greatly reduce each other's directional inductive effects. Examples are solid CO_2 in which the linear O–C–O molecules are in four sets parallel respectively to the four trigonal axes of a cubic lattice, and lead and barium nitrates in which the negatively anisotropic NO_3^- ions are in four sets with their planes respectively at right angles to the four trigonal axes of a cubic lattice.

Quantitative Relationships. The molecular refractivity of a cubic crystal may be calculated from its refractive index by means of the left-hand side of equation 2.13 b, and has the same significance as the molecular refractivity of other isotropic media, namely that it affords a measure of the polarisability or refracting power of the molecules (or the units arbitrarily selected as such*) in the crystal. In the case of anisotropic crystals we may similarly calculate molecular refractivities from each of the principal refractive indices (though the equation is not strictly applicable to such media), i.e. from ε and ω for uniaxial crystals, and α, β and γ for biaxial crystals, and thus obtain constants expressing the refracting power of the molecules for light vibrating along the principal optical directions.

---

* In ionic crystals or other crystals in which discrete molecules cannot be distinguished, a group of atoms must be arbitrarily chosen as the 'molecule', usually that corresponding to the conventional formula, e.g. NaCl for the sodium chloride crystal.

Reversing this procedure, some calculations have been made of the principal refractive indices of crystals from their structure and the polarisabilities of their atoms or atom groups, due allowance being made for the effects of neighbouring dipoles on one another according to the direction of the electric vector. Thus W. L. Bragg* calculated in this way the principal indices of the two forms of $CaCO_3$, calcite and aragonite, and obtained results which were correct to within 2 per cent. St. B. Hendricks and W. E. Deming† calculated the refractive indices of a number of oxalate crystals from the anisotropy and orientations of the oxalate group.

Another approach (K. G. Denbigh, C. W. Bunn and R. de P. Daubeny) has been the calculation of the indices of organic crystals on the basis of a system of *bond* polarisabilities instead of atom polarisabilities. For an outline of this work with references the reader is referred to C. W. Bunn's *Chemical Crystallography* cited at the end of this book.

Pleochroism (p. 94). Colour in organic crystals is known to be associated with the presence of certain groups known as *chromophores*, of which the following are important examples:

$$-C{=}C-, \qquad -N{=}N-, \qquad {=}C \underset{\displaystyle C{=}C}{\overset{\displaystyle C{=}C}{\big<}\big>} C{=}.$$

It has been found that the absorption of light is greatest when it is vibrating along the direction of the double bonds in these groups.

In coloured inorganic crystals absorption is greatest for vibrations along directions in which the ions are distorted.

---

* *Proc. Roy. Soc.*, 1924, **105** A, 270.
† *Z. Krist.*, 1935, **91**, 290.

3   THE POLARISING MICROSCOPE

The compound optical microscope, of which the polarising microscope is one type, is based essentially on the image-forming and magnifying properties of convex lenses, and we shall therefore begin by considering the characteristics of such lenses.

It should first be explained that the curved surfaces of all lenses used in microscopes and other standard optical instruments are *spherical*, i.e. are portions of the surface of spheres. In theory, some of the imperfections, or *aberrations*, in the performance of single lenses as image formers could be eliminated if they had surfaces of other shapes, but such aspherical surfaces are extremely difficult to make accurately. It is, however, comparatively easy to design grinding and polishing machines which, acting by oscillation and rotation about a fixed centre, will produce lenses having accurately spherical surfaces of any required radius, and by combining such components in various ways it is possible to compensate to a very large extent for their individual aberrations, as will appear later.

Fig. 3.1 *a* shows a thin biconvex lens, assumed to be in air. C is a singular point in the lens, called its *optical centre*, which is characterised by the fact that rays passing through it enter and leave the lens in the same or in parallel directions. If the lens has the same curvature on both faces, C coincides with its geometrical centre. OCI is its *principal axis*, i.e. the line passing through the centres of curvature of the faces.

Rays entering the lens are refracted according to Snell's law (p. 73). The general effect on a group of rays of monochromatic light diverging from an object point on one side of the lens, and at a greater distance from it than its focal length (see below), is to converge the rays on the other side, but if account is taken of all of these rays which can pass through the lens, it is found on applying Snell's law that they do not converge on a single image point. If, however, attention is confined to *paraxial rays*, i.e. rays which remain close to the principal axis because they start from a point on or near to the axis and make only a small angle with it, it is found that they do focus almost exactly on one

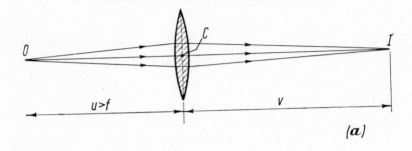

(a)

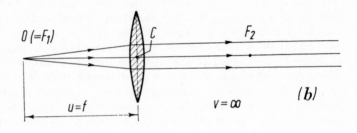

(b)

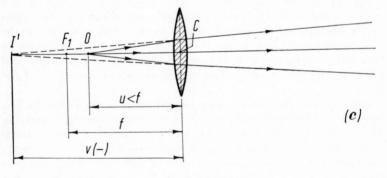

(c)

Fig. 3.1

point. Thus in the figure, paraxial rays from the point O pass through the point I.

Since the lens is thin we may neglect its thickness in comparison with the distances of the object and image points from it. Let us put $u = OC$ and $v = IC$ for these two distances respectively.

If O be moved nearer to the lens, a position will be found at which the paraxial rays no longer converge to a focus on the far side of the lens, but are parallel to one another (Fig. 3.1 *b*), i.e. $v = \infty$. The special value of u at this position is called the *focal length*, f, of the lens, and O is at the *first principal focus* F_1. (There is a *second principal focus* F_2 on the right-hand side of the lens, and at the same distance from it as F_1, corresponding to parallel rays travelling on the left-hand side.)

It may be shown that

$$\frac{1}{u} + \frac{1}{v} = \frac{1}{f} \quad . \qquad . \qquad . \qquad . \qquad . \quad 3.1$$

which is the fundamental lens equation. Applying the equation to case *b*, for example, we see that it correctly represents the situation, for if $v = \infty$, $1/v = 0$, and so $u = f$.

If O be moved still nearer to the lens (Fig. 3.1 *c*), the rays on the other side become divergent. We now have $u < f$, or $1/u > 1/f$, and applying Equation 3.1 we have

$$\frac{1}{u} - \frac{1}{f} = -\frac{1}{v},$$

which is positive, and therefore v is negative. The meaning of this is that the image is a virtual one. It is situated at I′ where the divergent rays to the right of the lens intersect when they are produced to the left.* It is called 'virtual' because it is a point from which rays only *appear* to come, e.g. to an eye placed on the right of the lens. No rays from O are actually focussed at I′, and no image would be received on a screen placed there. The image seen in a mirror is another example of a virtual image.

Figs. 3.2 to 3.4 treat the case of an object of finite size, but small in relation to the diameter of the lens, represented by the vertical arrow of height h. Again considering only paraxial rays of a given wavelength, and first assuming that $u > f$ (Fig. 3.2), we obtain an image

---

* The sign convention adopted here is that all distances to the object or to a real image are taken as positive, and distances to virtual images as negative. There is, however, another convention in use in which all distances to the right or upwards are taken as positive, and those to the left or downwards as negative, as in co-ordinate geometry.

h', which is inverted with respect to the object. Any point on the image is given by the intersection of at least two rays from the corresponding point on the object. In Fig. 3.2 we have used for the foot of the arrow the ray travelling along the principal axis OCI and a paraxial ray just below it. For the point of the arrow we have chosen the ray O′CI′ passing through the optical centre of the lens, and (for a reason which will become apparent presently) the ray O′HFI′, which before refraction by the lens, i.e. over the portion O′H, is parallel to the axis. By similar triangles, the ratio of the size of the image to that of the

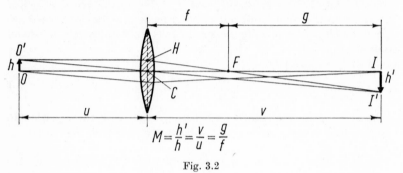

$$M = \frac{h'}{h} = \frac{v}{u} = \frac{g}{f}$$

Fig. 3.2

object, i.e. the magnification M, is equal to that between their respective distances from the lens, thus

$$M = \frac{h'}{h} = \frac{v}{u} \qquad . \qquad . \qquad . \qquad . \qquad 3.2$$

But since O′H is parallel to OC, F is a principal focus and CF $= f$. By making use of this and the properties of similar triangles we obtain the following expression for M:

$$M = \frac{h'}{h} = \frac{II'}{OO'} = \frac{II'}{HC} = \frac{FI}{CF} = \frac{g}{f} \text{ (putting } g \text{ for FI)} \qquad . \quad 3.3$$

We shall return to this result when discussing the magnifying power of a microscope (p. 119), g being then identified with what is termed the optical tube length of the instrument.

In Fig. 3.3 i, the object is at the focal distance f from the lens, and so rays diverging from any point on the object become parallel after passing through the lens. If the eye were brought to the position shown, where the beams of parallel rays corresponding to different object points cross, it would see an infinitely distant virtual image of the object, since each beam would be brought to a focus on the retina of the eye. This introduces us to the principle of the simple magnifying lens, and the magnification for the situation represented may be defined as the ratio between the sizes of the images formed on the retina respectively by the virtual image and by the object itself if it were

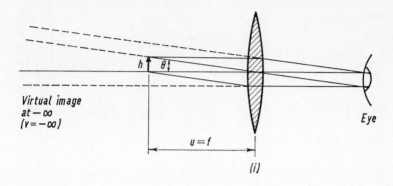

Virtual image
at −∞
(v = −∞)

Eye

u = f

(i)

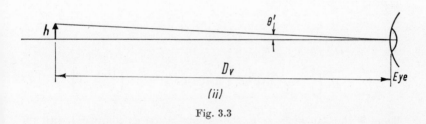

(ii)

Fig. 3.3

viewed without the lens at *the least distance of distinct vision*, D_v, which for the normal eye is conventionally taken as 10 in. or 25 cm. (Fig. 3.3 *ii*). This ratio is equal to that between the tangents of the angles subtended at the eye by the image ($\angle\theta$) and the object ($\angle\theta'$). Thus we have for the numerical value of the magnification

$$M = \frac{\tan\theta}{\tan\theta'} = \frac{h}{f}\cdot\frac{D_v}{h} = \frac{D_v}{f} \qquad . \qquad . \qquad . \qquad . \qquad 3.4$$

Alternatively, to indicate that the image is a virtual one, we may write $M = -D_v/f$ (where D_v and f are the numerical values of these quantities). In practice we are usually concerned only with the numerical value of the magnification and can ignore the sign.

In Fig. 3.4 the object has been moved a little nearer to the lens so that the virtual image is at the distance D_v from it. If the eye is placed close to the lens, so that the distance from eye to image may also

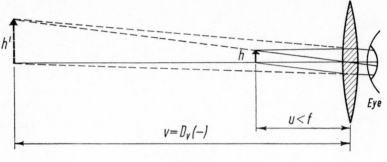

Fig. 3.4

be taken as D_v (or $-D_v$ according to our sign convention), the magnification will be as follows:

$$M = \frac{h'}{-D_v} \cdot \frac{D_v}{h} = -\frac{h'}{h} = \frac{v}{u} = -\frac{D_v}{u}$$

$$= -D_v \left(\frac{1}{f} + \frac{1}{D_v}\right) \text{ (from equation 3.1)} = -\left(\frac{D_v}{f} + 1\right) \quad . \quad 3.5$$

There is thus an increase in the magnification as compared with the case in Fig. 3.3. We cannot, however, obtain any further increase in the magnification by moving the object still nearer to the lens, because if we do this the divergence of the rays emerging from it will be too great for the eye to focus them.

To take an example of these two cases, suppose that $f = 1$ in. Then if the virtual image is at infinity (Fig. 3.3), $M = -D_v/f = -10$, whereas if it is at the distance D_v (Fig. 3.4), $M = -(D_v/f + 1) = -11$, an increase of 10 per cent in the numerical value.

Aberrations of Lenses. The cases discussed above have been confined to the passage of monochromatic paraxial rays through a thin biconvex lens. For these light conditions, similar results would be obtained with thin convex lenses of other types (plano-convex and meniscus lenses) and, as regards sharpness of focussing, with thick convex lenses also, though with these it would be necessary to take account of their thickness in expressing their performance quantitatively.

Under other conditions, single lenses show focussing defects, the

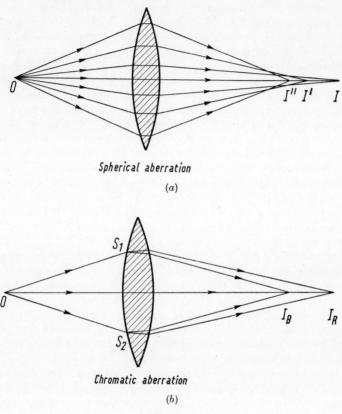

Spherical aberration

(*a*)

Chromatic aberration

(*b*)

Fig. 3.5

most important of which are *spherical aberration* and *chromatic aberration*. Spherical aberration is illustrated in Fig. 3.5 *a*. Extra-paraxial rays diverging from an image point O are brought to foci, I′, I″, which are nearer to the lens than that for the paraxial rays (I), and become progressively nearer as the divergence of the rays increases.

Chromatic aberration arises because the refractive index of a lens, and therefore its refracting power, increases with decrease in the wave-length of the light (p. 61), so that if white light is used, the blue rays are brought to a focus nearer to the lens than the red rays (and the rest of the spectrum at intermediate positions). Thus in Fig. 3.5b, I_B and I_R are the focal points for blue and red light respectively, corresponding to the incident rays of white light OS_1, OS_2.

It must be noted that (a) each colour will have its own spherical aberration, and (b) paraxial rays of white light suffer chromatic aberration, just as do non-paraxial rays.

Other kinds of aberrations for non-paraxial rays are associated specifically with object points which do not lie on the principal axis, and are due to the fact that the effective curvature of the lens surfaces is different for rays lying in different planes in the incident cone of light. Qualitatively the nature of these aberrations can be demonstrated by a simple experiment. An image of a pearl or opal electric light bulb, situated at a distance of several feet, is cast on a paper screen by means of a simple convex lens, and focussed as sharply as possible. The lens is then tilted slightly, so that the bulb is a little 'off-axis', when it will be seen that the image is drawn out into a blur in the direction at right angles to the axis of tilt. This effect is known as *coma*, from the comet-like appearance of the image. If the lens is tilted further, and also moved nearer the screen, a bright focal *line* parallel to the axis of tilt will appear, and if it is then moved away a little from the screen, while maintaining the tilt, another bright line, but at right angles to the axis of tilt, will be seen. This effect is termed *astigmatism*.

Two further aberrations which are associated with extended objects are *distortion* and *curvature of field*. In distortion the magnification of the outer parts of the image is either greater or less than that of the central parts, while curvature of field means that the image lies on a curved surface instead of on a plane.

Aberrations can be reduced very considerably, and for selected wavelengths eliminated completely, by combining lenses of different shapes and materials in various ways. The design of such lens systems depends very much on the purposes for which they are to be used. The lens combination in a camera, for example, which has to form a flat, well-corrected image of an object of great extent, is quite different from that of a microscope objective which has to deal with an object field much smaller than the aperture by which the light enters. The whole subject of lens aberrations and the methods of correcting for them is exceedingly complex, and its details fall outside the scope of this book. Some idea of the ways in which chromatic and spherical aberrations are dealt with in the optical components of microscopes will, however, be given in the section which follows. For further information the reader must consult more advanced works, such as those by B. O. Payne and R. S. Longhurst given in the list at the end of this book.

The Compound Microscope. Consideration of equations 3.4 and 3.5 will show that quite high magnifications are theoretically attainable with single lenses of very short focal length. Thus from 3.4 we see that for a lens having $f = 1$ mm., $M = 25/0 \cdot 1 = 250$. In the seventeenth and early eighteenth centuries, much important pioneer work was done with microscopes based on such single lenses, notably by van Leeuwenhoek, and during this period these instruments were preferred by many serious workers to the more convenient compound, or double, microscope (the principle of which was known from quite early in the seventeenth century), because they gave a much superior image. The reason for this lay in the fact that when a single lens is used as shown in Fig. 3.4, but in white light, the images for different colours, though not coincident, subtend much the same angle at the eye, so that they are seen superposed on one another and chromatic aberration is, in effect, largely annulled. In the early compound microscopes there was no correction for chromatic aberration and the images which they gave had strongly coloured borders in consequence.

The disadvantage of the high-power single lens microscope lay in the fact that the lens had to be extremely small to obtain the necessary very short focal length, and this in turn meant that the working distances between eye and lens, and lens and object, were also very small, resulting in much discomfort and eye strain in the use of the instrument. In the compound microscope this is avoided, and at the same time a larger field of view is obtained, by effecting the magnification in two stages. The late eighteenth, and nineteenth centuries saw the development of methods of counteracting lens aberrations, and the application of these to the compound microscope firmly established it as a serious scientific instrument.

The principle of a typical compound microscope is shown in Fig. 3.6. Light is reflected by the adjustable *mirror* M through the convex lenses C and N, which together constitute the *condenser*, the purpose of which is to converge the light upon the object X. The mirror is silvered on both sides, one of which is plane and the other concave. The concave side is only used in certain special cases to be dealt with later. At, or somewhat below, the lower focal plane of the condenser is situated the *substage iris diaphragm* G, by means of which the convergence of the illuminating beam may be controlled.

An enlarged and inverted image of the object (the *primary image*, X″) is formed by the *objective* O and the lower lens, or *field lens*, of the *eyepiece* or *ocular* E, in the lower focal plane F of the upper lens, or *eye lens*, of E. The eye placed at Q where the emerging bundles of parallel rays cross (the so-called *Ramsden disc*) sees an enlarged virtual image X′ of the primary image X″ apparently at an infinite distance.

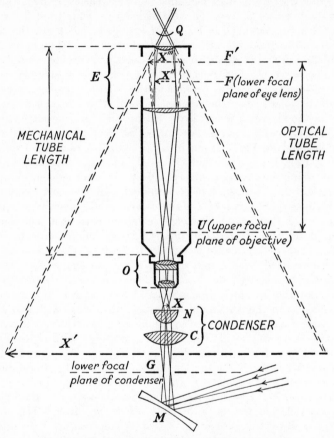

Fig. 3.6. The compound microscope (diagrammatic).

The magnification of the instrument may be defined as the ratio of the sizes of the images formed on the retina of the eye (1) by the virtual image X′, and (2) by the object X if it were viewed by the unaided eye at the least distance of distinct vision (cf. Fig. 3.3).

The magnification can also be expressed as the product of the magnifying power of the objective and that of the eyepiece. The magnifying power of the objective is equal to g/f_0, where f_0 is its focal length,* and g is the *optical tube length*, which is the distance between the upper focal plane of the objective, U, and the plane F' in which the primary image (X''') would be formed if the field lens of the eyepiece were not present (cf. Fig. 3.2 and equation 3.3). It must be distinguished from the *mechanical tube length*, i.e. the distance between the top of the body tube and the upper shoulder of the objective (see figure). g differs for different objectives on the same instrument, because the levels of their upper focal planes are not the same. However, it is governed mainly by the fixed mechanical tube length, which (for a given eyepiece) determines where the primary image is to be formed. With high- and medium-power objectives, which have upper focal planes at approximately the same level, g does not change very much, and equation 3.3 shows that the magnification is approximately inversely proportional to the focal length. With low-power objectives, however, the upper focal planes are higher up the tube, and so g is appreciably reduced.

The magnifying power of the eyepiece is equal to D_v/f_e, where f_e is its focal length, i.e. the focal length of the whole combination, and D_v is the least distance of distinct vision (cf. equation 3.4). In the figure the eyepiece shown is of the so-called Huygens type, which is that usually fitted. Other types are mentioned later. It is characterised by having no external focal plane on the field lens side, and only the eye lens is actually concerned in magnifying the primary image. The field lens acts with the objective to produce this image, which is smaller than that which would be produced by the objective alone (cf. X'' with X''' in the figure). Thus the expressions given above for the magnifying powers of the objective and eyepiece may at first sight appear to be unrelated to this case. However, it may be shown that

$$\frac{\text{Size of } X''}{\text{Focal length of eye lens}} = \frac{\text{Size of } X'''}{f_e},$$

so that the result is the same as if in fact an image X''' was formed by

---

* A combination of two or more lenses, such as a microscope objective, has a focal length as a whole (f) which is determined by the position of its principal foci, F_1, F_2, just as for a single thin lens. Whereas in the latter case, however the focal length is the distance of either of the principal foci from a single point, namely the optical centre of the lens, for a lens combination there are *two* points P_1 and P_2 on the axis (called the *principal points*) from which the focal length has to be measured, thus $f = F_1P_1 = F_2P_2$. These points are such that if an object were situated at P_1, there would be a virtual image of the same size at P_2. Thick single lenses have to be treated similarly. For further details consult Longhurst, or other advanced text (see Appendix 1).

the objective and magnified by a lens or lens combination having a focal length f_e. Thus the expression

$$M = \frac{g}{f_0} \times \frac{D_v}{f_e} \qquad . \qquad . \qquad . \qquad . \quad 3.6$$

gives the correct value of the total magnification (M) of the instrument.

Most makers nowadays mark objectives and eyepieces with their magnifying powers in round figures, thus '40 $\times$ ', '10 $\times$ ', etc., and by multiplying one figure by the other an approximate value for the total magnifying power for a given combination of objective and eyepiece may be obtained.

By combining a negative (concave) lens made of a glass with a high dispersion ('flint glass') with a convex lens made of one with a low dispersion ('crown glass'), as shown in Fig. 3.7 *a* and *b*, it is possible to bring rays of two widely separated colours, say blue and red, to the same focus, and at the same time reduce the residual dispersion for other colours to a degree that is unimportant for most purposes. Such a combination is called an *achromatic doublet,* and microscope objectives in which chromatic aberration in counteracted in this way, e.g. the one in Fig. 3.6 which consists of two such doublets, are called *achromatic objectives.* The doublets are usually given a plano-convex shape as shown in the figures, since this shape gives freedom from spherical aberration also under certain conditions (see below).

Better colour correction is given by *apochromatic objectives,* which contain combinations of lenses of fluorite (calcium fluoride) with glass lenses and bring rays of three colours, blue, green and red, to the same focal plane. They have, however, the defect, inherent in the design, that the size of the image is slightly different for different colours, and this produces colour effects in the outer parts of the field when they are used with a Huygens eyepiece. To correct for this defect a special *compensating eyepiece* must be used instead.

For all ordinary optical crystallographic work achromatic objectives are perfectly satisfactory, and, as far as the writers are aware, only objectives of this type are ever offered as having been specially selected for polarisation microscopy because of freedom from strain, as is the practice of most manufacturers.

The principal ways in which corrections for spherical aberration are made are as follows: (*a*) the refraction is divided between a number of refracting surfaces, i.e. two or more weaker lenses are used instead of one stronger one. In this way the angle which a ray makes with the normal to any one surface is kept as small as possible, and conditions approximate to those for paraxial rays; (b) use is made of the fact that with some types of lenses there exist, for any given wave-length, certain conjugate (i.e. corresponding) object and image points for which there

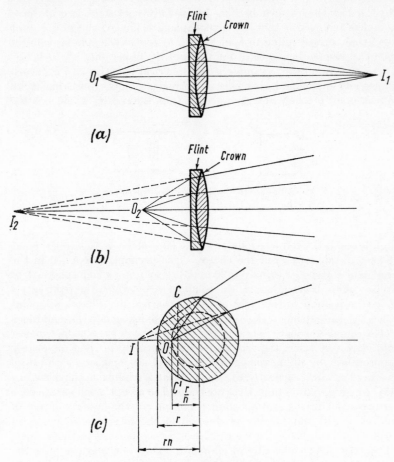

Fig. 3.7. Aplanatic points.

is no spherical aberration. Such conjugate points are termed *aplanatic*. For example, the plano-convex achromatic doublet has two pairs of aplanatic points. One pair consists of an object point O_1, outside the principal focus, and a real image point I_1, as shown in Fig. 3.7 a. The

5

other consists of an object point O_2, inside the principal focus, and a virtual image point I_2, as shown in Fig. 3.7 *b*. Typical achromatic *low-power objectives* (3 to 5 × ; Fig. 3.8 *a*) consist of one such doublet acting as in Fig. 3.7 *a*, while achromatic *medium power objectives* (say 10 ×), like that shown in Fig. 3.6, usually consist of two of these doublets arranged so that the virtual aplanatic image point of the lower one (that corresponding to I_2 in Fig. 3.7 *b*) acts as the aplanatic object point corresponding to O_1 in Fig. 3.7 *a* of the upper one.

Another important example is the spherical lens (Fig. 3.7 *c*), which along any diameter has a pair of aplanatic points, consisting of an object point O inside at a distance r/n from the centre, where r is the

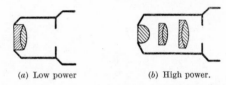

(*a*) Low power   (*b*) High power.

Fig. 3.8. Typical achromatic objectives (diagrammatic).

radius and n the refractive index of the lens, and a virtual image point I at a distance rn from the centre. This principle is applied in the design of *high-power objectives* (30 to 95 ×) by using a hemispherical, or hyper-hemispherical, lens as the component by which the light enters (e.g. the portion to the right of CC' in the figure). The object point then lies just outside the lens, giving an approximation to the conditions for a complete sphere, while in the oil immersion type of high-power objective (see later) these conditions are actually realised, or closely approached, by filling the space between object and lens with an oil having the same, or nearly the same, refractive index as the glass. In this way high-power objectives are enabled to accept a wide-angle cone of rays, and this is an important condition for the best resolution of object detail, and for the production of the interference figures of crystals, as will be shown later. The other components in these objectives (Fig. 3.8 *b*) take care of chromatic aberration and complete the process of converging the light to form a real image.

Since the positions of the aplanatic points of a lens depend on the wave-length, it is not possible to correct an objective for spherical aberration exactly for all wave-lengths. Achromatic objectives are corrected for one colour (green) and apochromatic objectives for two, but there is a considerable reduction in the spherical aberrations for other colours.

It will be clear from the above remarks that an objective will only give its optimum performance if it is used at the distance from the object, and therefore at the optical tube length, for which it was corrected. It is therefore inadvisable to transfer an objective from its own microscope to one having a different mechanical tube length, since this will alter the optical tube length at which the objective has to work. Another condition affecting image quality is the thickness of the cover slip over the preparation, since variations in this thickness affect, in the optical sense, the object-objective distance because of refraction of the light by the slip. Most objectives are corrected for a cover slip thickness of 0·17 mm., or else for use with uncovered objects, e.g. polished surfaces of metals and ores (see Table on p. 131). These considerations apply particularly to high-power objectives.

Other points connected with objectives will be dealt with in the section on resolution (p. 129).

Turning now to consider the Huygens eyepiece (Fig. 3.6), we first observe that its construction is very much simpler than that of the average objective. The main reason for this is that, owing to its distance from the objective, it only has to accept rays which make comparatively small angles with the axis. Its two plano-convex lenses are made of the same glass, and the lower (field) lens has a focal length which is between one and a half and three times that of the eye lens, while the distance between the two is approximately one half the sum of the focal lengths. For such a system it may be shown that (a) the deviation of the light is shared equally between the four surfaces so that spherical aberration is reduced to a minimum, and (b) the focal length is the same for all colours. (b) does not mean that the principal foci for all colours will coincide, for the principal points (p. 119) for different colours are not the same, but it does mean that the different images will subtend the same, or much the same, angle at the eye, and so will give the effect of being combined, as in the case of the single-lens microscope (p. 117).

The separation of the lenses in the Huygens eyepiece is such that the combination has no external focal plane on the field lens side. Anything which has to be viewed at the same time as the object, such as cross hairs, linear scales for making measurements, and the circular stop defining the field of view, has therefore to be situated at the lower focal plane of the eye lens (F, Fig. 3.9 a), so as to coincide with the real image formed by the objective and the field lens (X″, Fig. 3.6). Measurements on the object made with a linear scale in this position may, however, be subject to errors, because the scale is viewed with the eye lens alone whilst the object image seen is the result of refraction by both field lens and eye lens.* For such purposes the Ramsden positive type should be used (Fig. 3.9 *b*). This consists of two plano-convex lenses of equal focal length with their convex sides facing inwards, and separated by a distance equal approximately to one-third of the sum of their focal lengths. The focal plane lies outside the combination at F′, and the object image is formed by the objective in this plane. The image of a scale placed here is subject to the same

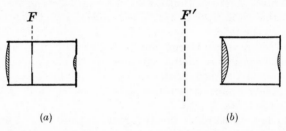

(a)   (b)

Fig. 3.9. Eyepieces (diagrammatic); (a) Huygens, (b) Ramsden.

distortions as the object image, since both are viewed through the two lenses of the combination.

In the simple type of Ramsden eyepiece shown in Fig. 3.9, the conditions for achromatism are not satisfied, though the resulting defect is not serious. If necessary this defect can be eliminated by using an achromatic doublet as the eye lens. Such achromatised Ramsden-type eyepieces are sometimes called Kellner eyepieces.

The Polarising Microscope. This is essentially a compound microscope provided with calcite polarising prisms or, more usually nowadays, polarising filters, e.g. discs of 'Polaroid', above and below the stage, and some means of altering the orientation of the object (usually in one plane only) with reference to the plane of vibration of the light incident upon it. Provision is also made for the insertion of auxiliary lenses and compensators into the path of the light through the instrument.

The arrangement of the main components in a typical modern polarising microscope is shown diagrammatically in Fig. 3.10. Optical components corresponding to those in Fig. 3.6 are lettered similarly,

* If no other eyepiece is available, serious error can be avoided by checking the values of the scale divisions at different distances from the centre of the field against the stage micrometer with which such eyepiece scales are calibrated (usually a transparent scale one millimetre in length divided into a hundred parts, mounted on a slide).

and need not be listed again. The incident light passes through the Polaroid disc P, which is termed the *polariser*, and is thus constrained to vibrate in one plane only. P can be rotated in its own plane, the angle of rotation being read against a fixed mark from divisions engraved on the metal ring in which it is mounted. A second Polaroid disc A is mounted in the body tube of the instrument, and is termed the *analyser*. (This is usually not rotatable, but is so in some instruments of advanced type.) When the polariser P is in the '0°' (or '180°') position, in which it is usually located by some form of spring catch, its vibration plane, i.e. the vibration plane of the light transmitted by it,* is at right angles to that of the analyser, assuming that this also is in its '0°' position if it is rotatable. When arranged thus in relation to one another the polariser and analyser are said to be 'crossed', and they will not permit light to reach the eyepiece E so long as the medium between them is entirely isotropic, because the light transmitted by the polariser is completely extinguished by the analyser, according to the principle underlying Malus's experiment (p. 74). Cross-hairs (or a crossline graticule) situated in the eyepiece at H indicate the vibration

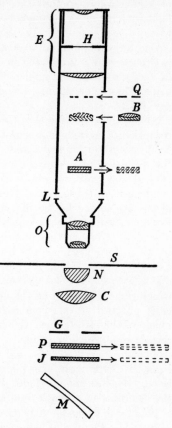

Fig. 3.10. Typical polarising microscope (diagrammatic).

directions of the polariser and analyser when they are in the crossed position. In order that the cross-hairs may be sharply focussed, the eye lens is usually mounted on an inner sleeve so that it can be moved up or down in relation to the rest of the eyepiece.

The analyser is in a sliding or rotating mount, so that when it is

* It is a convenient common practice, though admittedly somewhat loose, to speak of the vibration plane, or vibration direction (p. 55) of a polarising device in this sense.

not required it can be moved to one side as indicated by the arrow in the figure. In some instruments the polariser can also be withdrawn, or swung aside, so that the object can be examined in unpolarised light, but for most purposes there is no particular advantage in doing this.

The object, mounted on a glass slide, is laid on the *stage* S. This is circular and is graduated in degrees around the edge. It can rotate in its own plane, and angles of rotation are measured, either against a fixed mark, or against a vernier enabling readings to be taken to, say, $0.1°$.

Above the objective O is the *slot* L through the body tube, for the reception of various compensators, the purpose and use of which will be described in later chapters. The direction of the slot is at 45° to the vibration planes of the polariser and analyser when they are in the crossed position. In some instruments it is possible to insert compensators through a slot in the eyepiece at the lower focal plane of the eye lens. Slotted objectives are also supplied by some manufacturers, the slot in this case being at the upper focal plane of the objective. One or other of these alternatives is necessary when using compensators bearing scales which have to be focussed. In the second case the scale is focussed by inserting the *Bertrand lens*, B. This lens and the eyepiece act together to constitute a low-power microscope which can be focussed on the upper focal plane of the objective.* The chief purpose of this combination is, however, to give an enlarged image of the interference figures which are formed in this plane under certain conditions, and which will be described more fully in Chapter 5. Above the Bertrand lens, and often attached to the same mounting, is an iris diaphragm, or a pinhole stop, Q, the purpose of which is to isolate the interference figure of the crystal occupying the centre of the field of view when several are present.

Below the polariser may be inserted a finely ground glass disc, or *diffuser*, J. The use of this component will be described and discussed more fully in the later section on illumination in this chapter.

Polarising Devices. Although polarised light can be produced by reflection and refraction by isotropic media as already shown in

---

* To allow for the fact that the position of this plane in the microscope differs with different objectives, the Bertrand lens in some microscopes is mounted so that it can be moved up or down and thus critically focussed. In cases in which it is fixed, its position will have been chosen to suit high-power objectives, for it is with these that it is most commonly used. Some focussing is still possible, however, by adjusting the level of the eye lens in the eyepiece.

Chapter 2, p. 74, the only polarising devices suitable for use in the polarising microscope are based on the double refraction of light by anisotropic media. Two principles are employed: (1) one of the two polarised rays produced by double refraction is deflected sideways by total reflection at an inclined surface whilst the other passes on, this being what happens in the Nicol prism and other types of polarising prisms constructed of calcite; (2) the medium is intensely pleochroic (p. 94) in the sense that it absorbs one of the rays so strongly that its transmitted intensity is negligible. This is the principle of 'Polaroid', and similar polarising filters.

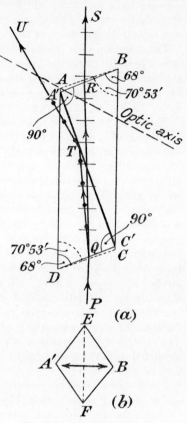

Calcite polarising prisms. The original design was due to Nicol (1828) and thus bears his name. The end faces of an elongated cleavage rhombohedron of Iceland spar (ABCD, Fig. 3.11 *a*) are ground and polished to make slightly different angles with the axis as shown (A'B, C'D). The rhombohedron is then cut diagonally (A'C'), and cemented together again with Canada balsam. Rays entering the prism parallel to the axis, or making a small angle with it (e.g. PQ) undergo double refraction. For the extraordinary ray the refractive index of the

Fig. 3.11. The Nicol prism.

calcite is very near to that of the balsam, and so this ray is transmitted (QRS). The ordinary ray is associated with a much greater index than that of the balsam, and strikes it at an angle greater than the critical angle of incidence.* It is therefore totally reflected and passes

* When a ray of light strikes a boundary between two media from the side of the one with the greater refractive index, it is totally reflected if its angle of incidence is greater than that for which the angle of refraction into the second medium is 90°, i.e. for which the refracted ray just grazes the boundary. This limiting angle of incidence is called the *critical angle*.

out of the side of the prism (QTU). Fig. 3.11 *b* shows an end view of the prism and the direction of vibration of the transmitted light.

Other types of calcite polarising prisms (e.g. Glan-Thompson, Ahrens) have end faces which are normal to the axis, and are more suitable for use in a polarising microscope since they do not produce any lateral displacement of the light beam.

The insertion of a calcite prism analyser into the body tube, as at A in Fig. 3.10, alters the focus of the microscope and introduces some astigmatism into the image, unless suitable correcting lenses are fitted above and below the prism to render parallel the light passing through it.

Polarising filters. The most familiar of these in the English-speaking world are the types known by the omnibus term 'Polaroid', which have been developed by the Polaroid Corporation of America.* The earliest of these filters consisted of a plastic film containing a mass of sub-microscopic needle-shaped crystals of herapathite oriented parallel to one another. Herapathite is a complex sulphate and iodide of quinine, and its crystals are strongly pleochroic. The orientation of the needles was effected by extruding a suspension of the herapathite crystals in a viscous solution of the plastic through a narrow slit, the needles tending to turn themselves parallel to the direction of flow. Later types have consisted of films of long-chain polymers (of which polyvinyl alcohol is one) which have been stretched to orientate the chains and then treated with either iodine or certain dyes, the molecules of which become adsorbed in a regular manner on the polymer. The vibration direction of strong absorption is that parallel to the polymer chains. Yet another type consists of a polyvinyl alcohol film which has been stretched and then dehydrated to give polyvinylene, which is itself intensely pleochroic.

The Polaroid used for microscopes is of particularly high quality, and is of one or other of these later types. The actual filter is protected by being mounted between optically flat discs of glass.

The extinction obtained with crossed Polaroids of high quality is as good or even better than that obtained with crossed calcite prisms. The use of Polaroid in the microscope also has the following advantages. (1) A Polaroid analyser in the normal position in the body tube intro-duces no astigmatism into the image. Further, a change of focus on withdrawing the analyser may be very simply avoided by mounting a disc of glass of the same thickness in the same mount, in such a way

* For an account of this development see E. H. Land, *J. Opt. Soc. Amer.* 1951, **41**, 957. See also Shurcliff, W. A., *Polarized Light* (Harvard Univ. Press and Oxford Univ. Press, 1962).

that the glass takes the place of the Polaroid when the latter is in the 'out' position. (2) In cases in which an auxiliary analyser above the eyepiece is required (p. 193), the small depth of space occupied by a Polaroid disc as compared with a calcite prism, allows the eye to be brought close enough to the eyepiece to view the whole field easily. (3) Polaroid polarisers can be made much wider, and therefore capable of passing a much wider beam of light, than is possible in the case of calcite prisms, the cross-sectional dimensions of which are limited by the scarcity and very high cost of large pieces of Iceland spar of optical quality. The ability to make use of a wide beam of light leads to considerable simplification in the design of the condensing system, as will be explained later in this chapter in the section on illumination. In view of the widespread use of Polaroid in modern polarising microscopes, and of the fact that there are also large numbers of instruments fitted with calcite prisms in use, it has become desirable to have a general term which covers both types of polarising devices. A. F. Hallimond has proposed the term 'polars',* and we shall use this term in the remainder of this book, unless a particular type of polarising device is referred to.

Resolution. So far in this chapter we have discussed the formation of images solely in terms of *geometrical optics*, i.e. by considering only the directions pursued by rays that are imagined either to have emanated from, or passed directly through an object, and then to have suffered refraction at the lens surfaces in accordance with Snell's Law. This treatment enables us to find the position and size of an image, but can tell us nothing about the degree to which the image reproduces, or *resolves*, the fine detail of the object. This is because the treatment takes no account of the wave nature of light.

The *resolving power* of an optical system is expressed inversely by the *limit of resolution*, i.e. the smallest distance by which two points can be separated in the object and still be recognised as distinct in the image produced by the system. In a microscope this property is determined solely by the objective (assuming that the object is correctly illuminated; see later), since the eyepiece merely serves to magnify the primary image formed by the objective.

The fundamental reason for the existence of this limit of resolution is that light, as a result of its wave nature, spreads sideways, i.e. undergoes *diffraction*, when it passes through a small aperture, or grazes the edge of an obstacle, as we have already noted on p. 52 in connection

* Hallimond, A. F. *Manual of the Polarising Microscope* (Cooke, Troughton and Simms, 2nd Edn., 1953, reprinted 1956), p. 32.

with Young's experiment. In Abbe's theory of microscopic resolution (*ca.* 1873) attention is confined to the diffraction of the incident light by the object, which is regarded as a fine periodic structure or a combination of such structures. In Rayleigh's theory (1896) the object is regarded as being self-luminous (which it rarely is, though this condition may be approached under certain conditions of illumination) and the diffraction considered is that occurring at the edge of the objective aperture. The theories lead to very similar results for the limit of resolution, for they depend on the same basic fact, namely

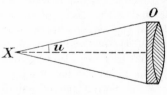

Fig. 3.12

that the whole information about the object that is communicable by light waves at all* is contained, as it were, in the light, both direct and diffracted, streaming in all directions from the object, and the more of this light that is taken in by the objective, i.e. the wider the angle of the cone of rays that it accepts, the more faithfully will the image reproduce the object detail.

As a working rule based on these theories, which is in fact well borne out in practice with well-corrected objectives, it may be taken that:

$$\text{Limit of resolution} = \frac{\lambda}{2n \sin u} = \frac{1}{\text{resolving power}} \qquad . \ 3.7$$

where λ is the wave-length of the light used, n is the refractive index of the least refractive medium separating object and objective, and u is the half-angle of the maximum cone of rays which the objective can accept from the object, as shown in Fig. 3.12. With the usual 'dry' objectives, the medium just referred to is air, and so n is sensibly equal to 1. The quantity $n \sin u$ is known as the *numerical aperture* of the objective (symbol N.A.). Thus the limit of resolution is proportional to the wave-length of the light, and inversely proportional to the N.A. of the objective.

* Structural details which are on a scale appreciably smaller than the wave-length of light, are by this very fact not reproducible in an image formed by light waves.

The following table gives the numerical apertures and other data for a typical range of objectives:

DETAILS OF ACHROMATIC OBJECTIVES MANUFACTURED BY
VICKERS INSTRUMENTS LTD.

Focal length		Magnifying power	Working distance (mm.)*	N.A.	u (degrees)
Inches	mm.				
$1\frac{1}{3}$	33	3	43·0	0·1	6
1	25	5	17·0	0·15	9
$\frac{2}{3}$	16	10	5·0	0·28	16
$\frac{1}{3}$	8	20	1·5	0·5	30
$\frac{1}{3}$	8	20	1·7	0·5	30†
$\frac{1}{6}$	4	40	0·71	0·65	40
$\frac{1}{6}$	4	40	0·83	0·65	40†
$\frac{1}{6}$	4	40	0·37	0·85	58
$\frac{1}{6}$	4	40	0·49	0·85	58†
$\frac{1}{12}$	1·8	95	0·12	1·30	59‡

* The distance between the end lens of the objective and the object when the microscope is in focus.
† These objectives are corrected for use with specimens not covered by a cover-slip, such as polished sections of metals or of ore minerals studied by reflected light.
‡ Oil immersion objective (see below).

In the case of *oil immersion* objectives, such as that given last in the table, a high numerical aperture is obtained by filling the narrow space between the end lens and the cover slip over the object with 'immersion oil'. This is usually thickened cedar wood oil, but others are marketed for the purpose, and if a special one is recommended by the makers of the objective, it is best to use it. Immersion oils have a refractive index of 1·51–1·52, and provided that there is no medium with a lower index anywhere between the condenser and the objective, the resolving power will be raised in proportion to this value, i.e. as compared with the performance of a 'dry' objective of the same angular aperture, as is shown by equation 3.7. A reason for using oil with this particular value is that it is approximately the same as the refractive index of glass, and this contributes to the elimination of spherical aberration in the objective, as already explained on p. 122.

Magnification. The magnifying power of an objective depends, as we have seen, on its focal length, and is not *necessarily* connected with its resolving power, i.e. with its N.A. In practice, however, objectives are designed so that these two properties do go more or less hand in hand (see table above, for example), and there are two reasons for this. Firstly, the full resolving power of a given objective cannot be realised visually unless the magnification of the object exceeds a certain minimum value, because the eye itself has a limited resolving power. (Neighbouring image points which fall on the same nerve ending on the retina are not resolved.) Secondly, magnification in excess of that required comfortably to bring out the detail which the objective is capable of resolving is valueless—*empty magnification* it is commonly called—besides unnecessarily restricting the amount of the object which appears in the field of view.

The actual total magnification (that of the objectives times that of the eyepiece) required in any case depends on a number of factors, principally the nature of the object and its contrast, the illumination, and the observer's eyesight, but *a useful rule is that it should lie between* 250 *and* 1000 *times the N.A. of the objective*. Thus for an N.A. of 0·80 it would be between 200 × and 800 ×.

The Mechanical Construction of the Polarising Microscope. Those parts of the microscope which support the body tube, stage, and substage, and are concerned with the focussing of the instrument and the centring of its optical components, are known collectively as the *stand*. Most polarising microscopes and other optical microscopes in use today have stands of one or other of the types shown in Figs. 3.13 and 3.14. In these figures the components which have already been referred to in Figs. 3.6 and 3.10 are given the same distinguishing letters. The drawings do not illustrate the instruments of any particular manufacturer, but show the general lay-out to which most instruments of these two types conform.

Fig. 3.13 shows the older and more conventional *hinged stand*. The curved *arm* supports the body tube at its upper end, and the stage, substage, and mirror at its lower end. It is hinged at V to the *foot*, which is approximately U-shaped. The hinge enables the optical axis of the instrument to be adjusted to any angle between vertical and horizontal, either to secure the most comfortable viewing position or for some special purpose, e.g. if it is desired to project an image of the specimen on a screen which, given a sufficiently powerful illuminant, can conveniently be done with the microscope in the horizontal position.

The microscope is focussed by moving the body tube up or down by means of a rack and pinion mechanism. In addition to this movement (*coarse focussing*), a much slower and more sensitive one may be produced by additional mechanism giving *fine focussing*. In the figure K and D are the milled heads on the near side of the instrument which

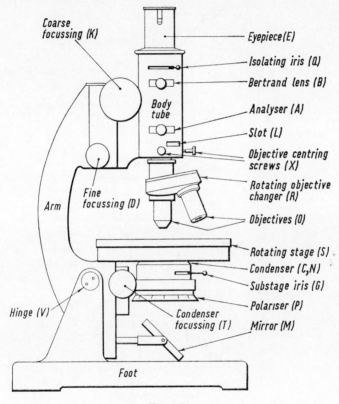

Coarse focussing (K)

Eyepiece (E)

Isolating iris (Q)

Bertrand lens (B)

Analyser (A)

Body tube

Slot (L)

Objective centring screws (X)

Rotating objective changer (R)

Fine focussing (D)

Arm

Objectives (O)

Rotating stage (S)

Condenser (C,N)

Substage iris (G)

Polariser (P)

Hinge (V)

Condenser focussing (T)

Mirror (M)

Foot

Fig. 3.13

operate these two movements respectively. There are corresponding heads on the other side, so that the instrument can be focussed with either hand. Usually one of the heads operating the fine focussing movement is graduated so that small vertical distances in the specimen, e.g. the thicknesses of crystals, can be measured (p. 159).

Another rack and pinion mechanism, operated by the head T enables the condenser (C,N) to be focussed (see next section on illumination).

The substage iris G, and, commonly, the polariser P, are in the same mount as the condenser and so move with it.

Fig. 3.14 shows the type of instrument with a *fixed stand*, which has been introduced in the last twenty years and has become very popular.

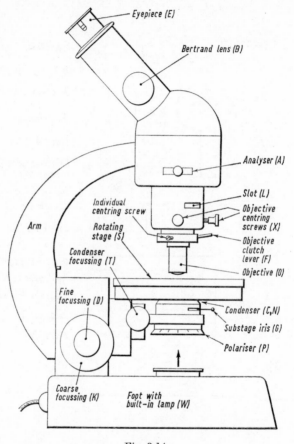

Fig. 3.14

As far as polarising microscopes are concerned, this type has been mainly confined to larger instruments for research work, examples being those of Vickers Instruments Ltd., York, England, and the ranges of polarising microscopes made by E. Leitz, Wetzlar, Germany, and Carl Zeiss, Oberkochen, Germany. The main features of the design are as follows. (1) The arm and its attachments are fixed (apart from focussing movements) so that the optical axis remains vertical. (2) By means of a prism at the top of the body tube, the light beam is bent so as to enter an inclined eyepiece, thus giving greater comfort in viewing. In some instruments the eyepiece is inclined in the opposite direction to that shown in Fig. 3.14. (3) The focussing controls (K,D) are set low down, so that the hands can rest on the bench while using them, and they are coaxial, so that no time need be wasted in groping from one to the other. In some instruments one mechanism, coarse or fine, moves the stage instead of the body tube, while the other moves the arm and attached body tube; in others both mechanisms operate the stage. The fine focussing control is graduated as in most hinged models. (4) The lamp (W) with its associated condenser, iris, and filter holder (see next section) is built into the single broad foot of the microscope, so that once it has been properly adjusted, it gives a correctly centred illuminating beam as soon as it is switched on. If, however, a more powerful external illuminant is required, a mirror as used on hinged stands can be fitted to the foot. The focussing mechanism of the condenser is similar to that on hinged models.

We shall now consider some mechanical points which affect both types of stands.

Methods of changing objectives. A simple and (if well made), satisfactory fitment for this purpose is the *revolving nosepiece*, which consists of a revolving mounting screwed to the lower end of the tube, and carrying two or more objectives of different powers, any one of which can be brought into position merely by turning the mounting; a spring catch ensures that each one is correctly located. It is assumed that the objectives are *parfocal*, i.e. focus at approximately the same relative position of body tube and stage, as is usually the case with objectives made for the same microscope. If this is not so, great care must be taken when bringing into position objectives having a small working distance; the tube must first be raised (or the stage lowered), so that the objective will not foul the specimen. This precaution applies equally to the method below. The microscope shown in Fig. 3.13 is fitted with a revolving nosepiece (R).

Another and extremely satisfactory method of changing objectives is by means of an *objective clutch*. Each objective is provided with a specially shaped collar with a centring adjustment (Fig. 3.14), which fits accurately another collar screwed to the end of the tube of the microscope. The objectives are held in position by a strong spring clutch or catch (F, Fig. 3.14), which may be easily released.

Centring the objectives. All polarising microscopes fitted with a revolving stage are provided with means of bringing the axis of rotation of the stage and the optical axis of the instrument into coincidence. This is obviously necessary, particularly when using high-power objectives, if a crystal brought to appear at the intersection of the cross-wires is to maintain that position, or even to remain in the field at all, as the stage is rotated. In many instruments the adjustment is effected by two lateral movements of the objective mounting at right angles to one another, actuated by screws with milled heads or with ends shaped to fit a special key (X, Figs. 3.13 and 3.14). For critical centring it is essential to have this type of mechanism on microscopes fitted with a rotating nosepiece (unless the objectives can be individually centred on the nosepiece, as described below). It is advisable to have it even when each objective has its own centring collar (Fig. 3.14) and is secured by a spring clutch (F, Fig. 3.14), because centring is apt to be upset slightly by the ordinary handling of the instrument (e.g. sliding the analyser in and out) and this can usually be corrected much more quickly by turning the screws on the body tube than by recentring the objective collar.

With the ordinary rotating nosepiece it is usual to find that each objective requires a slightly different setting of the centring screws. To avoid this, some Continental manufacturers (C. Reichert, Vienna; E. Leitz, Wetzlar; Carl Zeiss, Oberkochen) supply objectives having an individual centring adjustment operated simply by turning a knurled ring, so that each objective on the nosepiece can be centred once for all.

To avoid the necessity for centring objectives at all, some microscopes are provided with mechanism for rotating the polars simultaneously, the stage being kept stationary. Examples are the Swift 'Dick' model (James Swift and Son Ltd., London), in which the mechanism consists of toothed gearing, and the Leitz 'SY' and the Bausch and Lomb 'LD' models in which the polars are linked by means of a bar.

Centring the condenser. Microscopes for advanced work are usually fitted with centring controls to the substage, enabling the condenser and substage iris to be brought exactly into line with the optical axis of the instrument. The centring of these components will be referred to again in the next section.

Illumination. From the preceding treatment we see that the maximum resolution is obtained with a given objective when its angular aperture is filled with light, i.e. when the object is illuminated by a cone of light having an apical angle equal to this aperture. This condition must also be established when using objectives of high aperture to obtain interference figures of crystals. Other optico-crystallographic observations, however, are concerned with the propagation of light along specific directions through the crystals, and in making these observations the incident beam must often be narrowed down to a near-parallel pencil, thus sacrificing resolution.

It is the function of the microscope condenser and the substage diaphragm, acting in conjunction with the source of light (nowadays almost always some form of electric lamp) to supply illumination appropriate to the observation to be made, and before describing ways of producing different conditions of illumination, some preliminary remarks on these items will perhaps be helpful.

The condenser. The condenser usually fitted to low- and medium-priced microscopes is of the two-lens Abbe type, shown in Figs. 3.6 and 3.10. This simple combination possesses considerable chromatic and spherical aberration, but it is nevertheless perfectly adequate for most general work. It has a maximum N.A. of about 1·2 when oiled to the preparation. Owing, however, to its spherical aberration, its full N.A. cannot be realised in such a way as to illuminate evenly the field of view or the back focal plane of the objective, unless one illuminates considerably more of the object than appears in the field of view. This produces 'glare' in the object image, because light falling on the preparation outside the field of view is scattered by details in the object, and some of this scattered light finds its way into the objective. To get rid of glare, the substage diaphragm must be closed somewhat, so that the objective aperture is not completely filled and some resolution is lost.

Various types of corrected, or *achromatic*, condensers are available, which differ in the extent to which chromatic and spherical aberrations have been reduced. The best of these approach in construction the complexity of a high-power objective, and when oiled to the slide have a N.A. of about 1·4. A corrected condenser should always be used when critical resolution at high powers is needed, or when using a high-aperture oil immersion objective to obtain wide-angle interference figures. The degree of correction necessary will depend on the problem, and in cases of doubt the advice of the makers of the instrument should be sought. For work on interference figures it is essential that the N.A. of the condenser be at least equal to that of the objective.

In microscopes fitted with a calcite prism as polariser, it is necessary to mount the upper lens, or lens combination, of the condenser (e.g. N in Figs. 3.6 and 3.10) so that it can be easily swung in and out of the path of the light. This is made necessary by the limitations imposed by the narrow beam of light which is passed by a calcite prism (p. 129). A condenser consisting of a fixed lens combination, which has a width appropriate to such a narrow beam, cannot meet all requirements of both high- and low-power objectives. Thus if it is designed to fill the field and aperture of high-power objectives, it will be incapable of filling the field of low-power objectives, because its focal length will be too short and only the centre of the field will be illuminated. It will only be possible to fill the field by removing the upper component and thus increasing the focal length.

The wide beam of light passed by a Polaroid polariser makes it possible to use a wide condenser of the type usually fitted to biological microscopes. The focal lengths and N.A.'s of such condensers are large enough to meet the requirements of a wide range of objectives, with no other adjustments than the setting of the substage iris to give the correct convergence to the light beam, and the focussing of the condenser. (Only the former of these adjustments is necessary in the system of illumination in which the diffuser is used; see below.)

To appreciate these points more clearly the reader may first refer to Fig. 3.15 *a* and *b*, which show respectively a narrow condenser CC_1 and a wide one CC_2, represented for simplicity by single refracting surfaces. Both condensers refract a parallel beam to a cone of the same angle, and therefore have the same N.A., but their focal lengths, f_1, f_2, are very different, that in *b* being the greater. The relation between focal length and area of object illuminated (i.e. field-filling ability) follows from the fact that this illuminated area is, under proper conditions of illumination, an image of the light source formed by the condenser, which is working like an objective 'in reverse', i.e. with the object (the light source) instead of the image at a more or less fixed distance from the lens system. Under these conditions the image of a source of given size will be *smaller* the smaller the focal length, as the reader may confirm for himself by drawing ray diagrams like Fig. 3.2 but interchanging object and image.

Many modern microscopes retain the condenser with removable upper component even though they are fitted with a wide or fairly wide polarising filter as the polariser. There are various reasons for this, one being that users who have been accustomed to this form of condenser continue to demand it. It is, however, the case that some achromatic condensers have rather short focal lengths, and that even with an instrument fitted with a long-focus Abbe condenser, it may be difficult to fill the field of a very low-power objective, especially if an eyepiece taking in a large field is used (see later). In such cases, the removable upper component is certainly a convenience.

The lamp. The simplest form is an ordinary 60 or 100 watt lamp with an *opal or milk-glass bulb*, running directly off the mains. It must be enclosed in a well-ventilated housing, with a circular opening about $1\frac{1}{2}$—2-in. in diameter for the emission of the light. This opening should be provided with an iris diaphragm, or a series of circular stops of different sizes, so that the effective size of the source may be varied. There should also be a holder for filters in front of the opening so that the colour or intensity of the light may be changed if desired.

There are many commercial types of these lamps available, but from the above description it is clear that it would be easy to make

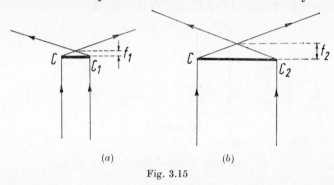

(a)   (b)

Fig. 3.15

one from simple materials and with the minimum of workshop facilities. The great advantage of this lamp, apart from its simplicity, is that it provides a large source of even intensity, so that the large field of view of low-power objectives can be fully and evenly illuminated (see later). For photomicrography and for some high-power work, particularly if colour filters are used, the intensity is rather low, though it is generally adequate for routine work in white light with all 'dry' objectives.

Low-voltage high-intensity lamps offer a more versatile form of illumination. The bulbs in these lamps have a small closely-coiled filament, the length of the coil being 2–3 mm., or a closely-spaced group of such coils, giving a larger area of source of the order of 3 mm. square, and work on 6 or 8 volts at a current of 5 to 6 amperes, through a small transformer. The bulb is mounted behind a condenser of about $1\frac{1}{2}$-in. focal length, and the distance between the two can be altered so that the light beam can be focussed. In front of the condenser there is an iris diaphragm and a filter holder. Although the wattage of these lamps, 36 to 48, is less than that of the opal bulb type, they are far more efficient, because much more of the light goes where it is wanted, namely in the direction of the microscope mirror. In the opal bulb lamp the light is scattered at the glass surface, and particularly when the diaphragm is closed down to suit the small fields of view of high-power objectives, only a small fraction reaches the microscope.

The above refers to lamps which are separate from the microscope. Built-in lamps (Fig. 3.14) are of the high-intensity type, but are generally of much smaller wattage than those just described, 15 watts (6 volts at 2·5 amps) being a common value.

Methods of Illumination Suitable for Polarisation Microscopy. These are shown in Figs. 3.16, 3.17 and 3.18. In these much simplified

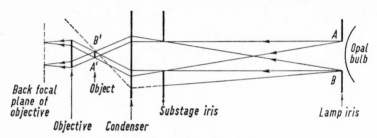

Fig. 3.16. 'Critical' illumination.

diagrams refraction at the objective, the microscope condenser and, in 3.17 and 3.18, the lamp condenser is represented as taking place at a single plane, and the light is shown as passing direct from the lamp to the microscope as though this were in the horizontal position, i.e. reflection at the microscope mirror is not represented. (This reflection is only a trivial circumstance in the usual way of using a microscope, and, provided that the flat side of the mirror is used, as in the normal procedure, it has no influence on the convergence or divergence of rays entering the microscope.)

'Critical' illumination. Fig. 3.16, represents what is termed 'critical' illumination, in which an image of the light source is formed in the plane occupied by the object. It used to be thought that this condition had to be satisfied if the best resolution was to be obtained, but it is now known that this is not necessary, and that the only really essential requirement for optimum resolution is that the aperture of the objective be filled. However, the arrangement of the illuminating system to give critical illumination is one in which the control of the convergence of the light falling on the object, and of the area of the object which is illuminated, is easy and straightforward, and it is the preferred method

for polarisation microscopy when the source of light is large and featureless, as with the opal bulb, or if a high-intensity lamp with a piece of ground glass in the filter holder is used.

In describing how critical illumination is established we shall first assume that the condenser of the microscope can be readily focussed, i.e. moved up and down, by a rack and pinion mechanism for example. A mounted preparation showing plenty of detail is placed on the stage, and the substage iris diaphragm is about half closed. A suitable preparation is a polycrystalline film made by melting an organic substance between a slide and cover slip and allowing it to crystallise (see p. 278), or a fine-grained rock section. The lamp is set up with its opening 6 to 8 in. from the microscope mirror (flat side), and the lamp iris, AB in the figure, is partly closed. The preparation is focussed, using a medium or low-power objective ($\frac{2}{3}$ to 1 in.) and a medium-power eyepiece, say 10 ×, and the image A'B' of the lamp iris is then focussed on the plane of the preparation by racking the condenser up or down. The quality of this image will depend on whether, and to what extent, the condenser is corrected. An Abbe condenser, for example, gives a poor image with strongly coloured borders, but in any case the sharpest image obtainable should be sought. (It is hardly necessary to add that in this and all other adjustments of the illuminating system of a microscope, the mirror should be adjusted so as to give the most even illumination of the field.) The lamp iris is then opened until the image A'B' just fills the field.

Next the back of the objective is inspected, either by simply removing the eyepiece and looking down the tube, or by inserting the Bertrand lens. If the substage iris is now closed, a sharp or reasonably sharp image of it will be seen, and, assuming that the objective has been correctly centred beforehand, this image should appear central with respect to the back lens of the objective.* (If it does not, the condenser and iris require centring, and if no means of doing this is provided on the instrument, it is best to return it to the makers for adjustment.) The iris is then opened until the back lens of the objective

* To avoid parallax effects, it is desirable that this image be formed at or near the back lens of the objective. When the iris is situated in the lower focal plane of the condenser (or focal region if the condenser is uncorrected), as in Figs. 3.6 and 3.16, the image is formed in the upper focal plane of the objective, which is near to the back lens with high-power objectives, but far above it with very low-power objectives. To bring the image nearer to the objective in this latter case, and also because it is easier constructionally, the iris is often placed somewhat below the focal plane of the condenser. This has little effect on the position of the image formed by high-power objectives, because their focal lengths are so short. A normal setting of the Bertrand lens now gives a sufficiently sharp image of the iris with all objectives.

is just filled with light. This shows that the aperture of the objective is just filled, and rays such as BC in the figure, which pass through the preparation at more oblique angles than are necessary for this are stopped, thus eliminating one source of glare. Since an objective of low aperture, is being used, the back lens should also be quite evenly illuminated after this adjustment has been made, even though the condenser may be an uncorrected one, because only a narrow central cone of rays is being taken from it, and for these the spherical aberration is small.

The conditions shown in Fig. 3.16, have now been established, and it only remains to replace the eyepiece, or remove the Bertrand lens, and inspect the image of the object. If this appears to be too bright for comfort, and detail is difficult to make out, i.e. if glare is present, the substage iris should be closed a little so as to reduce the effective aperture of the objective to, say, between three-quarters and two-thirds of its full value, this being checked by removing the eyepiece, or using the Bertrand lens, as before. This will increase the contrast, and give an image which can be viewed without eye strain, but of course some resolution will have been lost. The effect of glare can also be countered to a greater or less extent by reducing the general intensity of the light by inserting a neutral (smoky tint) filter in the filter holder of the lamp. Such filters can be bought, or a series having different intensities can be made of pieces of exposed and developed photographic plate. Some compromise between contrast and resolution must often be accepted in microscopy, however, particularly when using high powers and an uncorrected condenser (see below). Much depends on the inherent contrast in the object, and if this is high, it may be possible to use all or nearly all of the objective aperture, especially if the light intensity is reduced by a neutral filter.

Once critical illumination has been established as described above, it can be altered to suit objectives of higher power, merely by adjusting the lamp iris and the substage iris to correspond with the change in field area and objective aperture. The first step, as before, is to adjust the lamp iris so that the area of the field of view is just fully illuminated, and then to inspect the back lens of the objective. If the condenser is an uncorrected one, it will probably be found that this cannot be both fully and evenly illuminated, even by opening the substage iris to its full extent. This is because of the spherical aberration of the condenser. The more oblique rays necessary to complete the filling of the objective aperture are brought to a focus too low down and 'undershoot' the objective. (In using the words 'too low down' here, it is assumed, as elsewhere in this section, that the microscope is in the usual vertical position, and not as shown in Fig. 3.16.) The filling of the objective aperture can, however, be completed by opening the lamp iris a little more. This increases the size of the image of the source (A'B'), so that a greater area of the top surface of the condenser is illuminated. Rays of the required obliquity are now provided by the outer parts of this area, and these rays travel high enough to enter the objective.

The illumination achieved in this way with an uncorrected condenser and a high-power objective would be correct for the observation of interference figures, since the most important requirement here is that the upper focal plane of the objective be fully and evenly filled with light. But owing to the fact that it has been necessary to illuminate more of the object than appears in the field, the object image will probably suffer from excessive glare for the reason already given, and to get rid of this it will be necessary to close the substage iris somewhat and accept some reduction in resolution. On the other hand if a well corrected condenser is in use, it may be possible to achieve the use of the full aperture of the objective, because all the light is put where it is wanted, and so it is not necessary to illuminate more of the object than appears in the field of view.

If the condenser has a removable upper component the method of obtaining critical illumination is the same in principle as that described above, but it must be remembered that the upper component must be swung aside when using low powers and in position when using high powers. For intermediate cases the rule is simply that the upper component should only be used if its presence is found to be necessary to complete the filling of the objective aperture.

When working at low powers with a condenser having a fixed lens combination it may be found that the image of the light source is not large enough to fill the field, even when the lamp iris is opened to its fullest extent. One way of increasing the size of this image is to move the lamp a little nearer to the microscope, but there is not very much that can be done in this way, because it is obviously inconvenient, and also undesirable, to have the hot lamp housing too near to the instrument. A better method is to interpose a converging lens of $2\frac{1}{2}$ to 4-in. focal length between the lamp and the condenser, and nearer to the latter, the best position being found by trial. Such a lens, called the 'subsidiary condenser', is provided on some microscopes. An optically equivalent method is to use the concave side of the mirror, but this is usually regarded as less satisfactory because of the astigmatism which this introduces into the illuminating beam. However, at the low powers in question this is unlikely to have any marked effect on the quality of the image in the microscope, and is undoubtedly the simplest solution.

Köhler illumination. The low-voltage high-intensity lamp enables the object to be illuminated much more strongly than is possible with the opal bulb, and such illumination is needed, for example, for photomicrography, for detecting very small birefringences, and for obtaining brilliant interference figures in monochromatic light in studies of dispersion (p. 226). This type of lamp cannot, however, be used to establish critical illumination as with the opal bulb lamp, except

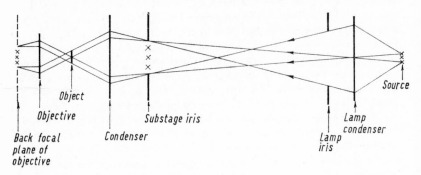

Fig. 3.17. Köhler illumination.

possibly at high powers, because the source is too small to fill the field of most objectives, and is uneven. (With a very small field, such as that of an oil-immersion objective, it may be possible to get rid of the unevenness by slightly defocussing the condenser.) This difficulty is got over by using the system known as Köhler illumination (Fig. 3.17). In this the image of the lamp filament (or filaments) is focussed on the plane of the *substage iris* by means of the lamp condenser, and the lamp iris is focussed on the plane of the object by means of the microscope condenser. The image of the source must be large enough to fill the lower aperture of the microscope condenser. This system is equivalent to critical illumination, but with the lamp *condenser* (which lies just behind the lamp iris) acting as the effective source, so that the irregularities of the filament do not appear in the field of view, while at the same time the full power of the lamp is utilised. Aperture and field are controlled respectively by the substage iris and the lamp iris as in critical illumination. Unfortunately from the standpoint of polarisation microscopy, the fact that the filament is imaged at or near the lower focal plane of the microscope condenser results in its being also imaged in the upper focal plane of the objective, so that this plane is unevenly illuminated and the proper observation of interference figures is hindered. If, however, the lamp bulb is of the type which has a group of closely spaced filaments, the hindrance is not serious, because the image of the group can be caused to cover the upper focal plane of the objective fairly evenly, and it can also be smoothed out somewhat by a small defocussing adjustment of the lamp condenser. Messrs. Carl Zeiss (Oberkochen) deal with this problem in their built-in illuminators by mounting a diffusing disc of 'hazed' glass (prepared by treatment with hydrofluoric acid, it is understood) immediately in front of the lamp bulb, in which position it is very close to the filaments of the special type of bulb used, and no serious loss of intensity results. With the ordinary high-intensity lamp, a piece of ground glass can be put in the filter holder when observing interference figures, but this will be so far away from the source that it will destroy the Köhler conditions completely, and the intensity will be much reduced. A simple solution which the authors have found satisfactory, and is equivalent to the Zeiss system, is to haze the glass of the bulb over a small area immediately in front of the filament or filaments by gently rubbing it with fine emery cloth, or carborundum powder, using water as lubricant.

There are alternative high-intensity featureless sources available, with which Köhler illumination meeting all requirements of polarisation microscopy may be established. Examples are (1) the 'Pointolite' lamp in which a bead of tungsten about 2·5 mm. in diameter is raised to incandescence, (2) the ribbon filament lamp in which a tungsten ribbon 2 mm. wide is used instead of a wire coil, and (3) the xenon arc. Such sources with their ancillary equipment tend to be expensive, and will usually only be required for special work. For further details the reader must consult more advanced works, such as B. O. Payne's *Microscope Design and Construction* (see Appendix I at end of this book).

The most convenient procedure for establishing Köhler illumination depends somewhat on the make of the lamp and of the microscope. For microscopes with built-in illumination the makers usually issue instructions, or will provide them on request, and these should be followed. When the lamp is separate the following procedure should be generally applicable. It is first necessary to see that the filament is correctly centred with respect to the lamp condenser,—an essential preliminary to any kind of use of an intensity lamp. The lamp is set up on a bench with the body horizontal, the iris is closed to reduce glare, and an image of the filament is focussed on a screen some 2 to 3 feet away by means of the condenser. Simple measurements with a ruler and stretched string will show whether the image is in line with the axis of the lamp, and any necessary adjustments can be made to the centring screws on the bulb holder, which are usually provided on these lamps. (If there are no centring screws, the bulb will have been pre-centred by the maker.) If the lamp bulb has been hazed (see above), a small ink spot may be made on the glass opposite to the centre of the filament and this spot is focussed on the screen.

With the lamp still on the bench the next step is to find by trial the distance l between it and the screen at which it gives an image of the source which will (taking its narrowest dimension) just fill the lower aperture of the condenser of the microscope. The lamp is then placed in position in front of the microscope, at a distance from the mirror which, plus that from the mirror to the substage iris (with the substage racked up to what is judged to be its normal position), is equal to l. The *lamp* iris is now closed down, focussed on the plane of the object with the microscope condenser, and then opened until the field is just filled, as in establishing critical illumination. Next the upper focal plane of the objective is examined by inserting the Bertrand lens, or removing the eyepiece, and the source is focussed on this plane by means of the lamp condenser.* If the source is featureless and cannot be marked, e.g. by an ink spot, as suggested above for filament lamps with hazed envelopes, it may be focussed by tilting the mirror slightly so as to bring the limit of the source into view, e.g. the edge of the filament in the case of a ribbon filament lamp. The mirror is afterwards recentred. If the lamp is of the type (the best) in which the position of the iris remains fixed and independent of the focussing of the source by the lamp condenser, Köhler illumination will now have been established, and it only remains to adjust the aperture and the illuminated area of the object to suit the observations to be made and the quality of the microscope condenser, as described for critical illumination. If, however, the lamp iris moves to and fro as the source is being focussed, some further adjustments of the microscope and lamp condensers may be necessary to secure the optimum conditions, because (1) the focussing of the source on the upper focal plane of the objective may have upset (2) that of the lamp iris on the plane of the object, and *vice versa* (since the substage iris usually moves with the microscope condenser). It is unlikely that these readjustments will be more than minor ones, unless the whole series of operations was begun with the microscope condenser far from its normal position. The best

---

* In some lamps the source is fixed and the condenser is moved to or from it; in others it is the source that is moved.

way to proceed is to make small changes to (1) and (2) alternately, and
check at each stage.

Illumination with high-intensity lamp and diffuser. A very convenient
system of illumination meeting the requirements of all routine work in
polarisation microscopy is shown in Fig. 3.18. It was originally proposed by A. F. Hallimond and E. W. Taylor and was incorporated as
an integral feature of the design of the first polarising microscopes
made by Messrs. Cooke, Troughton and Simms (predecessors to Vickers

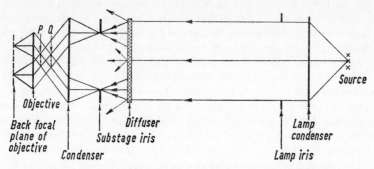

Fig. 3.18. Illumination with high-intensity lamp and diffuser.

Instruments Ltd.) to be equipped with Polaroid.* It was in fact only
made possible by the increase in the size of the condenser and in the
width of the incident beam permitted by the use of Polaroid, to which
reference has already been made. In this system the beam from a high-
intensity lamp is focussed so as to cover the area of a finely-ground
glass disc, the *diffuser*, situated just below the polariser (not shown in
the figure; see Fig. 3.10). From every point on the diffuser the light is
scattered in all directions. Much is lost by being scattered too far
sideways, but that which reaches the condenser strikes each point on its
lower surface from many different directions, with the result that the
convergent beam emerging at the top of the condenser consists of rather
wide bundles of parallel rays. Two of these bundles are drawn in the
figure. It will be noted that the region in which they intersect is of
considerable depth, so that an object could be situated at either P or Q,
say, and still be fully illuminated by rays in both bundles. This illustrates
one of the main advantages of the system, namely that no readjust-
ment of the height of the condenser to suit preparations mounted
on slides of different thicknesses is necessary, and so no focussing

---

* 'An Improved Polarising Microscope', *Min. Mag.*, 1946, **27**, 175.

movement for the condenser need be provided. This is the case in the Cooke 'Intermediate' and 'Research' models in which the condenser is held in a fixed position in a tubular mount by a clamping screw. (The condenser can, however, be clamped at different levels in this mount, so that it is possible, though not very convenient, to dispense with the diffuser and focus a light source on the object plane, i.e. to use critical or Köhler illumination, if desired.) Very even illumination of both the field of view and the upper focal plane of the objective are obtained by this method. Further, no particular advantage is gained by using a corrected condenser, and so the cheap Abbe type is adequate, provided that its aperture is sufficient for the work being done. The only adjustment necessary when changing from one objective to another, is to open or close the substage iris to suit the aperture of the new objective. The disadvantage of the system is that there is no control of the area of the object which is illuminated, because the diffuser prevents any image of the lamp iris being formed in the object plane. The only result of closing this iris is to reduce the total amount of light reaching the diffuser, and therefore the overall intensity of the light entering the microscope. Therefore when the substage iris is opened sufficiently to fill the aperture of a high-power objective, much more of the object than appears in the small field of view is illuminated, in fact practically the whole of the top lens of the condenser is flooded with light, so that the object image suffers badly from glare. This can only be eliminated by closing the substage iris somewhat, and sacrificing resolution. However, for routine optical crystallographic work, in which the emphasis is likely to be much more on optical properties than on the resolution of fine detail, this is not a great drawback.

'Parallel' Light. The treatment in the preceding sections on illumination assumes that the main aims are to obtain a well-resolved object image and to study interference figures. Many optical crystallographic tests are, however, concerned with the properties of the crystal for a single direction of propagation of the light (e.g. study of polarisation colours, effects of compensators, determination of refractive indices— see Chapter 4), and for these purposes the light must be rendered as nearly parallel as possible by closing down the substage iris to the smallest size consistent with adequate illumination. A better result may be obtained if the condenser is also lowered, but this is usually unnecessary. The most nearly parallel pencil is obtained if a second diaphragm of small aperture is provided in the substage assembly above or below the first, and not too near to it, or alternatively is inserted in the upper focal plane of the objective. It should be realised, however, that *strictly* parallel light is not obtainable in any of these ways, because of diffraction by the apertures controlling the beam— hence the inverted commas in the title of this section.

The closing of the substage diaphragm, particularly with high-power objectives, results in considerable loss in resolution, and a marked increase in contrast which the beginner may think represents an *increase* in resolution. Inspection of the image will show, however, that the increase in contrast is largely due to the formation of diffraction rings and haloes around prominent discontinuities in the image, and that the finer details visible with a more open setting of the iris have in fact been blurred out.

Heat Filters. Powerful sources of light emit a considerable amount of heat radiation, and the possibility of the specimen heating up must not be overlooked. Regard to this point is particularly important in refractive index work, for many of the liquids used alter in index considerably with change of temperature. Polaroid polarisers may also be damaged if directly subjected to a concentrated beam from a high-intensity lamp. The simplest form of protection is a piece of special heat-absorbing glass, placed in the filter holder of the lamp, and such filters are obtainable from microscope manufacturers. A type of glass suitable for this purpose is Chance ON 19 made by Chance Bros. Ltd., Smethwick, near Birmingham, England. Failing this the light may be passed through a parallel-sided glass cell filled with water. The minimum thickness of the water layer should be about 2 cm.

Monochromatic Light. For certain of the more advanced optical crystallographic determinations, such as obtaining accurate values for refractive indices and studying quantitatively the dispersion of the optic axial angle, it is necessary to use light which is monochromatic or approximately so. A suitable source is a modified form of spectrometer known as a *monochromator*. By means of this instrument, a narrow band of wave-lengths from any part of the spectrum may be directed into the microscope. The intensity of such a band is only a small fraction of that of the light entering the monochromator, and in order that it shall be adequate to illuminate the crystal it is necessary to use a high-intensity primary source, such as an arc. This consideration and the high cost of the instrument militate against its use for ordinary work.

For general purposes the most convenient source of light, which is strictly monochromatic (within the limitations outlined in the footnote on p. 62), is a type of *electric discharge lamp* which contains a volatile metal, and a small quantity of an inert gas, the purpose of which is to facilitate the initial discharge between the electrodes. As the lamp warms up, the metal vaporises and its characteristic frequencies are excited by the discharge. The light emitted also contains lines due to the inert gas, but their intensity is very low. A series of such lamps with sodium, cadmium, mercury, cadmium-mercury, and zinc fillings is supplied by the General Electric Company Ltd. (London), under the trade name 'Osira'. These lamps give a number of strong lines well spaced throughout the whole of the visible spectrum, and most of the lines can be readily isolated, or nearly so, by means of suitable filters.

The sodium lamp is the most generally useful, since it is customary to record optical data for sodium light (the doublet or D 'line' at 5896 and 5890 Å). For most work with the microscope it is unnecessary to use a filter with this lamp, since the intensity of the lines due to the inert gas is only about 1% of that of the D line. If specially pure sodium light is required, however, the inert gas lines can be eliminated by means of a suitable yellow filter. For example, the Ilford No. 606 Spectrum Yellow filter (see below), cuts out all but a doublet in the yellowish green region at 5688, 5683 Å, and the intensity of this is much reduced.

For many observations, light that is approximately monochromatic suffices, and this may conveniently be produced by passing white light through *filters* consisting of dyed gelatine films mounted between glass plates. The Ilford range of 'Spectrum' filters is satisfactory for this purpose.* The limits of the transmission band and the wave-length corresponding to the peak intensity of the band are given for each filter in the table opposite.

The figures given in the second column are the extreme limits of transmission, and with the normal illumination used for work with the microscope the light transmitted in the region of these limits will be of very low intensity. Thus the bands are effectively narrower than would at first appear.

These gelatine filters are easily damaged by heat, and must always be protected from the heat of the microscope lamp by interposing a piece of heat-absorbing glass or a water cell, leaving a space between the gelatine filter and the protecting filter.

Interference filters which transmit a narrow band of wave-lengths have been introduced during recent years. These consist of a layer of a dielectric, commonly cryolite (sodium aluminium fluoride), between metallised glass surfaces, and depend on interference

---

* Ilford Ltd., Ilford, London. Full details of these and other filters made by the Company are published by them in a brochure obtainable on request.

between the rays reflected respectively from the front and back surfaces, the transmitted wave-lengths being determined by the thickness of the dielectric layer. A particularly useful form is the *graded*, or

Ilford Filter	Limits of Transmission Band (Å × 10)	Wave-length of Peak Intensity (Å × 10) (approximate)
No. 601 Spectrum Violet . . .	385–475	430
No. 602 Spectrum Blue . . .	445–495	470
No. 603 Spectrum Blue-Green . .	475–520	490
No. 604 Spectrum Green . . .	500–545	520
No. 605 Spectrum Yellow-Green .	530–580	550
No. 606 Spectrum Yellow . .	560–610	575
No. 607 Spectrum Orange . .	575–720	600
No. 608 Spectrum Red . . .	625 to infra-red	680 to limit of visible
No. 609 Spectrum Deep Red . .	640 to infra-red	710 to limit of visible

continuous running filter, which is of elongated shape with the thickness of the dielectric varying continuously from one end to the other, and giving a change of transmitted wave-lengths over the whole spectrum. An example, manufactured by Schott and Gen. (Mainz), is supplied by Carl Zeiss (Oberkochen) mounted in a metal frame, which is calibrated in peak wave-lengths, and may be inserted in guides above the built-in illuminator of the Zeiss microscopes, or in front of a high-intensity lamp. Other such graded filters are made by Bellingham and Stanley (London), and by Bausch and Lomb (Rochester, N.Y., U.S.A.). The ability to change the wave-length rapidly and continuously in this way is a great advantage in studies of dispersion, and in 'variation' methods of determining refractive indices (p. 163).

The Use and Care of the Polarising Microscope. If the eyes are equally strong, fatigue may be avoided when working for long periods by using them alternately. The unoccupied eye should be kept open as less strain is thereby imposed, and with a little experience it should be found possible to concentrate the attention on what is seen through the microscope. It undoubtedly helps, however, if the vision of the unoccupied eye is blocked by a shade, made of cardboard and painted dead black, suitably attached at the side of the upper end of the microscope tube. A somewhat costly alternative is the *binocular eyepiece*, but the fitting of this to most microscopes interferes with the proper siting of the Bertrand lens, and is not therefore recommended for polarisation microscopy in which interference figures are being constantly studied.

The microscope must not be carried by any part above the fine adjustment mechanism, or the latter will be ruined. Most microscopes are best carried by holding the arm of the instrument with one hand and steadying the foot with the other.

When not in use, the microscope must be protected from dust either by replacing it in its case, or by covering it with a glass bell jar or a cardboard or plastic hood. Such covers may be obtained from firms dealing in scientific apparatus. It goes without saying that the microscope must not be used in any room in which corrosive fumes are generated. To prevent the entry of dust into the optical system of the microscope, the dust covers over slots for the reception of compensators must be kept closed when the slots are not in use. Unoccupied holes in the revolving nosepiece for changing objectives should be closed by screw caps.

Cleaning and lubrication of mechanical parts. New microscopes are usually accompanied by makers' instructions on these points, but if such attention should be necessary to an older instrument, about which no special information is available, the following notes will serve as a guide. It is assumed that the microscope is of the hinged stand type.

The stand may be cleaned with a rag moistened with benzene or xylene. Alcohol should never be used for this purpose. To clean the coarse focussing mechanism, the tube should be removed and the slides cleaned with benzene or xylene, and then lubricated lightly with paraffin or clock oil, or a good quality grease, removing any surplus. The teeth of the rack and pinion should be cleaned with a small stiff brush, but not lubricated. A little paraffin or clock oil may be applied to the shanks of the knurled heads where these enter the arm. (Immersion oil is *not* a lubricant, and should never be used as such.) This attention should only be necessary at very infrequent intervals, if the instrument is kept free from dust. If anything goes wrong with the fine focussing mechanism, the instrument should be returned to the maker for attention.

Lenses, Polaroids and Nicols. The microscope must not be subjected to sudden changes of temperature, for such treatment is liable to crack or otherwise damage the cementing films in these components. It must also be remembered that these films may soften if the instrument is kept in too warm a place, e.g. near a radiator, or if powerful artificial light is passed through it for long periods without first passing the light through a cooling cell.

It is essential that all lenses and polarising devices should be kept clean and free from dust. The upper ends of Nicols are usually provided with glass dust covers, but the lower ends sometimes need cleaning. This should be done only with a camel-hair brush, since more vigorous treatment is liable to scratch or otherwise damage them. Polaroid discs should never be cleaned by rubbing between the finger and thumb, as they may be thereby rotated out of their proper positions.

Lenses may be freed from dust with a warmed camel-hair brush, and cleaned by breathing on them and gently polishing them with a soft linen rag (not silk or cotton) kept specially in a closed box, or by using the special lens paper sold for the purpose. If this is not effective, the rag or paper may be *slightly* moistened with a little benzene or xylene, but not alcohol. Care must be taken that no liquid gets between the lenses. The eye and field lenses of slotted oculars should be unscrewed from time to time and their inner surfaces cleaned as above. This exposes the cross-hairs and great care must be taken that these do not get broken during the operation.

Immersion oil should always be removed from immersion objectives with lens paper as soon as possible after use, as the oil may oxidise and harden if left.

It must be remembered that high-power objectives are very close to the object when they are in focus, and so great care in focussing them must always be exercised to avoid breaking the slide, damaging the objective mechanically, or contaminating it with immersion liquids which may corrode the metal or dissolve the cement in the lens system unless quickly removed. The safest method for the beginner is to reduce the distance between the objective and the object cautiously (i.e. by lowering the tube or raising the stage, according to the type of focussing movement), until on looking sideways along the stage, only a thin streak of light can be seen between the objective and the cover slip. Only the fine focussing movement should be used in the final stages of this operation. When it is completed it can be assumed that objective and object are nearer to one another than corresponds to the position of focus, and by now slowly operating the fine focussing control in the opposite direction while looking down the tube, the object will be brought into view.

When unscrewing an objective from a microscope, or attaching one thereto, the tube should be racked up (or the stage lowered) and the unoccupied hand held underneath the objective to catch it in case it should slip through the fingers. As a further precaution against such accidents it is a good plan to stand the microscope on a piece of thick soft cloth when it is in use.

6

4 THE MICROSCOPIC EXAMINATION OF CRYSTALS

A. ORTHOSCOPIC OBSERVATIONS
('Parallel' Light)

The Optical Examination. The complete optical examination of any substance comprises the following four main stages, which it is convenient to summarise here.

(I) *Ordinary Light (Polars not inserted)*

Observations on colour; crystalline form, if developed; cleavage; fracture. Measurement of edge angles. The determination of the refractive index of isotropic crystals.

(II) *Polarised Light (Lower Polar inserted)*

The determination of the principal refractive indices of anisotropic crystals and observations on pleochroism and 'twinkling'.

(III) *Crossed Polars*

Distinction between isotropic and anisotropic substances. Observation of the extinction, whether straight, symmetrical or oblique, if the latter, whether dispersed or not; measurement of the extinction angle. Determination of the birefringence from interference colours and thickness; and of the fast and slow directions by means of compensating plates.

(IV) *Convergent Polarised Light between Crossed Polars*

Observation of interference figures, and determination of uniaxial or biaxial character. If the latter, estimation of the size of the optic axial angle. Determination of the positive or negative character of the substance. Dispersion of the optic axes and bisectrices.

In practice, the properties listed under ordinary light are made above the polariser, the removal of which in some microscopes is a time-consuming operation. Very often it will not be necessary to go through the whole of the above process, the desired result of the problem in hand frequently emerging after a partial examination.

I. EXAMINATION IN ORDINARY LIGHT

Colour. The colour of a pure substance is a definite property, but its appearance in transmitted light under the microscope varies greatly with the thickness of the crystal, and some substances which appear quite dark in grains of a few millimetres diameter become quite pale or almost colourless in minute particles. Care should therefore be taken in describing this property. It should, however, always be observed in order that a comparison may be made with any changes of colour due to pleochroism (see below).

Crystal Form and Habit. The shapes of crystals as they appear under the microscope are determined by the crystal system to which they belong, the habit they affect (since they usually lie on faces of well developed forms), and by accidental distortions occurring during growth. Platy crystals will lie on their larger faces, and will have the advantage that a comparatively large surface free from reflections from edges will be available for study, but they have the disadvantage of making observations in other directions difficult or impossible. In any crop grown on a slide many crystals will by unequal development of faces, mask the true symmetry, but there are usually a good number which approximate to the ideal shapes. Fig. 4.1 shows typical shapes of crystals belonging to the various crystal systems, the orientation being shown by Millerian indices. Distortion may result in certain forms imitating the normal forms of other systems. For example, distorted cubes (Fig. 4.1 *a*) may resemble tetragonal or orthorhombic forms, but their true nature is revealed by their isotropism (p. 172). The distinction between mis-shapen rhombs (Fig. 4.1 *q*) and monoclinic or triclinic forms (*s* and *u*) is revealed by their decentralised uniaxial interference figure in convergent light (p. 210). Optical properties should always be used to confirm the evidence of shape and edge angles. Tetragonal and hexagonal crystals usually lie on their prism faces (Fig. 4.1 *f, g, h, j*) but may present square or hexagonal basal plates respectively which remain dark between crossed polars (p. 182) and present central uniaxial interference figures. Twins may be recognised by re-entrant angles or by the fact that between crossed polars the various members of the twinned crystal do not extinguish simultaneously (p. 194). Crystals which are equant or stoutly tabular may present a number of different sections for study because they may lie on a number of faces belonging to separate forms.

Cleavage. The presence of cleavage is revealed under the microscope by fine parallel lines in one or more directions on the crystal faces, or

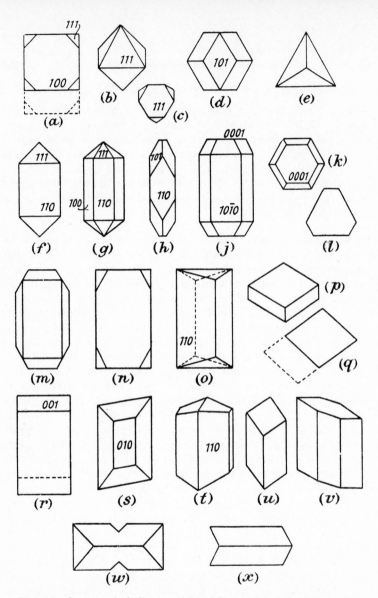

Fig. 4.1. Some typical shapes exhibited by crystals belonging to the various crystal systems as seen under the microscope.

Cubic: *a*, cube modified by the octahedron; *b* and *c*, octahedra; *d*, dodecahedron; *e*, tetrahedron.

Tetragonal: *f*, *g*, *h*, various combinations of prisms and pyramids.

Hexagonal: *j*, prism, pyramid and basal pinacoid; *k*, basal pinacoid and pyramid.

Trigonal: *l*, thin basal plate and two trigonal prisms; *p* and *q*, thick and thin rhombs.

Orthorhombic: *m*, *n* and *o*. The two former lying on pinacoids, and the latter on the prism (110).

Monoclinic: *r*, *s*, and *t*. The first a pinacoid form, lying on the (100); the second, pinacoid prism and dome, lying on (010); and the last, prism pinacoid and dome, lying on (110).

Triclinic: *u* and *v*, both crystals of copper sulphate, the first a pinacoidal form and the second, pinacoids and a prism.

The twinned forms are *w*, an orthorhombic twin of magnesium ammonium phosphate, and *x*, a twin of the monoclinic substance gypsum.

156

by the fact that the shapes of the fragments have been determined by the cleavage directions. The orientation of crushed grains or of detrital minerals is often controlled by the cleavage and can in certain cases be very characteristic. Good examples are provided by the triangular fragments of fluorite CaF_2, cleaved on the cubic octahedron {111}, or the rhomb-shaped pieces of the trigonal carbonates with cleavage parallel to {10$\bar{1}$1}. Where good pinacoidal cleavage occurs the surface of the crystal may be step-like in character, and each cleavage surface comes into focus on raising the objective. Fig. 4.2 *a*,

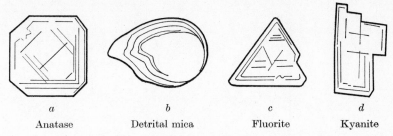

a	*b*	*c*	*d*
Anatase	Detrital mica	Fluorite	Kyanite

Fig. 4.2. Shapes of mineral grains determined by cleavage.

b, c and *d* shows examples of anatase, TiO_2; mica; fluorite; and kyanite, the triclinic form of Al_2O_3. Cleavage which is obscure may often be made more prominent by observing the crystal in oblique illumination (p. 162).

The Measurement of Edge (Profile) Angles. The angles between edges of idiomorphic crystals, or between traces of cleavages are often of diagnostic value and may be measured if the faces concerned are vertical or the traces of cleavage lie in a horizontal plane. The method of measurement is illustrated in Fig. 4.3. The intersection of the edges containing the angle is brought *near* to the intersection of the cross-wires and one of the edges is adjusted parallel to and nearly touching a cross-wire. The reading on the microscope stage is read and the stage turned until the other edge is parallel to the *same* cross-wire. The reading on the stage scale is again taken and the difference is either the included, or the supplementary, angle depending on which way the stage was turned. Such measurements may reveal the symmetry of the crystal, but since the method is not more accurate than about $\pm 0.5°$, conclusions about the symmetry should always be confirmed by the optical properties of the substance. For example, the ortho-rhombic substance carnallite, $KCl,MgCl_2,6H_2O$, crystallises from aqueous solution in six-sided plates having edge angles of nearly 60° and may be taken to be hexagonal, but as they are birefringent they cannot be of hexagonal symmetry parallel to (0001). The true polar angle (010:110 = 59°20′) gives an included angle of 120° 40′.

Measurement of Size and Thickness. Linear measurements under the microscope are made in such problems as the size analysis of sands or dusts where the amount of material is too small for other methods to be

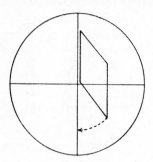 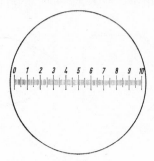

Fig. 4.3.   Measurement of   Fig. 4.4.
edge angles.   Eyepiece scale.

used; for the estimation in thin sections of the average grain size of rocks in descriptions of texture; to get data for modal analyses of rocks (i.e. in terms of the proportion of minerals present) and to determine the magnification of drawings of microscopic objects. The whole subject of microscopic size determination bristles with difficulties, and has given rise to a voluminous literature. It is not proposed to discuss the matter here but the reader is given a short selection of references below* in which other works on the subject are referred to.

Linear measurements of crystals under the microscope may be made by using a graduated mechanical stage; or by means of a transparent scale at the focus of the eye lens in a Huygens' ocular or more accurately at the external focus of a positive or Ramsden ocular (p. 124), calibrated as described below; or by using the more complicated screw-micrometer ocular, of which there are several types. In the first case, one side of

* Chayes, F., *Petrographic Modal Analysis*. (Wiley, New York, 1956). Holmes, A., *Petrographic Methods*, pp. 310–324. (Murby, London, 1921). Krumbein, W. C. and Pettijohn, F. J., *Manual of Sedimentary Petrography*, (D. Appleton Century Co., 1938) pp. 126–134, 176–181, 300–302. Larsen, E. S. and Miller, F. S., *Amer. Min.* 1935, **20**, 260. Rosenfeld, M. A., Jacobsen, L., and Ferm, J. C., *Jour. Geol.* 1953, **61**, 114–132.

the object to be measured is placed at the intersection of the cross-wires and then moved until the other side occupies a similar position. The difference between the two readings on the vernier of the stage gives the required length. The eyepiece micrometer is a piece of glass upon which has been engraved a scale consisting of fine lines one-tenth or one twentieth of a millimetre apart (Fig. 4.4). This is placed in the focal plane of the ocular. By placing upon the stage of the microscope a scale of known magnitude, the eyepiece scale may be calibrated for different combinations of objectives and oculars. The reader should familiarise himself with the size of the field seen with various combinations of oculars and objectives, as this will enable rapid approximate estimations of the sizes of crystals to be made. In drawings or photomicrographs of crystals, the magnification in diameters of the object should always be stated. This is the ratio between the actual size of the object and that of the picture.

It is sometimes necessary to measure the thickness of crystals or crystal plates, as for example in the measurement of birefringence. This may be done by using the fine adjustment screw of the microscope where this has been calibrated by the makers. With a high-power objective, say $\frac{1}{4}$ in. or $\frac{1}{6}$ in. (used because it has a small depth of focus), a fine scratch made upon a glass slide is carefully focussed by *raising the objective*. The crystal plate is then pushed into position above the scratch, and the upper surface of the plate is brought into focus by raising the objective again. The difference between the first and second positions of the micrometer screw gives the desired result. It is very important to note that the micrometer screw must be turned in one direction during a determination so as to get rid of 'lost motion' which would introduce serious error into the result. It is obvious that such measurements must be done upon dry and uncovered crystals.

In permanent mounts, as for example, thin slices of rocks or other materials, fairly accurate estimates of thickness may be made from the polarisation colours of any substances present whose birefringence and orientation are known (see p. 178).

Refractive Index. The accurate determination of refractive indices must be done in polarised light in the case of anisotropic substances, but the principles underlying the methods used under the microscope may conveniently be explained here, first of all with reference to isotropic crystals, which need only the use of ordinary (unpolarised) light.

If a colourless isotropic substance like glass is immersed in a colourless fluid, both having the same refractive index, the glass will become invisible in the fluid owing to the disappearance of refraction and reflection effects at the junction of the two substances. If the refractive indices are different, the *relief* or strength of the border between the two substances depends upon the magnitude of the difference. Practical use is made of this fact in the determination of refractive indices under the microscope, by immersing substances in different fluids of known refractive index, until the border phenomena disappear. When this happens, both substances have the same refractive index. In practice, when the border phenomena appear, it is necessary to know whether the refractive index of the fluid is higher or lower than that of the crystal. For, the relief of a substance with an index of 1·65 will be the same if it is placed in fluids with refractive indices of 1·70 or 1.60, the difference being the same in each case. Two methods are available, namely, (*i*) that of *central illumination*, commonly called the 'Becke method', and (*ii*) that of *oblique illumination*, or the 'Schroeder van der Kolk method'.

(*i*) *The method of central illumination.* If the junction between a crystal and an immersion fluid is sharply focussed with a high or medium-power objective (say $\frac{1}{4}$-in. or $\frac{1}{3}$-in. focal length), the two substances having different refractive indices, and then the image is thrown slightly out of focus by raising the objective (or lowering the stage), a bright line, the so-called 'Becke line', will appear near the junction and will move laterally towards the substance having the higher refractive index, broadening the while and becoming fainter. On depressing the tube, the phenomenon is reversed. The appearance of the Becke line shown in Plate I *a* and *b* opposite.

Various explanations of the phenomenon have been given. Becke's own explanation of the case in which the junction between the two substances is vertical is illustrated in Fig. 4.5 *a* in which A has the smaller refractive index. In slightly convergent light a bundle of rays, numbered 1 to 10, are refracted and reflected as shown, rays 6 to 10 being refracted in B towards the normal to the junction, rays 1, 2, and 3 being refracted away from the normal through A. Rays 4 and 5, however, meet the junction within the critical angle and so are reflected back on the same side of the junction to augment the effect of rays 6 to 10. The side of the junction towards the substance with the higher refractive index will be more strongly illuminated, giving the Becke line, which will appear to move towards B and become more diffuse when the objective is raised from the position of sharpest focus. Reference to the figure will show that the narrower the cone of light falling upon the junction the clearer will be the effect, as practically all the light emerging from A may be cut out. This may be done by

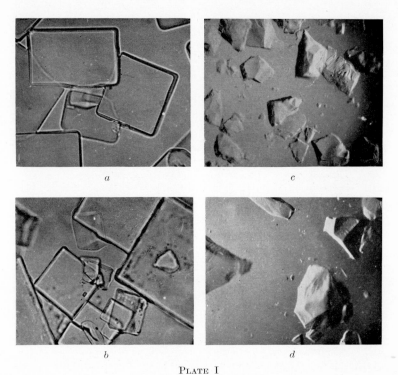

a c

b d

PLATE I

(See pp. 160–162)

Refractive Index Tests

(a) Becke test: index of crystal < index of liquid.
(b) Becke test: index of crystal > index of liquid.
(c) Van der Kolk test: index of crystal < index of liquid.
(d) Van der Kolk test: index of crystal > index of liquid.

to face page 160]

means of the substage diaphragm or by lowering the condenser. If the diaphragm is closed well down, good Becke lines may be observed with low power objectives. Vertical junctions such as have been described are not often met with in practice, but the rule that the Becke line moves towards the substance with the higher refractive index still applies as may be seen in Fig. 4.5 *b* and *c*, and Fig. 4.6. In these it is

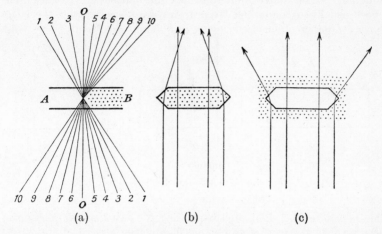

Fig. 4.5. The Becke test.

assumed that the light is 'parallel' (p. 148). Crystals or grains often present rude lens-like shapes due to the edges being thinner than the centre. It will be seen that when the refractive index of the grain is greater than that of the immersion fluid it acts as a double convex (converging) lens (Fig. 4.5 *b*), and when the conditions are reversed, as a double concave (diverging) lens (Fig. 4.5 *c*). Raising the microscope tube in the first case will cause the Becke line to move inwards illuminating more strongly the centre of the grain, and in the second case the adjacent field is more strongly illuminated than the grain. Should the light be weakly convergent and not parallel, the effect is the same. In thin slices junctions between substances are at various inclinations. Three representative cases are shown in Fig. 4.6 *a, b* and *c*, in which the substance with the greater refractive index is shaded. In the first case as at *a*, the higher refractive index overlaps the lower, but the rays meeting the junction are refracted towards the normal and so pass into the upper material with the higher refractive index. In the second case as at *b*, the junction is nearly vertical and rays meet the surface within the critical angle and once again are turned towards the substance with the higher index. In *c*, the substance with the higher refractive index underlies that with a lower one, but the rays being refracted away from the normal as shown once again fulfil the law of the Becke line.

The beginner is often nonplussed when he sees two Becke lines at a junction, which move simultaneously in opposite directions. The effect usually occurs when large grains are observed and the edges have a number of surfaces sloping in different directions. The 'false'

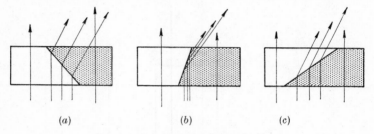

(a)   (b)   (c)

Fig. 4.6. Formation of the Becke line.

line may often be eliminated by closing the sub-stage diaphragm or alternatively the method of oblique illumination described in the next section may be used.

(*ii*) *The method of oblique illumination.* For this test the sub-stage diaphragm should be opened, a low-power objective used and oblique light obtained very simply by placing a card or a finger over half the mirror or by partly covering the lower opening of the condenser casing, or by merely tilting the mirror. Under these conditions it will be seen that when the substance has a higher refractive index than the immersion fluid a shadow appears on the same side of the *grain* as that on which the light was cut off, the opposite border being more brightly illuminated (see Plate I *d*, opposite p. 160). When the grain has a smaller refractive index than the liquid the positions of shadow and bright boarder are reversed (Plate I *c*). Care should be taken to see that the condenser always occupies the same position, because the phenomenon as seen in the microscope can be reversed by placing the object above or below the focus of the condenser.

The two methods of central and oblique illumination should be used together if possible, especially when deciding whether an exact match has been made between crystal and immersion fluid, or where owing to double Becke lines, the result may be in doubt.

Most of the fluids used in refractive index determinations by the immersion technique have a greater dispersion than crystals. That is to say the refractive indices of immersion fluids change greatly with the wave-length of light used, being higher for blue than for red, whereas the refractive indices of crystals change to a comparatively small extent for different colours of the spectrum. When therefore both crystal and liquid have the same refractive index for a wave-length of light near the middle of the spectrum, say for sodium light, the crystal will have a higher index than the liquid for the red end of the spectrum and a lower refractive index than the liquid for blue. If, now, the crystal is viewed in oblique white light, instead of the usual dark and bright borders, coloured fringes will be seen, one side of the crystal being bluish and the other reddish in colour. The blue fringe occupies the position which in blue light would be the bright border, and the red fringe the position that would appear bright in red light. In parallel light under similar conditions, blue and red Becke lines appear which move in opposite directions on raising the objective.

In monochromatic light an accuracy of ± 0.002 is attainable. With care where the habit is favourable and if the refractive index of the immersion fluid is determined at stage temperature, an accuracy of ± 0.001 may be achieved. It is best to approach the true value of the desired refractive index by a 'bracketing' procedure in which one determines the values which are just discernably below and above the correct value, after which a liquid may be made up if necessary for the final match. For instructions as to making mounts for refractive index determinations see pp. 268, 274.

Index Variation Immersion Methods. Improved immersion methods which give greater accuracy than the usual ± 0.002 of the method already described have been proposed by certain authors. The principles upon which these methods are based are (1) that the index of refraction of liquids increases with a decrease in the wave-length of light, and this dispersion is generally greater in liquids than in solids; (2) the index of refraction of liquids decreases as the temperature rises to a much greater extent than it does in solids for a similar rise, change in the latter being negligible over the range of temperature employed.

The methods are, briefly: the *dispersion method*, proposed by Merwin and Larsen,* by which the index of refraction of the substance is matched with the immersion fluid by altering the wave-length of the light used by means of a monochromator; the *single variation* method

* *Amer. J. Sci.*, 1912 (4), **34**, 42–7.

of Emmons* by which the indices of fluid and substance are matched by changing the temperature of the mount upon a warm stage; and the *double variation* method of the same author† in which both the wave-length of light and the temperature are changed, thus making it possible to determine the refractive index of the substance for any kind of light from the dispersion curves, which can be drawn after the refractive index of liquid and crystal has been matched at three or four different temperatures.

Immersion Media. Ideally the liquids used in refractive index work should be colourless, chemically stable and inert towards the substances with which they are used. As some organic liquids decompose in the light they should be kept in dark-coloured bottles of about 5 c.c. capacity having well-ground stoppers with dropping rods attached. It is useful to make up a set of liquids ranging in refractive indices from 1·35 to about 1·78 with intervals of 0·01. Each liquid should be miscible with those above and below so that determinations may be made to the third decimal place.

A list of immersion liquids is given opposite from which a selection within the limits mentioned above may be made. The indices for pure single chemical compounds are given to the third decimal place and refer to the D line at the temperature stated. The data for other liquids, mainly natural oils, are only approximate values for room temperature, since the indices vary with the source, concentration, etc. Some data for the decrease of refractive index with rise of temperature $(-dn/dt)$, and for the dispersion are included. It cannot be emphasised too strongly that the indices given in the list are only to be used as a general guide and each liquid should be tested on a refractometer before use. The liquids in a permanent set should be tested periodically, say, every three months.

* *Amer. Min.*, 1928, **13**, 504.
† *loc. cit.*, and Winchell, A. N., *Elements of Optical Mineralogy*, Part I (Wiley, New York, 1931), pp. 216–34.

Liquid	n	°C	dn/dt	Dispersion
Water	1·333	20	slight	—
Acetone	1·359	19·4	—	slight
Methyl acetate	1·359	20	—	—
Ethyl alcohol	1·362	18·35	−0·0004	slight
Methyl butyrate . . .	1·386	20	—	slight
Ethyl butyrate	1·393	18	—	slight
Ethyl valerate	1·393	20	—	slight
Paraldehyde	1·405	20	—	—
Amyl alcohol	1·410	14·6	−0·0004	slight
Ethyl monochloracetate . .	1·419	25	−0·00047	—
Ethyl bromide	1·424	20	—	—
1,2-Ethylene dichloride . .	1·444	20	—	—
Chloroform	1·446	18	—	—
Trimethylene chloride . .	1·446	25	−0·00049	—
Petroleum*	1.45	—	—	—
Lavender oil	1·46	—	—	—
Carbon tetrachloride . . .	1·466	12·3	—	—
Methyl thiocyanate . . .	1·466	25	−0·00054	—
Olive oil	1·47–1·48	—	—	—
Almond oil	1·47–1·48	—	—	—
Turpentine	1·47	—	—	—
Glycerine†	1·47	—	—	—
Medicinal paraffin‡ . . .	1·47–1·49	—	−0·0004	slight
Castor oil	1·48	—	—	—
Methyl furoate	1·485	25	−0·00045	—
Toluene	1·498	16·35	—	—
Benzene	1·501	20	—	—
p-Xylene	1·497	16·2	—	—
m-Xylene	1·500	14·85	—	—
o-Xylene	1·508	15·5	—	—
Sandalwood oil	1·51	—	—	—
Propylene bromide . . .	1·516	25	−0·00054	—
Cedarwood oil	1·51–1·52	—	—	—
Ethyl iodide	1·522	7	—	—
Ethyl salicylate	1·525	14·4	—	—
Monochlorobenzene . . .	1·525	20	—	—
Clove oil	1·53	—	−0·0005	moderate
1,2-Ethylene dibromide . .	1·538	20	−0·0006	—
Methyl salicylate . . .	1·532	21	—	—
o-Nitrotoluene	1·547	20·4	—	—
Aniseed oil	1·55	—	—	—
Mononitrobenzene . . .	1·553	20	−0·0005	—
Dimethylaniline	1·559	20	—	—

* Ordinary lamp oil.
† Takes up water from the air rather rapidly.
‡ Any medicinal oil, such as Nujol, may be used.

Liquid	n	°C	dn/dt	Dispersion
Monobromobenzene . . .	1·560	20	—	—
Benzyl benzoate . . .	1·57	—	—	—
o-Toluidine	1·573	20	−0·0005	—
Cinnamon oil	1·58–1·60	—	−0·0003	strong
Aniline	1·586	20	−0·0005	—
Bromoform	1·598	19·0	−0·0006	—
Cassia oil	1·59–1·60	—	—	—
Cinnamic aldehyde . . .	1·619	20	−0·0003	strong
Monoiodobenzene . . .	1·621	18·5	—	—
Carbon disulphide . . .	1·6295	18	—	strong
α-Monochloronaphthalene . .	1·632	21·6	—	moderate
s-Tetrabromethane . . .	1·634	25	−0·00053	—
α-Monobromonaphthalene . .	1·659	19·4	−0·0005	moderate
α-Iodonaphthalene . . .	1·699	25	−0·00047	—
Cadmium borotungstate solutions*	up to 1·70	—	—	—
Potassium mercuric iodide solutions†	up to 1·71	—	—	—
Methylene iodide‡ . . .	1·74	—	−0·0007	rather strong
Methylene iodide and sulphur .	1·74–1·79	—	—	—
Methylene iodide, sulphur and iodides§	1·74–1·87	—	—	—
Phenyldiiodoarsine . . .	1·84	—	—	—

* Klein solution. The concentrated solution is supplied commercially as a heavy liquid for separating minerals (its sp. gr. is 3·28). It may be diluted with water to give liquids of lower index, and these solutions may be concentrated again by evaporation if required. The solution is decomposed by lead, zinc, and iron.

† Sonstadt (or Thoulet) solution may be obtained commercially or prepared as follows: 6·75 gm. of HgI_2 and 5·75 gm, of KI are dissolved in 20 c.c. of water with stirring. The solution is evaporated on a water bath until a crystalline film forms on the surface. After cooling, the clear liquid is decanted from any solid which has crystallised out. The solution may be diluted with water to give liquids of lower index, and these may be concentrated by evaporation. It is very poisonous, acts upon metals, and attacks the skin.

A modification of this solution proposed by Wherry is as follows (*U.S. Dept. Agr. Bull.* 679 (1918)): Mix equal volumes of glycerine and water, and dissolve in the liquid 3·38 gm. of HgI_2 and 2·88 gm. of KI per c.c. Evaporate on a water bath to the point of incipient crystallisation, and decant from any solid. Dilute with glycerine to make liquids of lower index.

‡ Liberates iodine on exposure to light. Discolouration may be prevented by adding a piece of clean copper or tin, or a little mercury.

§ To 50 gm. of methylene iodide add 17·5 gm. of iodoform, 5 gm. of sulphur, 15·5 gm. of stannic iodide, 8 gm. of arsenious iodide, and 4 gm. of antimonious iodide. Warm to hasten solution, allow to stand, and filter off undissolved solids (Merwin, *J. Wash. Acad. Sci.*, 1913, **3**, 35).

In actual practice sets of refractive index liquids are usually made up of mixtures of a small number of substances, which should not have widely differing boiling points. F. E. Wright* proposed the following combination which has proved useful for inorganic substances and for some organic ones also.

Mixtures of—	n_D
Petroleum and turpentine	1·450–1·475
Turpentine and 1,2-ethylene dibromide or clove oil . .	1·480–1·535
Clove oil and α-monobromonaphthalene	1·540–1·635
α-monobromonaphthalene and α-monochloronaphthalene .	1·640–1·655
α-monochloronaphthalene and methylene iodide . . .	1·660–1·740
Methylene iodide and sulphur	1·740–1·790
Methylene iodide, iodoform, antimony iodide, arsenic sulphide, antimony sulphide, and sulphur	1·790–1·960

For organic substances which are soluble in most of the above liquids the solutions of cadmium borotungstate or potassium mercuric iodide given in the previous list may be used. In difficult cases where the substance under examination is soluble in both organic liquids and inorganic aqueous solutions it may be necessary to prepare special liquids saturated with the substance.

For substances with refractive indices above about 1·87, amorphous mixtures of sulphur and selenium, and of piperine with arsenic and antimony triiodides have been used. The crystals are heated on a slide with the immersion medium until the latter melts, a cover slip being then placed over the liquid. On cooling, the medium sets to a glass, in which the crystal particles are embedded. This method is only applicable to substances which are unaffected by the heating required to melt the medium, and is not therefore of general application but may be very useful for the study of rock minerals with high indices. A concise summary of the preparation and properties of such media is given by Larsen.†

In mixing two liquids of known refractive index to get an intermediate one, the following formula (which is true only for 'ideal' mixtures) may be used:

$$v_1 n_1 + v_2 n_2 = (v_1 + v_2)n, \qquad . \qquad . \qquad 4.1$$

where v_1 and v_2 are their respective volumes, n_1 and n_2 their respective refractive indices, and n the required refractive index.

---

* *The Methods of Petrographic Microscopic Research*, Carnegie Inst. Publ., No. 158 (1911), p. 96.

† *Microscopic Determination of the Non-opaque Minerals*, Bull. Geol. Survey U.S.A., No. 848 (1934), p. 18.

Refractive index liquids are supplied by a number of firms, some of which are listed in the Appendix.

Liquids having refractive indices below, say, 1·74 are easily standardised on a refractometer, and one of the Abbe type which needs only a drop of liquid should be at hand during an investigation. For liquids of higher indices it is necessary to use other methods, since the upper limit of an ordinary refractometer is determined by the refractive index of its prism which is rarely above 1·74. The most accurate of these

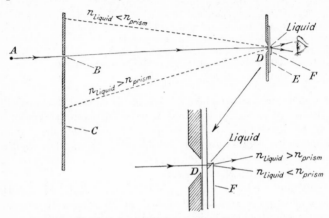

Fig. 4.7. Principle of Leitz–Jelley refractometer.

methods is to use a hollow prism and determine the refractive index by the method of minimum deviation as described in any textbook of physics. This method is, however, time-consuming and usually requires more than a few c.c. of liquid.* The most convenient methods for refractive index work are those which require only one drop of liquid, the refractive index of which may be read at once. Two instruments which fulfil these conditions will now be described.

The principle on which the Leitz–Jelley micro-refractometer is based is shown in Fig. 4.7. A source of monochromatic light A directs a beam through a slit B in a screen C, upon which is a vertical scale. The slit and scale are viewed through an aperture D in a stage plate carrying a glass plate E to which is cemented a small prism F. A drop of liquid is placed in the angle of the prism as shown. Light passing through the prism is refracted upwards or downwards according as its index is greater or less than that of the prism. In the former case the image of the slit appears on the screen, below its actual position; in the latter

---

* A small prism holding one drop of liquid is described by Larsen, *op. cit.*

case it appears above this position. The scale may be calibrated with substances of known index. By using white light the image of the slit is drawn out into a coloured band, thus affording a means of making a rough estimate of the dispersion of the liquid (strictly, relative to that of the prism). In this instrument the scale is calibrated for the direct reading of indices for sodium light from 1·33 to 1·92, the third decimal place being obtained by estimation. Instruments of this type are made by Leitz and by the Fisher Scientific Company (Pittsburgh, U.S.A.).

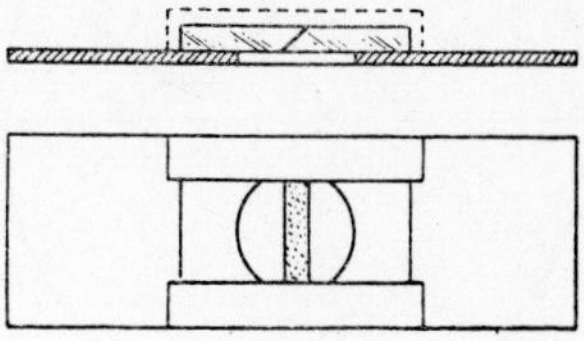

Fig. 4.8. Wright stage refractometer.

One of the most convenient instruments for determining the refractive index of a drop of liquid under the microscope is that of Wright.* The apparatus (Fig. 4.8) consists of two pieces of highly refracting lead glass (n_D 1·92), with an edge bevelled at 60°. One of these edges is polished and the other finished with a matt surface. The two pieces of glass are held in a metal slide above a circular opening, with the inclined edges in contact, the polished one uppermost. A drop of liquid is placed between the inclined surface, being held there by capillarity and its index of refraction is found by noting the position of the limiting refracted ray between the light and dark portions of the field. The observation should be made in convergent light, with a 16-mm. or $\frac{2}{3}$-in. objective, the Bertrand lens, and a micrometer scale in the eyepiece. The instrument may be calibrated by using three of four liquids the refractive indices of which have been accurately found upon a refractometer. The graph which results when the refractive indices are plotted against the divisions of the scale is a simple sine curve.

It should be understood that a fixed combination of objective, ocular, and tube length must be preserved when using this method. The accuracy is 0·001 units. An instrument of this kind is made by James Swift and Son Ltd. (London) who provide prisms to suit different ranges of refractive indices.

II. EXAMINATION IN POLARISED LIGHT (LOWER POLAR INSERTED)

When the lower polar has been inserted all the light which reaches the microscope stage is plane-polarised. If an anisotropic crystal is rotated in the plane of the stage above the lower polar, its two directions of

* Wright, F. E., *J. Wash. Acad. Sci.*, 1914, **4**, No. 11.

vibration for light passing through it will be brought successively parallel to the plane of vibration of the polariser (see Fig. 2.17, p. 76). In these positions all the light from the polariser will pass through the crystal without any change in the direction of vibration. In other positions the two vibration directions of the crystal will share the vibrations from the polariser according to the angle these make with the vibration direction of the polariser. Many substances do not seem to change their appearance on being rotated above the polariser while others show characteristic changes which will now be described.

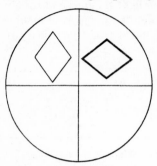

Fig. 4.9. Variation in relief.

Variation in Relief. It has been stated that the prominence of the border (relief) of a crystal depends on the difference between its refractive index and that of the immersion medium. It has also been demonstrated that in anisotropic crystals the refractive index varies with the direction of vibration of transmitted light. When a crystal section lies on the stage with one of its vibration directions parallel to that of the polariser it will show the relief appropriate to its refractive index for that direction, and when turned through 90° it will show the relief appropriate to the other refractive index. Sometimes the difference is too small to be apparent to the eye. When, however, the crystal has a large double refraction and the immersion medium has a refractive index near to one of those of the crystal the difference in relief is striking, the crystal coming into strong and weak relief alternately. This phenomenon is known as 'twinkling', and is well exhibited by the mineral calcite, $CaCO_3$, cleavage rhombs of which when immersed in a liquid with a refractive index of 1·56 appear successively on rotation above the polariser as shown in Fig. 4.9.

Variation in the Selective Absorption of Light. Pleochroism. The variation in the selective absorption of light with its vibration direction in coloured crystals has already been referred to in Chapter 2. It may be studied by rotating the crystal above the polariser, when changes in both intensity and tint will be observed in most cases.

In uniaxial crystals there are two principal absorption directions and therefore in this case the special term *dichroism* is used. One of these directions lies parallel to the optic axis which is the direction of vibration of the principal extraordinary ray, E, and the other lies at right angles to this direction and therefore gives the colour and the absorption characteristics of the ordinary ray O. The maximum changes in colour of a dichroic substance are to be seen therefore when the optic axis is lying in the plane of the microscope stage and the two principal vibration directions may be brought successively parallel to the direction of vibration of the polariser. Basal sections of uniaxial substances show no colour change on rotation, but present that which is characteristic of the O ray, because light travelling along the optic axis has the same ease of vibration in all directions, and the section therefore displays uniform absorption properties. Either the O or the E ray may have the greater absorption for a given wave-length.

Absorption is described in terms of the *absorption formula* $O > E$, or $E > O$, or it may be put in the form $\omega > \varepsilon$ or $\varepsilon > \omega$, using the corresponding indices of the rays. Changes of colour due to selective absorption of different parts of the spectrum are described in terms of the *pleochroism formula* thus (to take the example of brown tourmaline), O, dark brown, E, pale yellow. In addition to tourmaline, striking examples of pleochroism are shown by the pseudo-uniaxial mineral biotite which is intensely pleochroic in sections cut across the perfect basal cleavage, X (or E) being pale yellow and Y = Z* (or O) being dark brown; by magnesium platinocyanide, $Mg[Pt(CN)_4],7H_2O$, tetragonal, which is bluish-red for light vibrating along c, and carmine red for vibrations at right angles to it; and also by the tetragonal potassium copper chloride, $K_2CuCl_4,2H_2O$, which shows E, sky-blue and O grass green.

In biaxial crystals there are three principal absorption axes at right angles, light vibrating parallel to which may be absorbed in a different way for both intensity and colour. These axes are usually parallel to the axes of the indicatrix ellipsoid. In the orthorhombic system they coincide with both the ellipsoid axes and the crystallographic ones. In the monoclinic system, one of them, together with one of the ellipsoid axes, coincides with the crystallographic axis b. The other two, usually, but not necessarily,† coincide with those of the ellipsoid. In the triclinic system the absorption axes may not coincide with any of the ellipsoid axes.

The absorption formula for biaxial crystals is expressed X (or Y or Z) $\gtrless$ Y (or Z or X) $\gtrless$ Z (or X or Y). Or similarly, the refractive indices may be used to indicate the absorption, e.g. $\alpha > \beta > \gamma$. The

---

* X, Y and Z are common abbreviations for the ellipsoid axes OX, OY and OZ respectively.

† Laspeyres, H., *Z. Krist.*, 1879–80, **4**, 444.

pleochroism formula is expressed, to take a hypothetical case, X red, Y orange, Z light yellow.

In describing the pleochroism of crystals the changes in absorption should be correlated with the fast and slow directions of vibration in a crystal section, as determined with the quartz wedge or otherwise (p. 189). Thus, it may not have been possible to determine the directions of the axes of the ellipsoid, but the directions of fast and slow vibration having been determined upon a face which is described, the pleochroism could be written, for example, 'length direction of the face, fast, pale green; across the face, slow, yellow'.

It is convenient to notice here that the direction of vibration of the polariser may be determined by using the pleochroism of the rock mineral biotite, cut across the basal cleavage approximately parallel to the optic axis (see above). The mineral may be recognised in a section of biotite-bearing granite* by its perfect cleavage, brown colour and strong absorption. The direction of vibration of the polariser is indicated by the direction of the cleavage when the absorption is greatest, and this takes place when the cleavage lies parallel to one or other of the microscope cross wires.

III. EXAMINATION BETWEEN CROSSED POLARS

Isotropism and Anisotropism. By their behaviour between crossed polars, all non-opaque substances can be divided into two groups, namely isotropic and anisotropic substances (Chapter 2). The former remain dark like the field of the microscope whatever their orientation, whereas the latter will appear coloured on rotation in most orientations, and only in certain positions will become dark.

The reason for this difference in behaviour is that in isotropic substances light vibrates with equal ease in any direction, the wave surface being a sphere, and so when such a substance is on the stage there is no change in the direction of the light from the polariser and the field remains dark as though the stage were empty. On the other hand, when an anisotropic substance is placed above the polariser, the light from it on entering the crystal is doubly refracted, the two rays vibrating at right angles to one another and travelling with different velocities. Rotation of such a crystal on the stage will cause it to become dark, or *extinguish* at intervals of 90°, and between these positions the crystal will be illuminated, being brightest at 45° from the positions of extinction. The section extinguishes when the traces

* Obtainable from dealers in petrological specimens (see Appendix).

of its vibration directions become parallel to those of the polars, because in such a position the light from the polariser is not resolved in the crystal but passes on to the analyser unchanged, and so darkness results (see Fig. 2.17). The colours shown in the positions of illumination are known as *polarisation colours*. The formation of these will now be explained.

Polarisation Colours. Let us consider first the case of monochromatic light on its path from the polariser through an anisotropic crystal on the microscope stage and so to the analyser, the crystal not being in an extinction position. The light emerging from the polariser is plane-polarised (represented by E in Fig. 4.10), and on entering the crystal is resolved into two plane-polarised beams (shown as rays O' and E' in the figure), which have different velocities and vibrate at right angles to one another. Although one ray is retarded behind the other, the two cannot interfere since they do not vibrate in the same plane, but in general they combine to produce elliptically polarised light since their waves will have different amplitudes and emerge in different phases (p. 57). This elliptically polarised light will in the analyser (shown as a calcite prism in the figure), be resolved into four components, O' giving rise to O" and E", and E' to O''' and E'''. Of these O" and O''' are totally reflected and do not emerge from the analyser,* but E" and E''' now vibrating in the same plane may interfere to produce effects which depend on their respective amplitudes and phases. Ordinarily, a retardation of $\frac{1}{2}\lambda$ in one of two similar waves which follow the same path and vibrate in the same plane will produce darkness, as for example in the 'Newton's rings' experiment performed in monochromatic light. In the polarising microscope, however, darkness only results in the analyser when the fast and slow rays *from the crystal* differ by one wave length (or by any whole number of wave lengths). In other words, when the fast and slow rays emerging from the crystal differ in phase by one or more whole wave lengths, the components derived from them in the analyser will be out of phase by half a wave length and the algebraic sum of their respective motions zero. This will be explained by means of Fig. 4.11.

Let AA' be the direction of vibration of the analyser and PP' be the direction of vibration of light emerging from the polariser, OP' being its amplitude. In the crystal section RSTU, the light vibrates along VV' and WW' with amplitudes OC' and OC" respectively. When both waves have no phasal difference, they will pass through O together and reach their crest C' and C" simultaneously. When such is the case

* When Polaroid is used one of the components is absorbed.

the vertical components which may interfere in the analyser, OY and
OX, are seen to be equal and opposite, and darkness results. On the
other hand, if a difference of phase of $\frac{1}{2}\lambda$ or any odd multiple occurs,
it will be seen that when one wave reaches its crest at C', the other
will be in its trough at C'''. In these circumstances the vertical components OY, ZC''' will be equal and of the same sign, the resultant wave
having twice the amplitude and therefore four times the intensity.
It is important to notice that in the first case darkness will result no

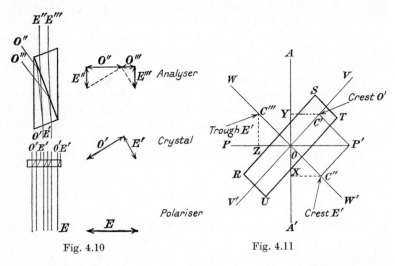

Fig. 4.10   Fig. 4.11

matter what the value of the angle between the directions of vibration
in the crystal and those of the polars, for in any position the components
passing through the analyser are equal and opposite. In all cases
where the phase difference is not a whole wave-length, the section is
illuminated except in the extinction positions, being most brightly lit
up in the 45° position when the vertical or analyser components are
greatest.

The amplitude of the analyser-passing wave is obtained directly
from the ellipse corresponding to the elliptical vibration of the light
emerging from the crystal. Thus in Fig. 4.12, POP' and AOA' are the
vibration directions of the polariser and analyser respectively, and OC',
OC'' the amplitudes of the components transmitted by the crystal, as
in Fig. 4.11. To take a particular case, if OC' is the slower of these
components, and the phase difference between them on emergence
from the crystal is between 90° and 180°, then the ellipse will occupy

a position in the circumscribing rectangle as shown (Fig. 2.5, p. 59), If LK and L′K′ are the tangents to the ellipse which are also perpendicular to the analyser vibration direction AOA′, then OL or OL′ is the amplitude of the analyser-passing wave.

For any crystal section, the amount of retardation of one wave behind the other depends upon two factors: (1) the difference in wave

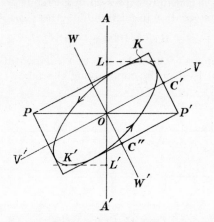

Fig. 4.12. Amplitude of analyser-passing component.

velocity of the beams in a direction normal to the plane of the section and (2) the thickness of the crystal plate. The wave velocities are related inversely to their respective refractive indices in the section, α' and γ'. If d be the thickness of the crystal plate, t_1 and t_2 the times taken by the two beams to pass through the section, and c the velocity of light *in vacuo*, then

$$\text{velocity of the slow beam, } \frac{d}{t_1} = \frac{c}{\gamma'}$$

$$\text{velocity of the fast beam, } \frac{d}{t_2} = \frac{c}{\alpha'}$$

$$\therefore t_1 = \frac{\gamma' d}{c} \text{ and } t_2 = \frac{\alpha' d}{c}$$

and

$$t_1 - t_2 = (\gamma' - \alpha')\frac{d}{c}$$

which expression gives the retardation in time of one beam behind the other. In terms of the thickness of the section the *relative retardation* or *optical path difference*, R, is derived by multiplying both sides of the equation by c thus:

$$R = c(t_1 - t_2) = (\gamma' - \alpha')d \qquad . \qquad . \qquad .4.2\,a$$

The relative retardation of a section is therefore its birefringence (the difference between its two refractive indices), multiplied by the thickness. Thickness is generally expressed in microns ($\frac{1}{1000}$ mm.), symbol μ, and relative retardation in micro-millimetres ($m\mu$), so that

$$R_{m\mu} = 1000(\gamma' - \alpha')d_\mu \qquad . \qquad . \qquad .4.2\,b$$

The phase difference between the two components on emergence from the crystal is given by multiplying the relative retardation by

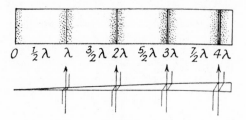

$$0 \quad \tfrac{1}{2}\lambda \quad \lambda \quad \tfrac{3}{2}\lambda \quad 2\lambda \quad \tfrac{5}{2}\lambda \quad 3\lambda \quad \tfrac{7}{2}\lambda \quad 4\lambda$$

Fig. 4.13. Quartz wedge.

$360/\lambda$, or by $2\pi/\lambda$, according as the answer is required in degrees or radians, λ being the wave-length expressed in the same units as the relative retardation.*

The effect of an increase of thickness resulting in a correspondingly greater relative retardation may be studied by viewing a wedge-shaped section of quartz or other anisotropic substance in monochromatic light between crossed polars. In the 45° position a series of alternating dark and light bands will be seen. The dark bands occupy positions where the retardation between the fast and slow beams is zero (at the thin end of a 'perfect' wedge) or a whole number of wave lengths, and the centres of the light bands mark the position where the retardation is $\tfrac{1}{2}\lambda$ or any odd multiple of this (Fig. 4.13). If now a change is made from monochromatic to white light, a series of coloured bands is seen, which are similar, *provided there is no dispersion of the birefringence* (p. 93), to those produced by the interference between reflections from the upper and lower surfaces of a thin wedge of air or liquid (Newton's scale). The explanation is as follows. The spacings of the extinction bands for different colours are proportional to the wave lengths. Thus

* Note that 1 $m\mu$ = 10 Å.

those for blue have the closest, and those for red the widest, spacings. This is illustrated in Fig. 4.14 in which λ and R are given in mμ. In white light the effect is as if the phasal difference for each colour were superposed. A vertical line on the diagram will show the phasal contribution each colour makes to the interference colour.

At the thin end of a perfectly made wedge (never achieved in practice), the phase difference is zero, and darkness results. As the increasing

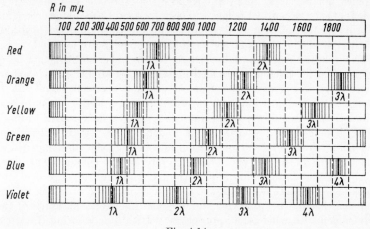

Fig. 4.14

thickness introduces a phasal difference between the fast and slow rays, greatest at first for the blues, a grey-blue tint is seen which merges into white at about R = 230 to 260 mμ, where all colours have some phasal difference but none is as yet extinguished. As the point R = 400 mμ is approached, and the middle of the violet extinction band is reached, yellow becomes strong, merging through orange into red, which is prominent about 500 to 560 mμ, because blue, green, and yellow are weak, and the red is still about 200 mμ away from the centre of its own extinction band. The colours mentioned comprise the *first* and *lowest order* of interference colours. The sequence of colours in the second, third, and fourth orders is given in the table included in Fig. 4.15, each order terminating with and including a red. As the thickness of the wedge increases, the colours become fainter and more complex, owing to the overlapping of the extinction bands for different parts of the spectrum, the fifth and sixth orders consisting mainly of pale pinks and greens. In still higher orders, these colours merge into 'whites of the higher orders'.

Examination between parallel polars may occasionally be useful, the polariser or analyser being rotated through 90°. This causes the light and dark bands in a wedge viewed in monochromatic light to change places and in white light the normal interference colours change to the complementary ones shown in the right-hand column of Fig. 4.15. The method may be used to distinguish between high whites and white of the first order, and to confirm the polarisation colour seen between crossed polars. It is important to note that the true complementary colours between parallel polars will only be seen if the wedge or section is truly at 45° between extinction positions, because in other positions the amplitudes of the analyser-passing components are unequal.

The relation between interference colours, the birefringence of a section and its thickness, are well illustrated by Michel–Levy's colour chart of birefringences, an outline of which is given in Fig. 4.16. If possible the student should try to examine a copy of the original chart which is unfortunately not now published. It is to be found in Idding's *Rock Minerals*, (Wiley, 1911) as a folder.* The vertical columns of the chart show relative retardation, R, in $m\mu$, the birefringence of the section and the sequence of normal interference colours. Thickness is shown horizontally in millimetres. If the birefringence and the thickness of a section are known, the interference colour which will be shown is located by following the diagonal line from the value of the birefringence to where the appropriate vertical line showing thickness cuts it, and the interference colour is to be found along the horizontal line through that point. Alternatively, if the birefringence and the polarisation colour of a section are known, it is possible to get an estimate of the thickness of the section which will be indicated where the diagonal from the value of birefringence cuts the horizontal line showing the polarisation colour.

In the above discussion, the term *birefringence of the section* was used. This should not be confused with the maximum birefringence for any one substance, that is the *birefringence of the substance*, which is the difference between the maximum refractive indices ($\varepsilon - \omega$) or ($\gamma - \alpha$). The methods of recognising sections showing the birefringence of the substance will be dealt with in Chapter 5. It will suffice to say here that they are parallel to the optic axis in uniaxial crystals and parallel to the optic axial plane in biaxial crystals, and that they are recognised by their properties in convergent light.

* Smaller versions of Michel–Levy's chart are to be found in Kerr's *Optical Mineralogy*, McGraw–Hill, 3rd edn. 1959, and in Chamot and Mason's *Handbook of Chemical Microscopy*, Vol. 1, (Wiley, 1958). James Swift and Son Ltd., 113, Camberwell Road, London, publish a brochure *Polarisation Colour Scale* which shows interference colours between crossed and parallel polars.

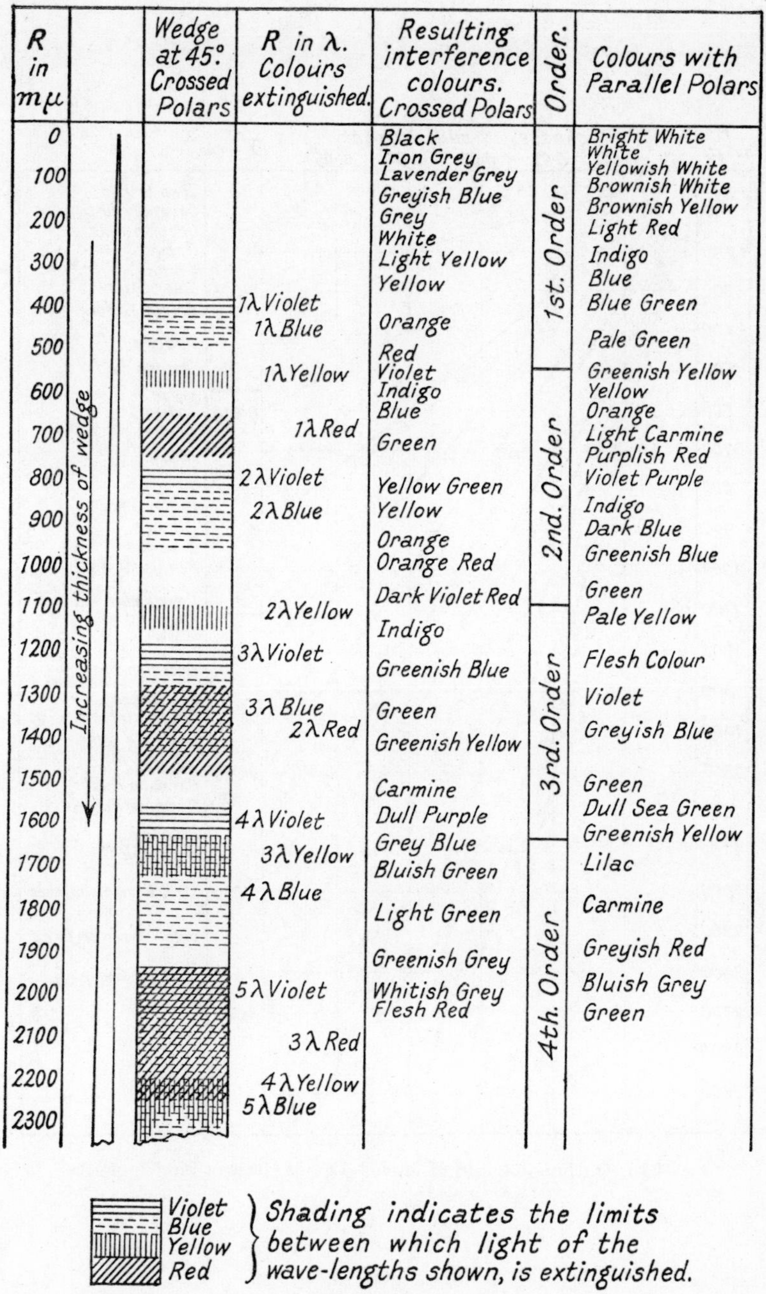

R in mμ	Wedge at 45°. Crossed Polars	R in λ. Colours extinguished.	Resulting interference colours. Crossed Polars	Order.	Colours with Parallel Polars
0			Black	1st. Order	Bright White
			Iron Grey		White
100			Lavender Grey		Yellowish White
			Greyish Blue		Brownish White
200			Grey		Brownish Yellow
			White		Light Red
300			Light Yellow		Indigo
			Yellow		Blue
400		1λ Violet			Blue Green
		1λ Blue	Orange		
500			Red		Pale Green
600		1λ Yellow	Violet	2nd. Order	Greenish Yellow
			Indigo		Yellow
			Blue		Orange
700		1λ Red	Green		Light Carmine
					Purplish Red
800		2λ Violet	Yellow Green		Violet Purple
900		2λ Blue	Yellow		Indigo
			Orange		Dark Blue
1000			Orange Red		Greenish Blue
1100		2λ Yellow	Dark Violet Red	3rd. Order	Green
			Indigo		Pale Yellow
1200		3λ Violet	Greenish Blue		Flesh Colour
1300		3λ Blue	Green		Violet
1400		2λ Red	Greenish Yellow		Greyish Blue
1500			Carmine		Green
1600		4λ Violet	Dull Purple		Dull Sea Green
			Grey Blue		Greenish Yellow
1700		3λ Yellow	Bluish Green		Lilac
1800		4λ Blue	Light Green	4th. Order	Carmine
1900			Greenish Grey		Greyish Red
2000		5λ Violet	Whitish Grey		Bluish Grey
			Flesh Red		Green
2100		3λ Red			
2200		4λ Yellow			
2300		5λ Blue			

Increasing thickness of wedge

Violet
Blue
Yellow
Red
} Shading indicates the limits between which light of the wave-lengths shown, is extinguished.

Fig. 4.15

179

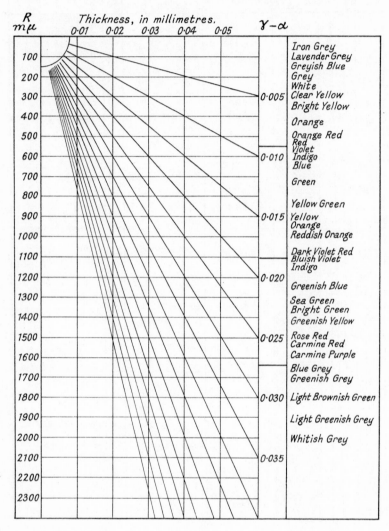

Fig. 4.16. Outline diagram of Michel–Levy's chart of birefringences.

Anomalous Polarisation Colours. Some substances display polarisation colours which do not match those of Newton's scale, and are therefore said to be *anomalous* or abnormal. These anomalies are due to one or more of the following causes: (1) selective absorption of part of the spectrum; (2) dispersion of the birefringence; (3) dispersion of the extinction directions.

The absorption of a very narrow band of the spectrum may leave a substance substantially colourless but will affect markedly the polarisation colours. Strongly coloured substances greatly affect the polarisation colours by masking them so that the colour between crossed polars is little different from that in ordinary light. An example of this is *o*-nitroaniline.

The normal sequence of Newton's colours is seen when the extinction bands for the various colours of the spectrum are as shown in Figs. 4.14 and 4.15. Dispersion of the birefringence has the effect of altering the relative positions of these bands with the result that the phasal differences are not the same as in the normal sequence. Calcite which shows this phenomenon has a birefringence of 0·185 for violet light and 0·167 for extreme red. The mineral apophyllite provides a striking illustration of this anomaly since the spacing for the extinction bands for all colours of the spectrum is nearly the same, and a wedge of the mineral shows a sequence of white and dark bands. In certain extreme cases the normal order of the extinction bands is reversed, those for red being more closely spaced than those for blue. This has the effect of replacing yellows by blue and blues by yellow. Anomalous colours are commonly seen in organic substances, for example *p*-nitrobenzaldehyde formed from fusion, but a number of minerals also display anomalies. Melilite, tetragonal, which according to Wülfing has a smaller double refraction for yellow (for which it is almost isotropic) than either red or green, shows strongly anomalous colours. Other minerals which show anomalies owing to dispersion of extinction directions are chlorite, zoisite and clinozoisite.

Extinction and Extinction Angles. A crystal will extinguish when placed between crossed polars in parallel light (1) if it is parallel to a circular section of the indicatrix, and (2) if it is parallel to an elliptic section of the indicatrix and its vibration directions are parallel to those of the polars. The first case is fulfilled in the case of cubic crystals, basal sections of uniaxial substances, and approximately so with optic axial sections of biaxial substances. The second case is fulfilled in all other sections of anisotropic substances provided there is no dispersion of the vibration directions or monochromatic light is used.

The distinction between circular sections of the indicatrix of aniso-tropic substances and cubic crystals is made in convergent light, when the former show characteristic interference figures (see next chapter). Basal sections of uniaxial substances extinguish completely and remain dark on rotation unless they are optically active and are thick enough to rotate the plane of polarisation appreciably (p. 97). Sections normal to an optic axis in biaxial crystals do not extinguish completely but are faintly and uniformly illuminated on rotation. This phenomenon may be connected with the fact that the optic axes are not directions of single ray velocity, and in certain cases dispersion of the optic axes in white light is a contributing factor. The appearance of such sections between crossed polars is very characteristic and reveals the fact that such crystals are biaxial even before examination in convergent light.

The *directions of extinction* in any crystal section are determined by the orientation of the indicatrix within the crystal (p. 91). If a direction of extinction is parallel to the length of the section, or to a single cleavage or prominent edge, it is said to be *straight* or *parallel*; if it bisects the angle between two cleavages or prominent edges it is called *symmetrical*; and in the case where it is neither symmetrical nor straight, it is *oblique* or *inclined*.

In all non-basal uniaxial sections straight and symmetrical extinctions obtain, since the axes of the crystal are parallel to indicatrix axes. The same applies in the orthorhombic system to all sections for which at least one vibration direction corresponds to a principal refractive index, i.e. all faces belonging to zones the axes of which are crystallo-graphic axes. *Faces not belonging to these zones which have symbols of the general type (hkl) will show oblique extinction.* This is illustrated in Fig. 4.17, in which HKL represents an (*hkl*) face, and AA' and BB' the optic axes, the optic axial plane being parallel to (010). The vibra-tion directions for light normal to the section HKL can be derived by the application of a relationship discovered by Biot and Fresnel. This states that the vibration, or extinction, directions in any section for light of perpendicular incidence are given by the trace of the plane which bisects the angle between the two planes which are normal to the section and which contain the two optic axes respectively. Thus in the figure the plane ACDA' is normal to HKL and contains the optic axis AA', and the plane BEFB' is also normal to HKL and contains the other optic axis BB'. The plane MNOP bisects the angle between these two planes and its trace NQ on HKL is one vibration direction, the other being at right angles to it. It will be seen that the extinction directions are not parallel to any of the edges of HKL, nor to the traces on the section of any common cleavage, such as that shown parallel to (010).

In the monoclinic system, one ellipsoid axis only is parallel to the crystal axis b, and the other two lie in the plane parallel to $b(010)$, with the result that in the zone $a(100):c(001)$ straight extinction is given (p. 93). On faces belonging to any other zone, oblique extinction obtains. Fig. 4.18 illustrates this by showing the orientation of the

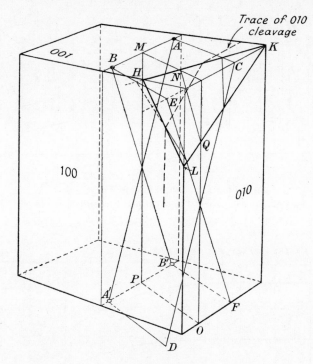

Fig. 4.17

ellipsoid in two monoclinic crystals. In (a) the plane containing the optic axes, or *optic axial plane*, is parallel to the one possible symmetry plane of the system, i.e. the (010), whilst in (b) it is normal to the (010) plane. The extinction angles in the prismatic zone for the mineral diopside, a monoclinic pyroxene, $CaMg(SiO_3)_2$, are also shown.

The variation in extinction angle around the prism zone of the monoclinic system needs further elucidation. On (100), as mentioned before, straight extinction prevails, and on (010) it is oblique with a value which depends on the tilt of the ellipsoid around the b axis. Between these two positions in the vertical zone the extinction angles

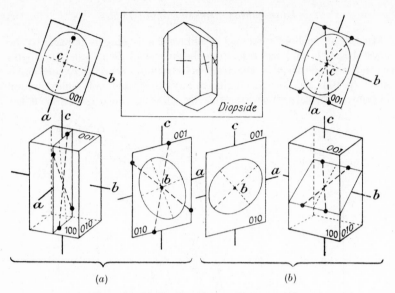

Fig. 4.18. Extinction of monoclinic crystals.
The optic axes are represented by broken lines terminated by large dots.

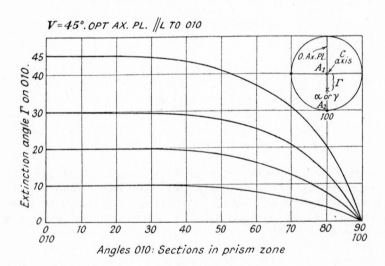

Fig. 4.19

with respect to *c* vary in ways which are determined by the values and orientation of the optical vectors. Three main types of variations occur as follows: (1) the extinction angle falls slowly from a maximum value on (010), and then rapidly to zero on (100) (Fig. 4.19); (2) the extinction angle decreases rapidly from a maximum on (010) to zero on (100) (Fig. 4.20); (3) the maximum extinction angle occurs *between* (010) and

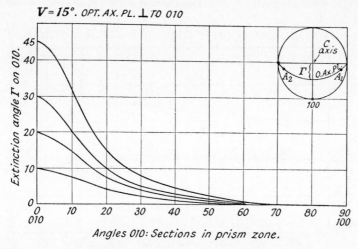

Fig. 4.20 (*Note:* Acute bisectrix is normal to (010).)

(100) (Fig. 4.21). The conditions which give rise to these three cases are shown respectively in Figs. 4.22, 1 (*i*) and (*ii*), 2 and 3. For case (1) the optic plane is parallel to (010) and *c* (the zone axis) lies in the quadrant containing the acute optic angle, as shown in 1 (*i*), or the optic plane is normal to (010) and *c* lies in the plane containing the acute bisectric and *β*, as in 1 (*ii*). For case (2) the optic plane is normal to (010), the acute bisectrix is *b* and *c* lies in the plane containing the obtuse bisectrix and *β*. For (3) the optic plane is parallel to (010) but *c* lies in the quadrant containing the obtuse optic angle.

In the monoclinic system two principal refractive indices may be measured on (010), but the discussion above will show that it would be unwise to depend on an extinction angle in order to decide whether the section was parallel to (010) or not. Figs. 4.19 and 4.21 will show that in cases (1) and (3) above a section might be 30° or more from (010) but still show almost the same extinction angle. Only in cases like that shown in Fig. 4.20 would one be justified in using an extinction angle

7

to locate the (010) section. It is much better to use convergent light (Chapter 5) to make sure of the orientation of a section on which refractive indices are being determined.

In the triclinic system, in general, no axis of the ellipsoid coincides with a crystal axis and oblique extinction results, although occasionally straight extinction may be found on one face; for example in a series of solid solutions formed from two isomorphous substances, the swing

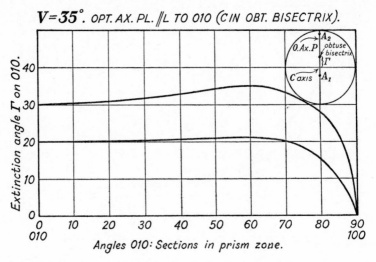

Fig. 4.21 (*Note:* Maximum extinction angle between 010 and 100.)

of the ellipsoid in sympathy with changing chemical composition may bring an ellipsoid axis parallel to one of the crystal axes.

In any section, complete extinction is only obtained in white light when the directions of extinction are the same for all colours, i.e. when the section is normal to a plane of optical symmetry for all colours. These conditions hold for all birefringent sections of uniaxial and orthorhombic crystals. In the monoclinic system, one axis of the indicatrix coincides with the crystal axis *b*, the other two lying in the one possible crystal symmetry plane of the system. Only this plane, therefore, acts as an optical symmetry plane, and only one axis, that parallel to *b*, is the same for all colours. Complete extinction will be given in the *a*(100):*c*(001) zone, and in other zones, i.e. on all faces which give oblique extinction, dispersion may be noticed. This is made clear by Fig. 2.32.

In the triclinic system, there is no coincidence between optic and crystallographic planes of symmetry, for the latter do not occur. In this case the extinction directions for different colours will not be the same.

When such dispersion occurs, it is said that the extinction is dispersed, or alternatively, that the bisectrices are dispersed. It should be

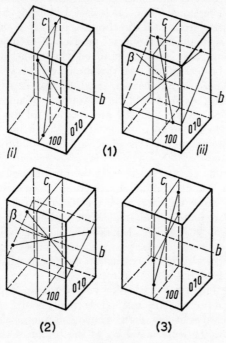

Fig. 4.22

mentioned that although this kind of dispersion exists in all monoclinic and triclinic crystals, yet in certain cases it is so slight as to be difficult of detection. Nevertheless, if many birefringent grains of a substance, orientated differently, give sharp and complete extinction in white light, it is extremely probable that it is uniaxial or orthorhombic.

The Measurement of Extinction Angles. Extinction angles should be measured in parallel light, and so the substage diaphragm should be almost completely closed. White light usually gives results sufficiently accurate for diagnostic or descriptive purposes, but where the extinction directions are dispersed monochromatic light must be used. To make a determination, first remove the analyser the better to see the specimen, and bring the crystal edge or cleavage parallel to a cross wire. The vernier reading is now taken, after which the analyser is inserted and the section turned to the nearest position of extinction, and a second reading of the stage position is taken. The difference between the two readings is the extinction angle. A number of determinations should be made and the average taken. It is useful to bring the section to the extinction position from both directions, especially if the birefringence of the section is small and the exact position of extinction difficult to see. If a single crystal is being examined, the extinction on a number of faces should be determined, and this should give an idea of the optical symmetry. Where a number of crystals are available presenting different sections, each should be examined. The simple rotation devices described on pp. 282–287 are very useful for examining the extinction angles in one zone, especially in the prism zones of monoclinic and orthorhombic crystals which are immediately differentiated by this means.

The 'bracketing' method has already been mentioned as an expedient for finding the exact position of exinction on sections of low birefringence, but more delicate methods are available by the use of so-called sensitive plates. The simplest method uses the *unit retardation plate* described on p. 190. This is placed in the diagonal slot above the objective and between crossed polars shows a violet tint or first order red. When a crystal is in the extinction position it will show the same colour as the plate, but a slight rotation of the substance will produce a second order blue or a first order yellow colour, depending on the direction of rotation. The method is really only satisfactory for colourless substances of low birefringence and upon isolated fragments which will allow the close matching of the colour of the field (due to the plate) and that of the crystal without difficulty.

In the second method a twinned plate of mica, known as the *Bravais plate*, is used in the slot of the microscope. It is made as follows. A small square is cut from a cleavage plate of muscovite mica of such a thickness as to show the violet tint between the first and second orders (approximately 0·1 mm.), so that its edges are parallel to the vibration directions. It is then cut across a diagonal, and one half is inverted. The two portions are cemented to a glass slip with the diagonals in contact, and the edges of the square parallel to those of the slip. The fast and slow vibration directions in the two halves are now opposed, as shown in Fig. 4.23. Between crossed polars both halves of the plate show the same colour, which remains unaltered when a crystal in the extinction position lies on the stage. A slight rotation of the crystal from this position results in the two halves of the Bravais plate showing different tints. It is important that the plate be accurately oriented in the slot, and for this reason it should be mounted in a well-fitting metal slider. Other types of twinned plates have been made. One of these, the Nakamura plate, uses right- and left-handed quartz for each half. It is used in the same way as the Bravais plate.

The exact description of extinction angles necessitates discrimination between the two vibration directions of the crystal plate, and a statement not only of the angle, but the vibration direction from which it was measured.

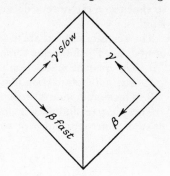

Fig. 4.23. The Bravais mica plate.

This involves the differentiation between the fast and slow directions in a section, and the angle is expressed in some such form as 'slow direction : crystal axis $c = 20°$'. If the orientation of the ellipsoid in the crystal has been elucidated, the vibration direction can be named according to the refractive index to which it corresponds, and the extinction angle described as, for example, '$\alpha:c = 20°$' or $\alpha^{\wedge}c = 20°$.

Distinction between the 'Fast' and 'Slow' Vibration Directions in Crystal Sections. To differentiate between the directions of vibration in a crystal section, a birefringent wedge or plate of which the vibration directions are known, is placed above or below the section between crossed polars and the difference the plate makes to the polarisation colours of the sections is noted. If the test plate or wedge is so placed that its vibration directions are similarly orientated to those of the crystal being examined, i.e. fast parallel to fast and slow parallel to slow, then the phasal difference between the two beams emerging from the crystal is increased, and the interference colours will rise in Newton's scale, but if the fast direction of the plate is superposed on the slow of the crystal, the phasal difference is reduced and the interference colours as viewed under the microscope will fall in the scale. Should the phasal difference be reduced to zero, *compensation* results and darkness, or a dark band, will be seen across the wedge at the position occupied by the colour which has been compensated. Superposing fast on fast, or fast on slow, is therefore equivalent to thickening or thinning the crystal section respectively. It should be noted that exact compensation in white light can only be achieved if the dispersion of the birefringence of the crystal is the same as that of the compensator, so that the relative retardations of the two are the same for all wavelengths.

The accessories used are of two kinds, namely, simple parallel plates, or wedges. The following three form the minimum equipment desirable.

1. The quarter undulation mica plate.
2. The unit retardation plate.
3. The simple quartz wedge.

The quarter undulation plate, or $\frac{1}{4}\lambda$ plate, is made of a cleavage flake of muscovite mica of such thickness that one vibration will be

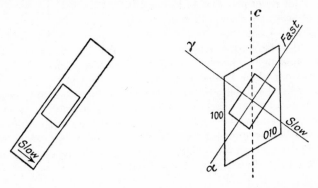

Fig. 4.24. The $\frac{1}{4}\lambda$ mica plate.   Fig. 4.25. Orientation of the gypsum plate.

retarded $\frac{1}{4}\lambda$ (for yellow light) behind the other, and the transmitted beam will be circularly polarised. Between crossed polars in parallel light, the plate gives a pale grey interference colour of the first order (R = about $150m\mu$). Muscovite is negative in sign, the acute bisectrix emerging nearly normal to the cleavage face, and so the vibration directions will correspond respectively to β and γ. The plate of mica is mounted between two thin slips of glass, with one vibration direction parallel to the long edge of the slide. The slow direction of vibration is marked by inscribing an arrow on the glass slide as shown in Fig. 4.24.

The plate is used as follows. The crystal to be examined is first placed in the extinction position and then turned through 45°, thus bringing one of the vibration directions parallel to the slot in the microscope tube. The mica plate is then inserted in the slot and the change in the interference colours is noted. A rise in the scale of colours shows that there is coincidence, and a fall, opposition in the corresponding directions of vibration.

The unit retardation plate is commonly made of a cleavage fragment of the transparent variety of gypsum (called selenite) although mica or quartz may also be used. The plate is cut of such a thickness as to have a retardation of 575 $m\mu$ (equal to one wave-length of yellow light), thus giving the 'sensitive violet' between crossed polars in white light. The orientation of the plate in relation to the cleavage piece from which it is cut is shown in Fig. 4.25. It is mounted similarly to the $\frac{1}{4}\lambda$ plate and used in the same way. When the birefringence of the crystal being examined is low, say grey of the first order, the difference in the resulting colours when vibration directions are (*a*) opposed and (*b*) coincident is very striking, being an orange of the first order in the first case, and a bright blue of the second order in the second case.

The mica plate has a relative retardation of one quarter that of the gypsum plate, and this makes it more useful for the examination of sections of relatively high retardation (second to fourth orders), because the polarisation colours are moved by it only a short distance in the scale. Confusion is likely to occur when using the gypsum plate since it moves the colours by a whole order and it is sometimes difficult to distinguish between, say, a third or fourth order red and doubt may arise as to whether the colours have been moved up the scale or down.

The simple quartz wedge is usually cut parallel to the *c* axis of the crystal and as quartz is uniaxial and positive the length of the wedge is slow. Quartz has the advantage also that it has a low birefringence and little dispersion of the birefringence. On placing the wedge in the 45° slot between crossed polars the colours of Newton's scale will be seen as the wedge is pushed in or out. The number of orders shown usually varies from four to six in different wedges. When the wedge is superposed above a crystal plate the colours will rise or fall according to whether the vibrations in wedge and section are opposed or not. If opposed, the colour of the section will be compensated by the corresponding colour of the wedge, and thus both the directions of vibration of the section are known (which fast and which slow) and also the position in Newton's scale of the colour shown by the section. If compensation is not achieved in the first position, the section should be turned through 90°.

When grains with thin edges or crystals with pyramidal ends are examined the interference colours will be arranged in contour-like forms as shown in Fig. 4.26 *a* and *b*, the higher colours being towards the centre or the thicker parts of the grain. On pushing in the wedge the colours will move outwards if the colours are raised (fast on fast) and inwards if the colours are lowered (fast on slow). The figures show the two cases, the small arrows indicating the direction of movement of the colour bands. Note that the length direction of the wedge is 'slow' in both cases. Should a 'fast' wedge ever be used, the direction of the movement of the colours would be reversed. The character of the length (whether fast or slow) of an elongated crystal or section is said to be positive if slow and negative if fast, and is described as the *sign of elongation* of the section. In uniaxial crystals elongated parallel to *c* the

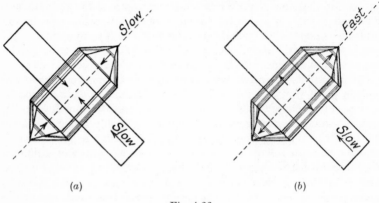

(a)   (b)

Fig. 4.26

sign of elongation determines the optical sign of the substance since positive crystals have a slow, and negative crystals a fast, length (E vibrating parallel to *c*).

Determination of the Birefringence of a Crystal Plate. If the thickness and the relative retardation of a section are known the birefringence may be found (p. 176). Measurement of thickness has already been described (p. 159) and it remains to show how the relative retardation is determined by means of the quartz wedge. The polarisation colour of the crystal plate is first of all compensated in the way already described and the order of the colour is found from the wedge by counting the orders as the wedge is removed. It may be necessary to remove the crystal from the stage while this is being done so that the colours of the wedge may be studied without difficulty caused by the interference tints of adjacent substances. When separate crystals are being examined there is usually enough of the field unobstructed for this to be done without removing the specimen. In grains, the colour shown by the thickest part is usually the best to use. It is often easy to determine the order of a colour in such cases by counting the reds from the margin (zero thickness) to the colour compensated. A refinement is to use a wedge with an arbitrary scale engraved upon it. The scale may be read by means of the Bertrand lens if placed in the upper focal plane of the objective which has to be of the type specially slotted for this purpose. Or it may be placed in a special slotted eye-piece which has an auxiliary analyser above it. The scale is calibrated by illuminating the field by means of sodium light (or other colour of known wave length). The black extinction bands which indicate relative retardations of whole numbers of wave lengths may then be used to calibrate the scale in terms of the wave lengths of the light used. Wedges cannot be constructed of quartz alone to show the zero band at the thin end, since this always breaks off in the grinding process so the first dark band will be that for a retardation of 1λ. After the scale has been calibrated in this way, parallel polars are then used when the former black and illuminated portions of the wedge change places, and the calibration for the series $R = \lambda/2, 3\lambda/2, 5\lambda/2$ etc., may be plotted. A graph may now be constructed showing R against the scale which is calibrated in terms of the wave lengths of light used, and these may be converted to micromillimetres by multiplying by the known wave length of the light in these units. Other more complex forms of wedges are in use but for information about these the student is referred to the more advanced texts (see Appendix I, p. 315).

As the determination of relative retardation depends on finding the position of the compensation band in white light, difficulties may arise if the substance shows marked dispersion of the birefringence (p. 181), particularly if the section is very thick. In such cases the birefringence may be determined directly from the two refractive indices. Other methods which have been devised for the special case of polymers (C. W. Bunn, R. P. Palmer), are described by N. H. Hartshorne in *Science Progress*, 1962, **197**, 29–33. Special compensators have been devised for the determination of very small birefringences such as may occur in some polymers and biological materials, and these are described in Hartshorne and Stuart, *Crystals and the Polarising Microscope*, 3rd edn. 1960, pp. 297–303.

Crystal Aggregates and Twinned Crystals. The optical properties of columnar or fibrous aggregates of crystals need no special mention, but the special case in which fibres or needles are arranged radially to form spherulites is interesting. When these are formed of aniso-tropic material, a black cross is seen between crossed polars in parallel light, similar in appearance to the isogyres of a uniaxial interference figure in convergent light (p. 204). The cross remains stationary on rotation of the stage. The sign of elongation of the fibres composing the spherulite may be determined in the usual way, even when they are too fine to be separately distinguished, for on the insertion of a plate or wedge, the interference colours in the two diagonal quadrants parallel to the accessory used will be raised or lowered with respect to the colours in the two opposite quadrants.

Twinned crystals of anisotropic substances are easily recognised between crossed polars because adjacent units of such crystals exhibit,

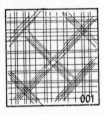
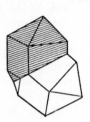
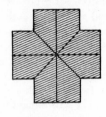

Fig. 4.27. Twinning   Fig. 4.28. Twin   Fig. 4.29. Cruciform
   in leucite.   of cassiterite.   twin of staurolite.

Twinned crystals between crossed polars 1.

in general, differences of illumination owing to their different orientation to the vibration planes of the polars.

Contact twins lying with their composition plane normal to the stage present no difficulty, but if the plane of junction is oblique to the microscope axis, a certain amount of overlap between the crystals will take place. In such a case, extinction will be impossible unless the vibration directions in each unit coincide. In interpenetration twins where no regular plane of junction exists, a similar effect will be produced.

The appearance of different types of twins is illustrated in Figs. 4.27 to 4.34, the directions of vibration of the polars being taken to be parallel to the edges of the page.

In crystals which are truly cubic, twins can only be detected by their outward form, but in the case of pseudo-symmetric cubic crystals, as leucite, $KAl(SiO_3)_2$, the twinning is seen on (001) as a series of fine bands alternately light and dark, lying parallel to the traces of the twin planes, which are those of the dodecahedral form {110} (Fig. 4.27).

Uniaxial crystals twin commonly in 'elbow' or geniculate shapes owing to the twinning axis being normal to a pyramid face. Each unit shows straight extinction (Fig. 4.28).

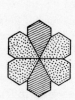 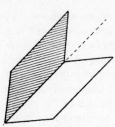 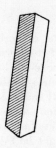

Fig. 4.30. Stellate twin of aragonite.

Fig. 4.31. Twin of gypsum.

Fig. 4.32. Twin of *o*-nitroaniline (γ form).

Twinned crystals between crossed polars 2.

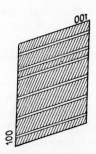 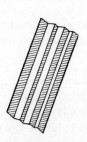 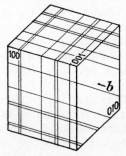

Fig. 4.33. Multiple twinning in diopside.

Fig. 4.34. Multiple twinning in albite.

Fig. 4.35. Albite and pericline twinning in plagioclase.

Twinned crystals between crossed polars 3.

 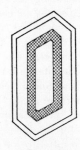 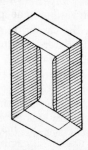

Fig. 4.36

Fig. 4.37

Fig. 4.38

Sections through zoned crystals of different types between crossed polars.

In the orthorhombic system common types are interpenetration twins of cruciform and stellate shapes (Figs. 4.29, 4.30).

In the monoclinic and triclinic systems twinning becomes of greater importance, both simple contact and multiple kinds being common. Fig. 4.31 shows a twin of gypsum lying on b(010), each unit having an extinction angle of 52° 30′, symmetrical about the composition plane. The twin of o-nitroaniline shown in Fig. 4.32 has no re-entrant angles, and might be taken for a hemimorphic form, because of its different terminations, but examination between crossed polars shows at once that it is a simple contact monoclinic twin on (100), each part of which has an extinction angle of 7°. In a crop of these crystals, however, some showing re-entrant angles are always seen, the case selected above being an isolated one.

In both the monoclinic and triclinic systems, in addition to simple contact twins on the pinacoid faces, multiple twins of various types are common. The latter may occur in conjunction with a simple contact twin, or two sets of multiple lamellæ may occur together. Fig. 4.33 shows lamellar twinning parallel to the basal plane in the monoclinic pyroxene diopside, $CaMg(SiO_3)_2$, and Fig. 4.34 that of the substance albite, parallel to (010). Fig. 4.35 shows the combination of the albite type of twinning with another set which has as its twinning axis, b, and is known as *pericline* twinning. The latter combination is characteristic of the potash feldspar microcline, $KAlSi_3O_8$, and the plagioclase feldspars, of which albite is an end member, display it commonly. Between crossed polars, sections in the (100):(001) zone will show cross hatching, owing to the twin planes being nearly at right angles.

Zoning. During the crystallisation of substances which form solid solutions, imperfect reaction between the solid and liquid phases may result in zoning of crystals. This may be continuous or discontinuous, that is, the crystal may vary in chemical composition gradually from centre to outer margin, or be composed of a series of distinct shells of different composition. In the first case, the crystal will give a continuous expanding wave of extinction from centre to margin when revolved between crossed polars, and in the second case, each shell will have its own distinct extinction angle (Figs. 4.36, 4.37). In other cases, certain ions of the mixed crystal may show a preference for the faces of a certain zone, thereby producing an 'hour-glass' structure (Fig. 4.38). A similar structure often results when crystals are grown from solutions containing dyestuffs, the dye molecules being concentrated preferentially on certain faces. (See for example, H. E.

Buckley *Crystal Growth*, Wiley, 1951). Zoned crystals of uniaxial systems will not show such expanding wave extinction since the extinction will be straight in any case. Orthorhombic crystals will also show straight extinction despite differences in composition from centre to margin, in all zones parallel to crystal axes. Sections cutting all crystal axes obliquely will cross different zones, and each part of the section will show a different extinction angle with respect to, say, the (100) or other cleavage. In uniaxial and orthorhombic crystals therefore a complete study of the crystals will involve investigation of variations in refractive index, birefringence and perhaps colour from centre to margin. In orthorhombic crystals also the value of 2V might vary significantly from centre to outer margin. An interesting case has been described by S. I. Tomkeieff* who investigated zoning in olivines which are orthorhombic ferro-magnesian silicates. A note of warning should be sounded here. Should it be suspected that the substance being examined might be zoned, it would be no use crushing the substance and finding the refractive indices on randomly oriented grains, by the method to be described on p. 239 since α might be found for a central piece and γ for a piece from the margin!

Optical Anomalies. Some crystals may show optical properties which are not in keeping with their outward symmetry. For example, some crystals which are outwardly cubic show varying amounts of double refraction between crossed polars, and certain uniaxial crystals may show biaxial interference figures in convergent light. Such anomalies may be due to various causes. Should a crystal be under strain its properties will be anomalous. The effects of mimetic twinning have already been referred to (p. 45), and the appearance of such crystals under the microscope between crossed polars reveals their true nature. Crystals of polymorphic substances sometimes undergo transformation without a change of external form, the result being an aggregate of very small crystals of the stable modification confined within the boundaries of the original unstable form. Such *pseudomporhs* as they are called exhibit confused optical properties which cannot be correlated with the external symmetry. For example, crystals of yellow mercuric iodide grown from the vapour are orthorhombic tablets parallel to (001). On being disturbed, transformation begins by the sudden appearance of the red modification in the form of bands parallel to the edges of the tablets. These bands spread sideways until the whole crystal is transformed, there being no change in the outward form of the plates. Another example is afforded by the unstable form

* *Min. Mag.*, 1939, **25**, 229.

of potassium nitrate which is deposited as rhombohedra from a warm solution of the salt. When these come in contact with a crystal of the stable modification, transformation sweeps rapidly through the rhombohedra but they retain their shape. In both cases the crystals lose much of their transparency and acquire a finely granular appearance. Between crossed polars they give no definite positions of extinction, owing to the random orientation of the small crystals and to the fact that they overlie one another, the effect being known as *aggregate polarisation*.

When optical anomalies are suspected in a crystal, various changes in the illumination should be made, such as inserting the converging lens if it is movable, and moving the position of the condenser or altering the size of the aperture of the iris diaphragm, the stage being well shaded from top light. It may then be found that the suspected anomalies have been nothing more than internal or external reflections from inclined faces. Irregular grains of cubic substances are sometimes difficult to make truly isotropic in appearance, until the above expedients have been tried, or the crystals have been immersed in a liquid with the same refractive index.

5 THE MICROSCOPIC EXAMINATION OF CRYSTALS

B. CONOSCOPIC OBSERVATIONS
('Convergent' Light)

Introduction. The examination of a crystal in parallel light between crossed polars reveals its optical character in one direction only, that parallel to the axis of the microscope. Very important additional information may be obtained by passing a strongly convergent beam of light through the crystal, when it is possible by various means, shortly to be described, to examine its optical character in many directions *at one and the same time*, by viewing between crossed polars not the image of the crystal, or *object image*, but another optical image formed in the principal focus of the objective by the strongly convergent beam of light. This image is called variously, the *directions image* (as opposed to the object image), the *image in convergent light*, or the *interference figure*. The appearance of some of these figures is illustrated on pp. 200 and 204.

When the microscope is used in this way it is said to behave as a *conoscope*, and the observations are described as *conoscopic* since they are made in convergent light.

The Microscope as a Conoscope. Fig. 5.2 shows the principle of the use of the polarising microscope as a conoscope. Light passing through the polariser P is made by the condenser C, N to concentrate upon the object X. The divergent rays pass through the objective and converge again in the upper focal plane U of the objective, to form a small real image, *each point in which is the focal point of light which has passed in a definite direction through the crystal*, hence the name *directions image*. The aperture of both condenser and objective should in general be large, since this enables a wide range of directions of propagation to be included in the interference figure (see Fig. 5.1). (When only the central part of an interference figure is of particular interest it may be advantageous to magnify this by changing to a system of lower aperture (cf. Fig. 5.1 *a* and *b*)). The interference figure cannot be seen in the ordinary way through the eyepiece because it lies far removed from the focal plane of the latter. Other methods are therefore used for examining the figures and will now be described.

Methods of Viewing the Interference Figure. The simplest method of all (due to Lasaulx) is to remove the ocular and view the small image in the focal plane U (Fig. 5.2) through the analyser direct. The interference figure is sharply defined but small, and as the ocular with its cross-wires or scale has been removed, accurate measurement on the figure such as the apparent angle between the optic axes (see later)

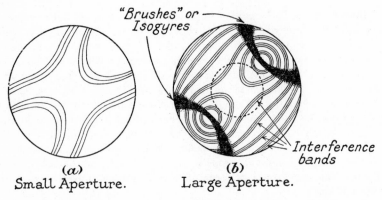

Fig. 5.1. Effect of aperture of objective on interference figure.
In (a) only the part of the figure within the dotted circle in (b) appears in the field of view.

cannot be made. *It should be noted that the interference figure as seen by this method is inverted with respect to the object image seen when the ocular is in place.* This makes no difference when the crystal presents a centred figure (as in Fig. 5.1), but must be taken into account when studying crystals giving inclined figures (as in Fig. 5.11, p. 210).

The most usual method employed is to insert in the body tube an auxiliary lens—the Bertrand lens (B, Fig. 5.2, and p. 126, Chapter 3)—most often situated above the analyser, and by means of it the interference figure may be brought into the focal plane of the ocular. The figures seen when the Bertrand method is used are not so sharply defined as they are by the Lasaulx method but are larger. The outstanding advantage of this method is that the ocular with its cross-wires or micrometer scale is retained, and these can be viewed simultaneously with the figure. Moreover the interference figure is *not* inverted with respect to the object image.

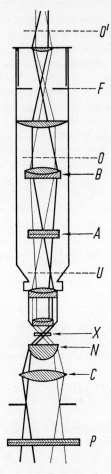

Fig. 5.2. The microscope as a
conoscope (diagrammatic).

Rays which pass through the crystal X
in the same direction are emphasised
equally in the drawing. Where such rays
are brought to a focus, viz. at U and
F, an interference figure is formed.
Where rays which emanate from the
same point on the crystal are focussed,
viz. at O and O', an object image is
formed. P, A, and B are the polariser,
analyser, and Bertrand lens respectively.

Methods of Isolating Interference Figures of Small Crystals. It often happens that in a mounted sample the particles are so small that more than one appears in the field, even when a fairly high-power objective is being used. In these circumstances it is necessary to isolate the interference figure of a selected grain. Various methods have been adopted to achieve this result, the principle underlying most of them being to use diaphragms either beneath the stage and so illuminate only the desired crystal, or in various positions above the stage with the object of cutting out all light which has not passed through the crystal. In order to do this satisfactorily, it is essential, as pointed out by J. W. Evans,* that the diaphragm shall coincide with a real image of the object, or with a focus conjugate to it. Two methods based on this principle are as follows.

1. This is a modification of the Lasaulx method. After the eyepiece is removed, a pinhole stop, say $\frac{1}{64}$ in. diameter, is inserted at the top of the body tube. This effects the isolation of the interference figure of a centred crystal because with the eyepiece removed an object image is formed at or near this level.

2. The Bertrand lens is used in conjunction with a diaphragm situated at the object plane above it (O in Fig. 5.2), most modern microscopes being provided with either an adjustable iris at this place, or a pinhole stop which comes into the correct position when the Bertrand lens is inserted. If the former, the desired crystal is centred and the iris closed until, without the Bertrand lens, only that crystal can be seen. In the latter case, the pinhole stop, though of fixed size, is usually small enough to effect the satisfactory isolation of quite small crystals. This applies also to method (1).

General Discussion of Interference Figures. When the microscope is used as a conoscope, the rays of light passing through a crystal plate follow different paths which will not only be longer the greater their inclination from the normal to the section, but will be normal to different sections of the indicatrix. It therefore follows that the interference figure from a parallel-sided plate will not show a uniform interference colour as the section does when its image is viewed in parallel light between crossed polars, but a series of curved interference bands is seen, coloured in white light and dark in monochromatic light, identical with those shown by the quartz or other wedges described in Chapter 4, p. 179. These interference bands are symmetrically arranged around the optic axis (or axes), and the central portion of the field shows the same interference colour as the crystal would do in parallel light,

* *Min. Mag.*, 1916, **18**, 48.

because the central rays are quite or nearly parallel to the axis of the microscope. In addition to these bands there are dark 'brushes' or *isogyres* (Fig. 5.1 *b*), the shape of which is determined by the positions of those points on the interference figure, where rays vibrating in directions parallel to the vibration directions of the polars are brought to a focus.

By the study of sections giving suitable interference figures the following optical characters may be determined:

In general

1. Isotropic substances may be differentiated from sections of crystals normal to an optic axis.

2. Anisotropic substances may be classified optically as belonging to uniaxial or biaxial crystal systems.

3. The positive or negative sign of the substance may be determined.

4. Taking thickness into account, qualitative estimates of the birefringences of different substances can be made from the figures given by sections normal to an optic axis.

In biaxial crystals

5. The direction of the optic axial plane may be found and the vibration directions of α, β and γ determined.

6. The size of the optic axial angle may be measured.

7. The dispersion of the optic axes may be studied and the crystal system determined.

UNIAXIAL CRYSTALS

Basal or Optic Axial Sections. If a basal section of a uniaxial substance is viewed in monochromatic light in one of the ways described above (p. 200), an interference figure will be seen consisting of concentric dark rings which are more closely spaced towards the margin of the field, and two isogyres which lie parallel to the cross-wires and intersect in the centre of the field (Fig. 5.3). If the stage is rotated the figure will remain unchanged, but if the polars are rotated simultaneously as in the Dick pattern microscope for example (p. 136), the isogyres will rotate with them, preserving at all times their right-angle relation. This will be understood from Fig. 5.4 in which the traces of the directions of vibration for different parts of the figure are shown.

In white light the isogyres remain dark but the rings are coloured, the colours seen being those of the polarisation colour scale of the substance, the lowest order being nearest to the centre of the figure.

The explanation of such a figure is as follows:

In Fig. 5.5 let ABCD be a section cut normal to the optic axis which is imagined to be in the plane of the paper, and let EE be parallel rays of a monochromatic convergent polarised beam of light,* entering the section. It will be seen that as the rays (except those travelling perpendicularly to the section) do not travel in the unique

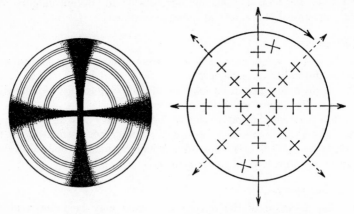

Fig. 5.3. Basal uniaxial inter-   Fig. 5.4. Vibration directions in
ference figure.   basal uniaxial interference figure.

The arrows represent two positions of cross-wires when the polars revolve.

direction of single velocity they are doubly refracted. At the upper surface there must emerge at all points rays O′ and E′ (as at X in Fig. 5.5), derived from a given pair of incident parallel rays EE, which from there onwards travel along the same path, vibrating of course in planes at right angles to one another. One of these rays (which one depending upon the optical sign of the substance) will have been retarded behind the other by an amount which depends upon the direction of their paths through the crystal. When the retardation of one ray behind the other is exactly one wave-length or any whole multiple of one wave-length, darkness results as explained in Chapter 4, p. 174. Since the extraordinary wave surface is an ellipsoid of revolution about the optic axis, all emergent rays having a given inclination to this axis consist of ordinary and extraordinary components differing in phase by the same amount. Emergent rays so allied to one another lie on the surfaces of an infinite number of geometrically similar cones coaxial with the optic

* A convergent beam of light may be regarded as being composed of convergent bundles of parallel rays.

axis, and the locus of their focal points in the interference figure is a
circle. This explains the series of concentric dark rings in the figure
when monochromatic light is used, each ring corresponding to a group
of cones for which the retardation is a whole number of wave-lengths.
It is obvious that the retardation becomes greater the greater the
inclination of the emergent rays to the optic axis, for with increase in
the inclination, the extraordinary rays differ in velocity more and more

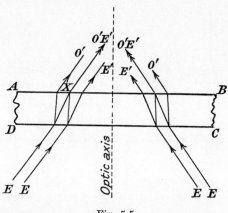

Fig. 5.5

from the ordinary rays, and also the thickness of crystal through which
the light has to travel gets greater and greater. Fig. 5.6 shows diagrammatically cones of emergent light corresponding to different retardations, each group of cones of a given inclination being represented for
simplicity by a single cone.

In Fig. 5.7 are shown the circular traces formed on the upper surface
of the crystal by two cones of O' and E' rays derived from the same
cone of incident light. We have seen that an ordinary ray vibrates in
the plane containing the ray and a line normal both to the ray and to
the optic axis, whilst an extraordinary ray vibrates in the plane containing the ray and the optic axis. The traces of these planes of vibration are denoted in Fig. 5.7 by small double-headed arrows. The
ordinary rays vibrate tangentially, and the extraordinary rays radially.
It is obvious that along the directions PP' and AA' which represent the
vibration planes in the polariser and analyser respectively, extinction
will result, and at 45° to these directions, between the dark rings, the
interference figure will be most brightly illuminated (p. 174). In the
central portion of the field the rays are normal to the section and travel

parallel to the optic axis. The field here will therefore remain dark. As far as the appearance of the figure goes, it does not matter whether the O′ or E′ rays are the more refracted. This depends upon the relative velocities of O′ and E′ in the crystal and determines the sign of the substance.

The number of rings of equal retardation seen around the central cross in a uniaxial figure, for a given combination of lenses, depends

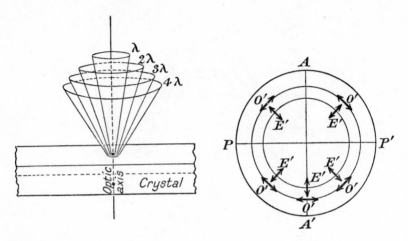

Fig. 5.6. Cones of equal retardation around the optic axis of a uniaxial crystal.

Fig. 5.7

upon the double refraction of the substance and the thickness of the section. The greater these two are, the more crowded around the cross will the rings be for a definite wave-length of light; and for a given thickness those for blue light will be more closely spaced than those for red.

Basal sections of uniaxial crystals which exhibit optical activity along the optic axis (Chapter 2, p. 97), give a characteristic figure in convergent light. Figs. 5.8 *a* and *b*, show two basal sections of quartz, the thinner one *a* appearing as a normal uniaxial figure because the section is not thick enough to rotate the plane of polarisation sufficiently for the eye to detect any change in white light. The other section (*b*) is thick enough for the plane of polarisation of light passing along the optic axis to be rotated sufficiently to produce an illuminated spot in the centre of the field. In white light this spot is coloured owing to the dispersion of the rotation (p. 98). If the section were studied in parallel light, it would show this same colour uniformly.

Sections Parallel to the Optic Axis (Optic Normal Sections). Optic normal sections are often presented by uniaxial crystals under the microscope, for prismatic habits are common, and such crystals (tetragonal, hexagonal, and trigonal) tend to lie with their optic axes

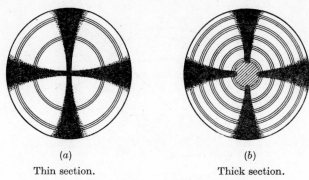

(a)   (b)
Thin section.   Thick section.
Fig. 5.8. Interference figures of quartz (basal section).

normal to the axis of the microscope. The figure given is very like that of the biaxial optic normal interference figure (p. 216), and consists of four series of hyperbolic isochromatic bands (or dark bands in monochromatic light) which are disposed symmetrically in quadrants as shown in Fig. 5.9, and which rotate with the stage. The bands are frequently very diffuse in white light, and always appear more clearly and can be distinguished in greater number in monochromatic light. Diffuse hyperbolic isogyres (similar in shape to those presented by biaxial crystals) enter the field as the stage is rotated, form a broad cross in the centre when the optic axis is parallel to one or other of the cross-wires, i.e. when the crystal is in the extinction position for parallel light, and swing out again in the direction of the optic axis. These isogyres move very rapidly and only occupy the centre of the field during the rotation of the stage through a few degrees, giving the impression of a momentary darkening of the whole field, for which reason the figure is often referred to as the 'flash figure'. The direction of movement of the isogyres is often extremely difficult to detect.

In white light, if the section be turned into the '45° position', as it is commonly called i.e. the position in which it is midway between two adjacent extinction positions), the direction of the optic axis is revealed by the fact that, starting from the centre of the figure, the colours fall in the polarisation colour scale in the two quadrants through which the optic axis passes and rise in the other two quadrants (Fig. 5.9). With thick sections, or sections of high birefringence, the fall in the two former quadrants may give place to a rise as the margin of the field is approached. For this reason, the sequence of colours must always be traced from the centre. The explanation of this fall and subsequent

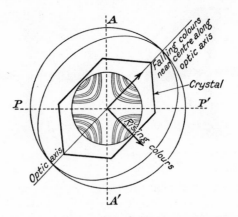

Fig. 5.9. A section parallel to c of a uniaxial crystal viewed in convergent light (small central circle) with a section of an appropriate (positive) wave-surface figure shown.

AA' and PP' are the directions of vibration of the analyser and polariser respectively.

rise is that the birefringence diminishes as the optic axial direction is approached, and this produces first a fall in the colours. As the rays become more oblique, however, the thickness of the crystal through which they must pass increases rapidly, and with thick or highly birefringent sections this may more than compensate for the fall in birefringence, and lead to a rise in the colours in the outer parts of the quadrants.

When a large number of interference bands appear in the field it is extremely difficult to distinguish the direction in which the colours fall. The best sections for the observation of this effect are those which are thin or of low birefringence, in which case the figure may present, for example, a red of the first order in the centre, yellow in the direction of falling colours, and blue in the direction normal to the optic axis giving a pattern like that in Fig. 5.10.

Sections lying obliquely to the Optic Axis. Certain uniaxial crystals, especially rhombohedral forms of the trigonal system, or pyramidal types of the tetragonal or hexagonal systems, may lie in such a way upon the slide that an *oblique, uncentred,* or *inclined* figure is given in convergent light, so that the centre of the cross is displaced from the intersection of the cross-wires in greater or less degree, according to the

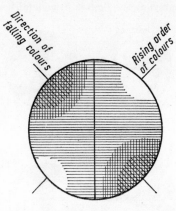

Fig. 5.10

angle which the optic axis makes with the axis of the microscope. On rotation of the stage the centre of the cross describes a circular path either within or outside the boundary of the field, the isogyres (if the centre is not displaced much beyond the margin of the field) preserving their parallelism to the cross-wires while sweeping successively across the field as shown in Figs. 5.11, *a–h.*

False Interference Figures. When using objectives of high power with crossed polars, a faint image appears resembling the dark cross of a basal uniaxial figure, even when there is no crystal in the field. This is due to the fact that the lower component of the objective has a strongly curved upper surface, and, as may be shown from optical theory, the plane of polarisation of the light from the polariser will be slightly rotated on refraction at such a surface, except where this plane is parallel or at right angles to the plane of incidence. These latter conditions only exist for rays travelling within those vertical principal sections of the lens which are parallel to the vibration planes of the polars, and so only these rays will be completely extinguished by the analyser; hence the dark cross. Elsewhere, owing to the rotation, the light will have a weak component which can pass the analyser.

On rotating the objective in its mount the cross remains stationary, provided that the glass of the lens is entirely free from strain. If, however, the lens is under strain, irregular shadows or a much distorted cross will be seen, and these will change their position as the objective is rotated. Such an objective is unsuitable for critical work.

The cross seen with an unstrained objective does not interfere with the observation of interference figures in general because it is so much

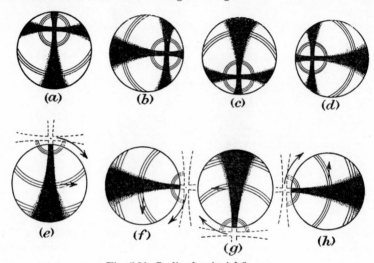

Fig. 5.11. Inclined uniaxial figures.

In the lower diagrams (*e*), (*f*), (*g*), and (*h*), the larger arrows show the direction of movement of the centre of the cross and the smaller arrows the direction of movement of the isogyres.

weaker than these, but when dealing with weakly birefringent material, care must be taken not to confuse it with a genuine figure due to the substance.

BIAXIAL CRYSTALS

Sections Normal to the Acute Bisectrix. When the section normal to the acute bisectrix is examined in convergent light, an interference figure similar to that shown in Fig. 5.12 is seen. This consists of two 'eyes' or *melatopes*,* which mark the points of emergence of the optic axes, surrounded by bands of equal retardation, dark in monochromatic light and coloured in white light. The inner bands surround each

* The term is due to Johannsen, A., *Manual of Petrographic Methods* (McGraw-Hill, New York and London, 1918) p. 420.

'eye' separately and are pear-shaped, or nearly circular if very close
to the 'eye'; the outer bands surround both 'eyes', and their form
changes from 'figure of eight' lemniscates to ovals as the margin of the
field is approached. Through the points of emergence of the optic axes
pass two isogyres, narrow and well defined at their centres, broader and
more diffuse towards the margin of the field. On rotation, the bands of
equal retardation move with the stage. The isogyres form a cross when
the trace of the optic axial plane (i.e. the line passing through both
melatopes) lies parallel to either cross-wire (Fig. 5.12 *a*), that arm of

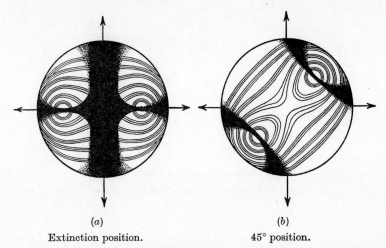

| (*a*) | (*b*) |
| Extinction position. | 45° position. |

Fig. 5.12. Biaxial interference figure given by a section normal to the
acute bisectrix.

the cross passing through the melatopes being narrower than the other.
In this position the crystal would be extinguished in parallel light.
Upon rotation from this position the cross breaks up into two hyperbolic brushes which are centred on the melatopes and lie as shown in
Fig. 5.12 *b*, when the trace of the optic axial plane is at 45° to the
cross-wires, the convex sides of the isogyres being towards the acute
bisectrix, which emerges in the centre of the field. The isogyres revolve
in a direction opposite to the movement of the stage.

The explanation of such an interference figure is as follows. Rays of
convergent light enter the crystal section, and, except along the optic
axes, double refraction takes place. Those rays the wave fronts of
which travel along the optic axes are brought to a focus in the interference figure at two points—the melatopes—which, being extinguished

by the analyser, appear dark. All other rays emerging from the crystal are made up of two components, differing in phase and vibrating in directions at right angles to one another (just as in the uniaxial case described above), and therefore resulting in interference in the analyser. Emergent rays for which the retardation is the same lie on conical surfaces surrounding each optic axis, the sections of the cones being nearly circular when the inclination to the optic axes is small, and becoming more pear-shaped as this inclination increases; at still greater inclinations, the surfaces merge so as to surround both optic axes. An example

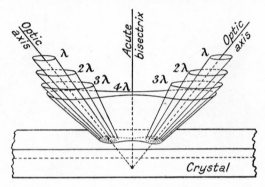

Fig. 5.13. Surfaces of equal retardation around the optic axes of a biaxial crystal.

of the relative arrangement of representative surfaces corresponding to retardations of λ, 2λ, 3λ, etc., for a given wave-length of light is shown in Fig. 5.13. Each surface (together with its allied parallel surfaces) produces a ring of focal points in the interference figure similar in shape to its trace upon a horizontal plane, and, as a comparison of Figs. 5.12 and 5.13 should show, this accounts for the shape of the bands of equal retardation in the interference figure. In white light the bands will be coloured.

The positions of the isogyres in the figure are determined by the directions of vibration at different parts of it. Fig. 5.14 shows the construction whereby these may be determined. MM' are the points of emergence of the optic axes. At any point on the figure, the directions of vibration may be found by joining the point to each melatope and bisecting the angles included between the lines thus drawn. This simple construction follows from the rule of Biot and Fresnel (p. 182). It will be seen that when the trace of the optic axial plane is at 45° from the cross-wires as shown, the directions of vibration parallel to those of the polars fall on curves which coincide with the shape of the isogyres of Fig. 5.12 *b*, whilst when it is parallel to a cross-wire, the isogyres form a cross as shown in Fig. 5.12 *a*.

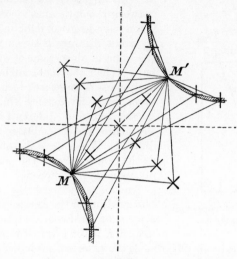

Fig. 5.14

Fig. 5.15. Interference figures given by plates of muscovite mica of different retardations (45° position).

The apparent distance between the melatopes is determined by the optic axial angle in the crystal, the index β, and the optical system of the microscope. As in uniaxial crystals the number of isochromatic curves is determined by the double refraction of the section and its thickness. Fig. 5.15 shows the interference figures given by muscovite mica in plates having (for perpendicular light) retardations of 1λ, 2λ, and 3λ (D line) respectively. The number of wave-lengths retardation is given by the number of dark curves between each melatope and the centre of the field, through which rays pass at right angles to the section. The angle between the optic axes is constant for any given wave-length of light and therefore the apparent distance between them remains the same in all sections of whatever thickness. When the acute angle between the optic axes is large (see below), the melatopes may lie outside the field of the microscope, and differentiation between the acute and the obtuse axial angle is difficult. When the axial angle is 90° the distinction between the acute and the obtuse angles disappears.

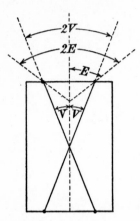

Fig. 5.16. Real and apparent optic axial angles.

The angle between the axes which is observed under the microscope with a dry system of lenses is not the actual angle (2V, Fig. 5.16) within the crystal but an apparent angle in air (2E) due to the external refraction of rays at the surface of the section. The relation between the real and apparent optic axial angles is given by the formula

$$\sin E = \beta \sin V \qquad . \ 5.1$$

where β is the intermediate refractive index of the substance.

The maximum angle of the cone of rays which can be accepted by a given objective depends upon its N.A. (p. 130), and hence there is a fixed size of 2E for which the melatopes lie on the margin of the field. From the relationship expressed in the equation above it follows that various sizes of V will give this value of 2E according to the value of the intermediate refractive index β. For example, if a dry objective of

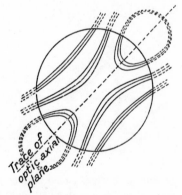

Fig. 5.17. Interference figure given by a section normal to the obtuse bisectrix (45° position), or an acute figure with 2E too large to be accepted by the objective.

N.A. 0·85 is used, the maximum value of E will be 58° (N.A. = $\sin u$ = 0·85 and u = 58°). The following table shows the values of V which will give E = 58° when β varies between 1·4 and 1·8. It also shows that when the melatopes lie outside the field (Fig. 5.17) an obtuse figure is not necessarily presented.

β	$\sin E/\beta \ (=\sin V)$	V.
1·4	$0·85/1·4 = 0·607$	37·5°
1·5	$0·85/1·5 = 0·566$	34·5°
1·6	$0·85/1·6 = 0·531$	32°
1·7	$0·85/1·7 = 0·500$	30°
1·8	$0·85/1·8 = 0·472$	28°

The use of an oil immersion objective (p. 131 Chapter 3) increases very much the true angle of the cone of rays within the crystal which can be accepted and hence makes it possible to bring both melatopes of large optic axial angles into the field. For example, two values of V for which the melatopes lie on the margin of the field when the objective has a numerical aperture of 1·30, and the immersion oil a refractive index of 1·515, are given below.

In this case

$$n_{oil} . \sin H = \beta \sin V \qquad . \qquad . \qquad 5.2$$

H being the external angle in oil corresponding to E in air and $\sin H = 1·30/n_{oil} = 1·30/1·515 = 0·858$ whence H = 59°.

β	$(n_{oil} . \sin H)/\beta = \sin V$	V.
1·4	$1·515(0·858/1·4) = 0·928$	68°
1·8	$1·515(0·858/1·8) = 0·722$	46°

It will be seen that when β is 1·8 the largest value for the acute angle (45°) can be brought within the field and at lower values of the index the obtuse figure can be seen.

Sections Normal to the Obtuse Bisectrix. As just shown, with a dry objective these sections give a figure consisting of lemniscate curves similar in shape to those of the acute figure, but the points of emergence of the optic axes lie well outside the field (Fig. 5.17). On rotation of the section, the isogyres swing into the field, and when the plane of the optic axis is parallel to the cross-wires, form a cross, and swing out again. They move more rapidly than those of an acute section, and remain in view for only a small rotation of the stage. When the optic axial angle is very small indeed this section approaches in character the optic normal section now to be described, and also to that shown by a section parallel to *c* of a uniaxial substance.

Sections Parallel to the Optic Axial Plane. These sections display an interference figure very like those given by vertical sections of uniaxial substances, in that the equal retardation bands are hyperbolic in shape and lie in four quadrants as shown in Fig. 5.18. Diffuse dark brushes

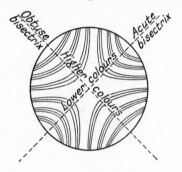

move rapidly into the centre of the field on rotation of the stage, momentarily darken the field and pass out again in the direction of the acute bisectrix. In parallel light between crossed polars the section is characterised by displaying the highest double refraction for the substance, α and γ lying in the plane of the section.

Fig. 5.18. Interference figure given by a section parallel to the optic axial plane (optic normal section). depicted in 45° position.

The two quadrants in which the acute bisectrix lies show lower colours at a given distance from the centre of the figure than do the other two quadrants, but when the optic axial angle, 2V, approaches 90°, this colour distinction becomes less apparent, until when the crystal is neutral it disappears altogether. The remarks about the difficulty of deciding in which direction the colours fall in uniaxial sections parallel to the optic axis (p. 208), apply in this case also.

The three types of biaxial sections described above lie normal to the planes of optical symmetry and are characterised by the formation of central dark crosses when the traces of these planes are parallel to the cross-wires. They are characteristically presented by pinacoidal faces of orthorhombic crystals.

Sections Normal to an Optic Axis. In these sections an optic axis emerges in the centre of the field, surrounded by nearly circular rings of equal retardation. A single dark brush passes through the centre of the field (Fig. 5.19), its curvature depending upon the size of the optic axial angle and the position of the optic axial plane with respect to the cross-wires. When the optic axial plane is parallel to one of these, the brush is also parallel to it and is straight, but if the section be rotated 45° from this position, the isogyre rotates in the opposite direction and becomes, in general, curved, the amount of curvature being greater the smaller the optic axial angle (Fig. 5.36, p. 237). It now lies across the optic axial plane and its convex side is directed towards the acute bisectrix. When 2V is 90°, the isogyre remains straight in all positions. Usually only one dark brush is seen in the field, but if the optic axial angle is small, a second optic axis may appear within the field towards the margin with its attendant isogyre (Fig. 5.20). In parallel light between crossed polars such sections are

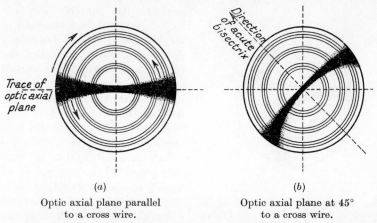

(a)	(b)
Optic axial plane parallel to a cross wire.	Optic axial plane at 45° to a cross wire.

Fig. 5.19.   Interference figure given by a section of a biaxial crystal normal to one optic axis (medium or large optic axial angle).

characterised by retaining a uniform faint illumination through a complete revolution of the stage, as already stated (Chap. 4, p. 182).

Sections Oriented Obliquely to the Bisectrices. Crystals having well developed prism or pyramidal faces usually lie so as to present sections which are not parallel to a symmetry plane of the indicatrix, and so more or less inclined interference figures are seen. For example, in Fig. 5.21 (i), (ii), (iii) and (iv), is illustrated an orthorhombic crystal with well-developed prism faces (110), the optic axial plane being coincident with the *ac* plane. It would lie on the stage as shown in Fig. 5.21 (ii), the plane containing the optic axes being tilted to right (or left). The interference figure would show the lateral displacement of the 'eyes' illustrated in Fig. 5.21 (iii), in which the orientation is such that the trace of the optic axial plane is parallel to the cross-wires. A rotation of the stage through 45° will give a figure similar to that of Fig. 5.21 (iv).

8

To take another example, should an orthorhombic crystal have well developed macro-domes, (101) (Fig. 5.22 (i)), it would tend to lie as in Fig. 5.22 (ii) when, if the optic orientation were the same as in the preceding case, the optic axial plane would remain vertical, but the acute bisectrix would not emerge in the centre of the field. The resulting interference figure would bear the aspect shown in Fig. 5.22 (iii) and (iv). In cases like those described above, where the section is normal to an optical symmetry plane, *when the crystal is in the extinction position for parallel light, one isogyre passes through the centre of the field and is straight and coincident with a cross-wire.* Where the section is not normal to an optical symmetry plane the isogyres do not pass through the centre of the field in the position where they become straight and parallel to a cross-wire.

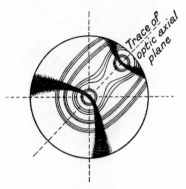

In pyramidal crystals the section presented lies inclined to all three principal planes of the indicatrix and the isogyres will assume a curved shape when intersecting the centre of the field. This character distinguishes oblique biaxial interference figures in which only one brush is seen, from inclined uniaxial figures of which the emergence of the optic axis is outside the field of view.

Fig. 5.20. Single optic axial figure given by a crystal with a small optic axial angle.

Fig. 5.23 *a*, shows a pyramidal orthorhombic crystal with the optic axial plane lying parallel to (010), the acute bisectrix emerging normal to (100). If such a crystal lies as shown in Fig. 5.23 *b*, the resulting tilt of the acute bisectrix is seen in the interference figures at (*c*), (*d*) and (*e*). The decentralised position of the straight isogyre should be noticed.

In general it may be said that the method of studying oblique interference figures is to place an isogyre in a position in which it is parallel to a cross-wire (if it can be seen in this position). If the isogyre now occupies the centre of the field the section is normal to an optical plane of symmetry. The stage should be rotated through 45°, the isogyre being watched closely to notice any change of shape, and the direction of the acute bisectrix and therefore the trace of the optic axial plane may be found from the direction of convexity of the brush. The complete figure may then be imagined by completing the outlines of

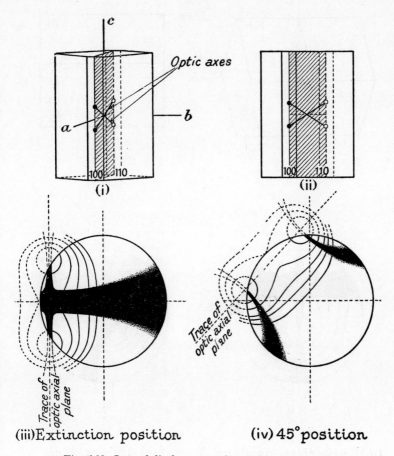

Fig. 5.21. Lateral displacement of acute bisectrix figure.

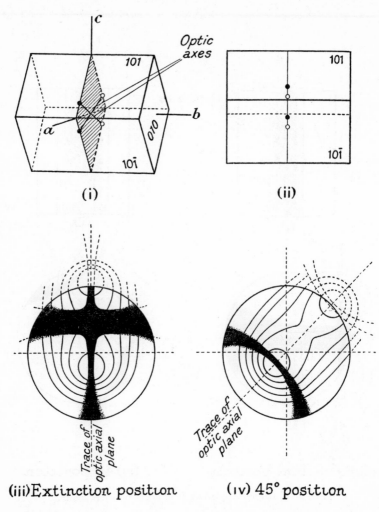

(i)

(ii)

(iii) Extinction position

(iv) 45° position

Fig. 5.22. Displacement of acute bisectrix figure along the trace of the optic axial plane.

the isochromatic curves. If a change to parallel light is now made the relation of the interference figure to the crystallographic directions may be found.

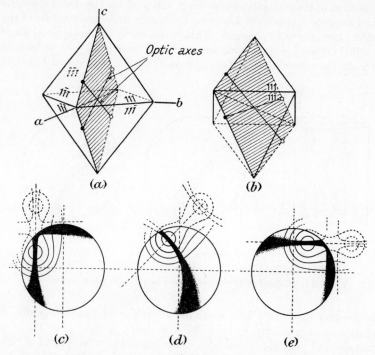

Fig. 5.23. Completely uncentred figure given by orthorhombic crystal lying on (111).

DISPERSION. EFFECT IN CONVERGENT LIGHT

Hitherto, the discussion of interference phenomena in convergent light has been pursued without emphasising the effects due to light of different colours. In Chapter 2, pp. 91–94, the changes in optical properties of crystals with light of different colours were explained and the effects of these changes with respect to interference phenomena in convergent light will now be dealt with.

In uniaxial crystals, although the values of ε and ω, (and therefore the size and shape of the indicatrix), vary with the wave-length of the light, the direction of the optic axis remains unchanged and the crossed isogyre maintains the same position for all colours.

In biaxial crystals, on the other hand, dispersion results in a variety of changes which, though frequently small, are sometimes large enough to have marked effects upon the interference figures. In the first place, dispersion of the refractive indices α, β, and γ, alters the size of the optic axial angle to a greater or less extent, because the *relative* values of the indices are generally changed. This variation in the optic axial angle is called *dispersion of the optic axes* and may occasionally be so large as to make the acute bisectrix for one colour (say red) the obtuse bisectrix

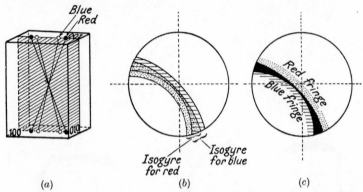

(a)   (b)   (c)

Fig. 5.24. Dispersion of the optic axes in orthorhombic crystals. 1.

for another (say blue) with resultant alteration of sign. Secondly, in addition to the change in both size and shape of the indicatrix in all uniaxial and biaxial crystals with variation in the wave-length of light used, in the monoclinic and triclinic systems the orientation of the indicatrix relative to the crystal axes varies also. This results in *dispersion of the bisectrices.*

Dispersion in Orthorhombic Crystals. In all substances belonging to this system the three axes of the indicatrix and those of the crystal coincide for light of all colours (Chapter 2, p. 93). The optic axial plane (containing α and γ) may be parallel to any one of the pinacoids (100), (010), or (001). The acute bisectrix may therefore emerge parallel to either a, b or c, the optic axial plane having two possible positions in each case.

An example of moderate dispersion is shown in Fig. 5.24 a, where the optic axial plane is parallel to (100) and the axial angle is greater for red light than for blue. It is evident that in white light, the isogyres of the interference figure in the 45° position will be composite, consisting

of the partly superposed isogyres for different kinds of light as shown in
Fig. 5.24 *b*, for red and blue.

The composite isogyre of Fig. 5.24 *b*, would have an appearance like
that illustrated in Fig. 5.24 *c*, namely, a dark brush fringed on its
convex side with red, and on its concave side with blue light. This is
due to the fact that the isogyre for any colour marks the positions in
which that colour is extinguished, and the other components of white
light reach the eye. In cases where the optic axial angle is greater for

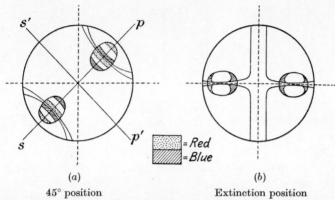

(a)   (b)

45° position   Extinction position

Fig. 5.25. Dispersion of the optic axes in orthorhombic crystals ($\rho > v$). 2.

red light (ρ), than for violet (v), as in Fig. 5.24, the fact is summarised
briefly by the formula $\rho > v$, and the opposite case by $\rho < v$.

Dispersion of the optic axes also affects the distribution of colour in
the colour bands of the interference figure. In cases of moderate
dispersion this effect is most evident in the immediate neighbourhood
of the melatopes, where also the coloured fringes of the isogyres show
up most clearly. In Fig. 5.25 *a* and *b*, the arrangement of colours
around these two points is shown diagrammatically for the case $\rho > v$.
The colours would be reversed for the opposite case. It should be noted
that in the extinction position the coloured fringes of the isogyres
disappear; and also that the figure is symmetrical about the trace of
the optic axial plane, *sp*, and about the optic normal, *s'p'*, this following
from the fact that only the optic axes and not the bisectrices are
dispersed.

Dispersion in Monoclinic Crystals. In the monoclinic system one of
the symmetry planes of the indicatrix lies parallel to *b*(010), i.e. to the

one possible symmetry plane of the system, whatever the wave-length of the light, and it follows that one of the axes of the indicatrix, either α, β, or γ, must be coincident with the direction of the b axis for all colours of light. Three cases are possible, and are illustrated in Fig. 5.26 (i), (ii) and (iii), the ortho-axis b being in turn acute bisectrix, obtuse bisectrix and optic normal. In (i) and (ii), the optic axial plane

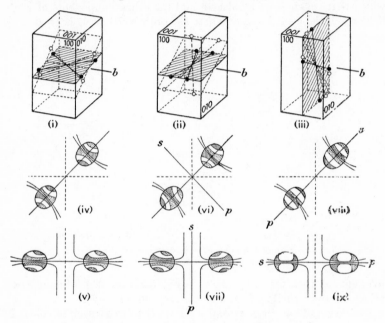

Fig. 5.26. Types of dispersion in monoclinic crystals.
Lines about which the interference figures are symmetrical are marked s p.

is normal to $b(010)$ and the plane of symmetry, and in (iii) it is parallel to $b(010)$. The cases figured represent a fairly large degree of dispersion but not so extreme as to lead to the phenomenon of crossed-axial-plane dispersion (p. 226), examples of which will be given below.

In addition to angular dispersion of the optic axes which is always present in some degree, dispersion of the bisectrices which happen to lie in the plane parallel to (010) takes place, as the result of a rotation of the indicatrix as a whole about the fixed axis b.

In the first case (Fig. 5.26 (i)), b is the acute bisectrix (α or γ), the obtuse bisectrix (γ or α) together with the optic normal lying in the symmetry plane (010). Dispersion takes place by a rotation of the optic axial plane around b, the melatopes of the acute axial angle rotating around the fixed bisectrix, and the obtuse bisectrix (together with the optic normal) being dispersed in the plane (010). This type of dispersion is called *crossed* or *rotated*, and the interference figure is seen to be centro-symmetrical (Fig. 5.26 (iv) and (v)).

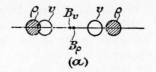

(a)

In the second case (Fig. 5.26 (ii)), b is the obtuse bisectrix, the acute bisectrix and the optic normal for each colour lying in the symmetry plane. A similar rotation of the indicatrix displaces the acute bisectrix normal to a line joining the melatopes of the figure. The positions of successive interference figures for different wave-lengths of light are thus parallel to one another (the dis-

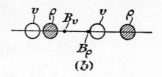

(b)

Fig. 5.27. Inclined dispersion in monoclinic crystals.

tance between the melatopes in successive figures being different, however, owing to dispersion of the optic axial angle). The dispersion is therefore called *horizontal* or *parallel*. The interference figure in white light will only be symmetrical with respect to a line normal to the traces of the optic axial planes. This type of dispersion is best recognised in the position in which the isogyres are crossed when the narrow bar joining the melatopes will be seen to be bordered by different colours above and below (Fig. 5.26 (vii)).

In the remaining case (Fig. 5.26) (iii)), the optic normal β coincides with the b axis and the optic axial plane for all colours lies parallel to the clinopinacoid (010). The optic axes and the acute and obtuse bisectrices are dispersed parallel to the clinopinacoid. With changing colour of light the position of the melatopes changes along the line joining them, and the interference figure will be symmetrical only with respect to the trace of the optic axial plane (Fig. 5.26 (viii)). Such dispersion is called *inclined*. The colour bands round one melatope will be more elongated than around the other, the actual order of the colours around the melatopes depending upon the amount of dispersion of the optic axes and bisectrices. Thus, in the case shown in Fig. 5.27 a, the isogyres in the interference figure will be fringed as shown in Fig. 5.26 (viii). Should, however, the dispersion be as great as that shown in Fig. 5.27 b, the colours around one melatope would be reversed.

Dispersion in Triclinic Crystals. In the triclinic system, there being no planes nor axes of symmetry by which the orientation of the indicatrix may be controlled, dispersion of both optic axes and bisectrices takes place irregularly and the interference figures are unsymmetrical. A possible case is shown in Fig. 5.28.

Crossed-Axial-Plane Dispersion. In certain biaxial substances in which the intermediate refractive index β lies near to either α or γ, the variation in size of the optic axial angle for a comparatively small change in the wave-length of light is very marked. If the acute interference figure of such a substance is observed in red light, and the wave-length is changed towards blue (by the use of a monochromator

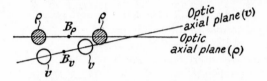

Fig. 5.28. Dispersion in triclinic crystals.

or a series of filters), it will be seen that the axial angle will become smaller as the wave-length is shortened, the substance becoming uniaxial for some intermediate colour of the spectrum. Further progressive change in the colour of the light will be followed by an opening of the optic axes in a direction at right angles to the former trace of the optic axial plane, the maximum size of angle being reached for violet light. The optic axial planes for red and blue light are normal to one another. This type of dispersion, called *crossed-axial-plane* dispersion, has already been briefly treated in Chapter 2, p. 94. The case of brookite mentioned there is illustrated in Figs. 5.29 *a, b* and *c*. The interference figure of this substance in white light (like that of most substances which show the phenomenon) is symmetrical but anomalous and without isogyres.

Other substances which show crossed-axial-plane dispersion are rubidium sulphate, Rb_2SO_4, and cæsium selenate, Cs_2SeO_4, which are orthorhombic,* and cæsium magnesium sulphate, $Cs_2Mg(SO_4)_2,6H_2O$ and the corresponding selenate, both monoclinic. If none of these is available *p*-nitrobenzaldehyde provides a convenient example.† If a little of this is melted between a slide and a cover slip and slowly cooled (p. 278), many of the resulting crystals will be oriented with the acute

---

* Tutton, A. E. H., *Crystallography and Practical Crystal Measurement* (Macmillan, 2nd ed., 1922), Vol. 2, 1058.

† Davies, E. S., and Hartshorne, N. H., *J. Chem. Soc.*, 1934, 1830.

bisetrix normal to the slide, and on these the dispersion may be readily observed by means of a series of colour filters.

In monoclinic crystals, crossed-axial-plane dispersion involves a change in the orientation of the optic axial plane from (010) to a plane normal to this, or *vice versa*, i.e. between the orientations shown in

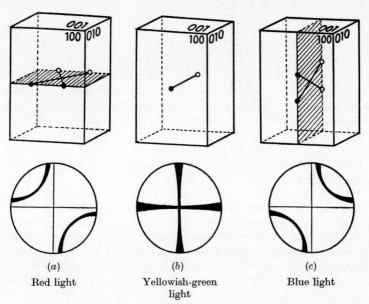

(a)	(b)	(c)
Red light	Yellowish-green light	Blue light

Fig. 5.29. Crossed-axial-plane dispersion of brookite.

Fig. 5.26 (i) or (ii) and (iii). It will be apparent that this change may be accompanied by the types of dispersion illustrated in these figures.

Dispersion Resulting in Change of Optical Sign. In certain uniaxial crystals in which the birefringence is small, dispersion may result in a change of sign. The example of torbernite has already been mentioned in Chapter 2, p. 94.

In some biaxial crystals a change of sign takes place because dispersion of the optic axes results in the optic axial angle passing through a value of 90°. This is shown by the mineral danburite, $CaB_2(SiO_4)_2$, which is optically negative for red, yellow and green, but positive for blue. (See also J. Mitchell Jr., and W. M. D. Bryant,[*] for some organic examples.)

[*] *J. Amer. Chem. Soc.*, 1943, **65**, 128.

Measurement of Dispersion. Accurate measurements of the amount of dispersion should be made in monochromatic light of different wave-lengths. The dispersion of the bisectrices in monoclinic and triclinic crystals is determined by measuring extinction angles for light of different colours on specific faces instead of making observations upon the interference figures.

DETERMINATION OF THE OPTICAL SIGN OF A CRYSTAL BY OBSERVATIONS UPON INTERFERENCE FIGURES

The differences between positive and negative crystals have already been explained in Chapter 2. They may be summarised briefly for the purpose of this section by means of the four diagrams in Fig. 5.30 which give the traces of the directions of vibration and relative velocities of convergent rays in basal sections of uniaxial crystals, and the principal vibration directions in sections of biaxial crystals normal to the acute bisectrix.

The problem of determining sign, therefore, resolves itself into finding out (1) in uniaxial interference figures, whether the radial or tangential direction of vibration is the faster, and (2) in biaxial crystals, whether in the acute interference figure the optic normal direction giving the refractive index β (i.e. the normal to the line joining the melatopes) is faster or slower than the ray vibrating parallel to the trace of the optic axial plane, this ray giving either α in positive, and γ in negative crystals.

The accessories used for this purpose are the mica plate ($\frac{1}{4}\lambda$ retardation); the gypsum or selenite plate (unit retardation plate); and the quartz wedge. The principles underlying the use of these accessories have already been explained in Chapter 4, pp. 189–192, and need not be repeated here. It will only be necessary to describe their application to the present problem. In general, it may be said that the gypsum plate is better adapted for use with sections having low double refraction, the mica plate and quartz wedge being more convenient for sections with higher birefringences.

It cannot be too strongly emphasised that in the following discussion, the phenomena illustrated in the diagrams are true only for the conditions described, and care must be exercised to see that the orientation of the interference figure, plate or wedge, and microscope slot, are identical with those given in the text before using the diagrams as a guide in practical work. It is always best to work out each case from first principles.

Uniaxial Crystals. On viewing a uniaxial interference figure with a $\frac{1}{4}\lambda$ retardation plate in the 45° slot of the microscope, it will be seen that the black isogyres are now first order greyish-blue (the colour due to the plate), the circular colour bands are slightly moved radially

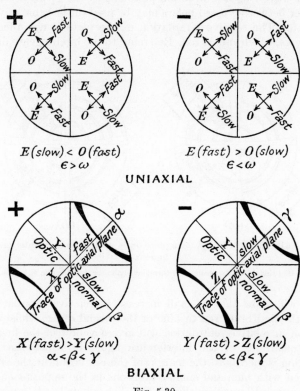

E (slow) < O (fast)   E (fast) > O (slow)
$\epsilon > \omega$ $\epsilon < \omega$

UNIAXIAL

X (fast) > Y (slow)   Y (fast) > Z (slow)
$\alpha < \beta < \gamma$ $\alpha < \beta < \gamma$

BIAXIAL

Fig. 5.30

towards the centre of the field in one pair of diagonally opposite quadrants and outwards in the other pair, becoming discontinuous at the isogyres, and there appear two dark spots near the intersection of the isogyres on a line at 45° to them (Fig. 5.31 *a* and *b*). The diagonal upon which the spots lie is the direction in which the relative retardation is reduced by $\frac{1}{4}\lambda$ (the effect being like 'thinning' the section) and the dark spots mark the positions at which exact compensation results. In this quadrant the vibrations of the plate and section are opposed.

Fig. 5.31 *a* shows that since the plate has a 'fast' length the vibration in the same direction in the section must be 'slow', and as this is the vibration direction of E, the crystal must be optically positive. The opposite case is shown in Fig. 5.31 *b*.

A unit wave-length retardation plate of gypsum giving a red of the first order between crossed polars may be used in the same way as the mica plate. The relative retardation of the plate is not affected by the isogyres, which appear red. Reference to the birefringence diagram,

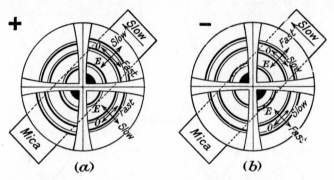

Fig. 5.31. Effect of the $\frac{1}{4}\lambda$ mica plate on $+$ and $-$ uniaxial interference figures.

The thin rings show the positions of the colour bands before insertion of the plate.

p. 179, will show that a small increase in relative retardation will change the first order red to blue of the second order, whilst a slight reduction in relative retardation will give a yellow of the first order. In the quadrants of the interference figure in which the relative retardation is increased, the margin of the isogyres near the cross will be fringed with blue and similar positions in the opposite quadrants will be occupied by yellow (Fig. 5.32). The colour bands suffer altera-tion in position as in the case when the mica plate is used, but the relative retardation of each ring is altered by exactly 1λ instead of $\frac{1}{4}\lambda$ for light of a definite wave-length. The positive and negative uniaxial cases with a fast length gypsum plate are shown, the various bands being labelled with the retardation they represent.

When the quartz wedge is used, the results are exactly analogous to those seen when the mica and gypsum plates are used, except that the movement of the colour bands is continuous as the wedge is pushed through the microscope slot thin end first, the movement being towards the centre in the quadrants in which the colours are raised (increased relative retardation), and away from the centre in the opposite quadrants where the colours are lowered in response to a decrease in relative retardation. In Fig. 5.33 the movement of the colour bands in positive

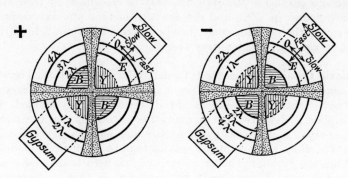

Fig. 5.32. Effect of unit retardation gypsum plate on + and − uniaxial interference figures.

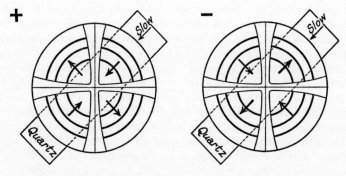

Fig. 5.33. Effect of quartz wedge on + and − uniaxial interference figures.

and negative uniaxial interference figures is indicated by the small stout arrows, a quartz wedge with its slow direction of vibration parallel to its length being used, orientated NE–SW with respect to the crosswires.

When inclined interference figures are presented, such as those shown in Fig. 5.11, the same methods may be adopted as those just detailed. The stage is revolved, the movement of the straight isogyres is noted and a quadrant is selected the orientation of which in relation to the complete figure is known. The test is then made with one of the plates or a wedge, the latter being used upon very inclined figures of which only the colour bands may be seen.

Sections parallel to the optic axis may be recognised by their interference figures (p. 208), and the direction of the optic axis deduced. The sign of the substance may then be determined in parallel polarised light by use, e.g., of the quartz wedge.

Biaxial Crystals. The methods for determining sign in biaxial crystals are conducted in exactly the same way as those for uniaxial crystals, and any of the three accessories already mentioned may be used. The mica plate is, however, not in general so satisfactory in the case of biaxial crystals as are the gypsum plate and quartz wedge, the colour effects of which are much more striking than those of the $\frac{1}{4}\lambda$ plate.

When the gypsum plate or quartz wedge is used to determine sign, the interference figure should be orientated so that the melatopes make an angle of 45° to the cross-wires, and the directions of vibration in the plate lie parallel to the principal vibration directions in the crystal section. The optic axial plane lies through the melatopes and the β vibration direction lies normal to this. The underlying principle of the method is to determine whether the β direction is faster or slower than that in the optic plane, and so find out whether α or γ is the acute bisectrix.

Consider the case of a positive biaxial section normal to the acute bisectrix. If this section is orientated so that the melatopes lie NE–SW, the fast direction of vibration (α) will be parallel to the line joining the melatopes and the slow direction (β) will lie normal to it. If now a quartz wedge with slow length is inserted parallel to the trace of the optic axial plane of the crystal (fast), then the colours will be lowered. As the wedge is pushed in the lemniscate colour bands will move out in the direction of the optic normal, bands of smaller retardations replacing those of higher values (Fig. 5.34 (i)). The phenomena for positive and negative crystals in different orientations is given in Fig. 5.34 (i)–(iv).

When a unit retardation plate is used, the phenomena for biaxial crystals are analogous to those given by uniaxial crystals. The isogyres, which become red on insertion of the plate, are fringed near the melatopes with yellow on the sides facing those portions of the field in which the retardation has been reduced, and blue on the opposite sides. Fig. 5.35 *a* and *b*, show the disposition of the coloured fringes for positive and negative biaxial interference figures, using a 1λ retardation plate with fast length, in a NE–SW direction. These diagrams should be carefully compared with those for uniaxial crystals (Fig. 5.32), when it will be seen that the disposition of the colours with respect to the 45° diagonals is the same, i.e. for the conditions stated, in positive

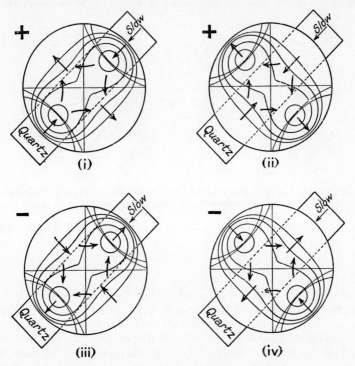

Fig. 5.34. Effect of quartz wedge on + and − biaxial interference figures (acute bisectrix).

crystals yellow NE–SW, blue NW–SE, and *vice versa* for negative crystals.

It should be remembered that the optical effects (directions of movement of colour bands, etc.), obtained for any given orientation of an acute interference figure and plate or wedge, will be reversed if the obtuse figure is examined.

On partial biaxial interference figures the same procedure as for complete figures is followed after the direction of the acute bisectrix has been determined by turning the isogyre 45° from its straight position (if it can be seen), and noting the direction of its convexity, which is the required direction. Should the isogyre leave the field in the diagonal position its curvature cannot be determined with certainty and another section should be sought.

On sections parallel to the optic axial plane (p. 216, Fig. 5.18), the optical character may be determined in parallel light as described for

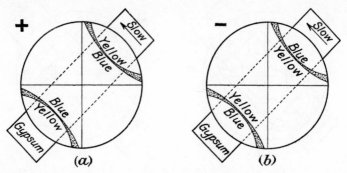

Fig. 5.35.　Effect of unit retardation gypsum plate on + and − biaxial interference figures (acute bisectrix).

optic normal sections of uniaxial substances, after deducing the direction of the acute bisectrix as given on p. 216, the acute bisectrix direction being slow (γ) for positive, and fast (α) for negative substances.

MEASUREMENT OF THE OPTIC AXIAL ANGLE

In this section we shall only describe some simple methods of determining the optic axial angle, which are applicable to crystals in ordinary mounts between a slide and a cover slip. Other (generally more accurate) methods involve the use of rotation apparatus, such as the single-axis apparatus to be dealt with in Chapter 7, or the universal stage, details of which will be found in some of the advanced works cited in the Appendix.

It is possible to calculate the value of 2V if all three refractive indices are known. These may be determined under the microscope as described in pp. 237–240. The formulæ given below show the relation between the refractive indices and half the acute angle for positive and negative crystals respectively, $V\alpha$ being half the negative acute axial angle and $V\gamma$ that for positive crystals:

$$\cos^2 V\alpha = \frac{\gamma^2(\beta^2 - \alpha^2)}{\beta^2(\gamma^2 - \alpha^2)} \qquad . \qquad . \qquad . \quad 5.3\,a$$

$$\cos^2 V\gamma = \frac{\alpha^2(\gamma^2 - \beta^2)}{\beta^2(\gamma^2 - \alpha^2)} \qquad . \qquad . \qquad . \quad 5.3\,b$$

Alternatively it is possible to calculate any principal refractive index from a knowledge of V and the other two refractive indices, and this may be useful when γ is too high to be measured directly. A warning must, however, be sounded here because unless the refractive indices are known with great accuracy large errors may occur. The subject is mentioned again on p. 298.

The most rapid and convenient methods of measuring the optic axial angle under the microscope are those in which observations are made upon interference figures of which one or both of the melatopes appear in the field. Several factors militate against absolute accuracy. In the first place the primary interference figure at the principal focus of the objective is actually formed upon a slightly curved surface, and what is really observed by the eye is an orthographic projection of the figure. Secondly, in thin sections the isogyres may be so diffuse as to make it difficult to determine very accurately the points of emergence of the optic axes. It must be remembered that the size of the optic axial angle depends upon the wave-length of light, and that therefore a precise determination can only be made in monochromatic light. The dispersion of the optic axial angle in many substances is, however, so small that a mean value, sufficiently definitive for diagnostic purposes, can be obtained in white light. It is possible in the most favourable cases to approach within 1° of the true value of 2E (the apparent angle in air, p. 214) by these methods using monochromatic light.

Measurements upon the figures are made by means of a scale placed in the focal plane of the ocular (or at a conjugate focus where it may be viewed simultaneously with the interference figure). A simple linear scale (Fig. 4.4 p. 158) which can be placed at 45° to the cross-wires will do for the Mallard method (see below), but a 0·1 mm. co-ordinate micrometer scale, i.e. a grid, is much better for the method which uses the curvature of the isogyre, and makes the plotting of the positions of the isogyres upon diagrams a simple matter. While a number of ingenious methods have been evolved for use in difficult situations such as when both two melatopes are outside the field, the authors believe that the two methods described below are sufficient for all practical purposes when rotation methods are ruled out.

The Mallard Method (Two Melatopes in the Field). E. Mallard showed that half the apparent distance between the melatopes of a biaxial interference figure, as measured on an eyepiece scale, is proportional to the sine of the angle which the optic axes make with the bisectrix, and a constant factor which depends upon the lens system of the microscope. The relation between the apparent axial angle, E, and half the apparent distance between the melatopes D, is given by Mallard's formula

$$D = K \sin E$$

K being the *Mallard constant*.* In order to find K for any lens system of the microscope, D is measured in terms of the eyepiece scale upon an interference figure the optic axial angle of which is known. An example will make the method clear. A plate of barytes cut normal to the acute bisectrix with 2E = 63° 10′ gave D = 12, in the 45° position, using a Reichert No. 5 objective and a Reichert No. III ocular. K therefore works out to 22·9. One good determination will usually suffice for ordinary work, but two or three determinations should be made upon substances having very different values of 2E for greater accuracy. Once the Mallard constant (sometimes denoted by M), is known, the value of 2E for any section showing a central (or slightly inclined figure) having two melatopes in the field may be found, and the apparent angle reduced to the true angle (2V) by means of the formula

$$\sin E = \beta \sin V$$

where β is the intermediate refractive index of the crystal. In microscopes where an arrangement exists for altering the position of the Bertrand lens, the Mallard constant must be determined not only for a fixed combination of ocular and objective but also for a definite position of the Bertrand lens.

Instead of working out the angular equivalents of D by means of the Mallard formula each time, the divisions of the microscope scale may be calibrated once for all for any fixed lens system by means of three or four substances of known 2E and a graph constructed showing the relation of E and D.

Estimation of 2V on Optic Axial Sections. It has already been stated that when the angle 2V is 90° the single isogyre of the optic axial section is straight and pivots around the centre of the field (the 'compass figure'). In uniaxial crystals (2V = 0°), the basal section gives a figure in which the angles between the isogyres are 90°, and when 2V is very small the acute figure approximates to that of the uniaxial one, each separate isogyre in the 45° position being sharply curved, the two arms of each brush forming an angle of nearly 90° between them. The amount of curvature of the isogyres in the 45° position is clearly a function of the size of the optic axial angle, though it depends somewhat upon other

---

* In practice one may use the whole distance 2D thus merely doubling the value of K.

factors such as the mean refractive index of the crystal. It may therefore be used to estimate the size of the optic axial angle. Fig. 5.36
shows approximately the course of the middle line of the isogyre in
optic axial sections for values of 2V between 0° and 90°, at intervals of
15°. The field of view shown is that given by an average microscope
using an objective of about 0·80 N.A., and it will be noted that when
2V is less than about 25° the other isogyre of the interference figure is

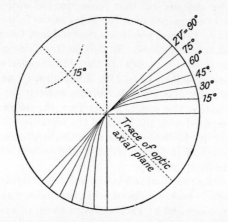

Fig. 5.36. Curves showing approximately the relation of the shape of the
isogyre to the optic axial angle (2V), in a section normal to one optic axis
(45° position).

also seen. The curves are based on those given by F. E. Wright* for
different cases, and may be used to estimate optic axial angles to
perhaps ±10°. Comparison of an actual isogyre with the curves is
simplified and at the same time made more accurate by plotting it
upon squared paper with the aid of a co-ordinate micrometer scale, as
mentioned above.

THE DETERMINATION OF THE REFRACTIVE INDICES OF BIREFRINGENT CRYSTALS

The immersion method of determining refractive indices has already
been described in Chapter 4 with special reference to isotropic crystals.
Now that the study of crystals in parallel and convergent polarised
light has been dealt with, the reader is in a position to understand how
the method may be applied to birefringent crystals.

* Wright, F. E., *Methods of Petrographic Microscopic Research*, 1911, p. 155.

In the first place, by using the method in ordinary unpolarised light as for isotropic crystals, the *mean* refractive index of a birefringent substance may be determined, and in certain cases this may be of diagnostic value, especially if the birefringence is low. It is, however, always more satisfactory, to determine the principal refractive indices of the substance, or, at least, the indices shown by a particular section of it, and this can be done because in polarised light the two refractive indices shown by any crystal (not presenting an optic axial section) may be separately compared with the index of the immersion liquid in the following way. Crossed polars are inserted and the stage is turned until the crystal is extinguished. In this position, one of the vibration directions of the crystal is parallel to that of the polariser (which may be ascertained as described in p. 172, if not already known), and the light transmitted by the crystal vibrates entirely in this direction (p. 76). On removing the analyser therefore, the index for this direction may be compared with the index of the liquid by either the Becke, or Schroeder van der Kolk test. The stage is then turned through 90°, when a comparison of the other index of the crystal with that of the liquid can be similarly made.

To determine the principal refractive indices, crystals lying so as to present these indices must be examined in the above way, such crystals being variously recognised by their outward form, polarisation colours, the nature of their extinction, or their interference figures as will now be described.

Uniaxial Crystals. Every section has ω as one of its indices, so that the determination of this index may be readily made. ω is also the sole index shown by optic axial (basal) sections, which may be recognised by their isotropism in parallel light, and by their characteristic interference figure consisting of concentric rings of colour and a black cross (p. 204).

ε is shown only by sections containing the optic (and c) axis. Crystals with a well-developed prism form (parallel to c) usually lie on a vertical face and so present $\varepsilon\omega$ sections. Such crystals can often be recognised by their appearance (e.g. Fig. 4.1); they give straight extinction and optic normal interference figures. It may also be recalled that the birefringence is a maximum for crystals so orientated, and that they therefore show the highest polarisation colours in relation to their thickness.

The determination of ε on irregular material, which is too finely divided to give satisfactory interference figures, may be made by examining a number of grains showing the highest polarisation colours, taking as ε the value found which differs most widely from ω. Obviously the correctness of the result depends upon the grains being orientated at random, so that some present $\varepsilon\omega$ sections. A marked rhombohedral or basal cleavage might result in an overwhelming proportion of the grains being bounded by faces parallel to these directions, when examples lying so as to show ε would be rare or absent. An attempt must therefore be made to roll the grains into other positions, and test for ε again. Various methods of 'crystal-rolling' are discussed on pp. 279–280, Chapter 7.

Biaxial Crystals. Sections giving centred interference figures show principal refractive indices as follows:

FIGURE	OPTICAL SIGN	INDICES SHOWN
Acute bisectrix	$+$	α, β
Acute bisectrix	$-$	γ, β
Obtuse bisectrix	$+$	γ, β
Obtuse bisectrix	$-$	α, β
Optic normal	$+$ or $-$	α, γ
Single optic axis	$+$ or $-$	β

The sections with the above orientations are the principal and circular sections of the indicatrix. In addition to these, any section which is perpendicular to a principal section of the indicatrix, i.e. to an optical symmetry plane of the crystal, shows one of the principal refractive indices, namely that for light vibrating at right angles to the symmetry plane concerned. Such sections give the type of inclined interference figure described on pp. 218, 220, in which, in the extinction position, one isogyre is straight and passes through the centre of the field. In this position, the principal index shown is that for light vibrating at right angles to the direction of this isogyre. The optical sign and the relation of the vibration direction to the optic axial plane determine whether the index is α, β or γ.

The principal indices may be determined on finely divided irregular material in random orientation by a method similar to that described for uniaxial crystals namely by examining a large number of grains showing the highest polarisation colours and taking as α and γ respectively the lowest and highest indices found. β is given by those grains showing a uniform illumination between crossed polars on rotating the stage.

Acicular and fibrous crystals present all the indices of the substance during rotation about the axis of elongation, a fact which is useful if the crystals will 'stay put' in many different positions of rotation. If the extinction is straight along the axis of elongation at all positions of rotation, the index along the length must necessarily be constant and a principal index.

A point of interest and importance is that no section of a biaxial crystal can have indices which are both above, or both below β. In some cases this affords a means of determining β, for if one grain is found with a lower index of, say, 1·635, and another with an upper index of this same value, then β is 1·635.

Use of Rotation Apparatus for Determining Refractive Indices. The methods described above are those which are applicable to ordinary mounts of crystals between a slide and a cover slip. Other methods which are applicable to crystals large enough to be manipulated individually, and which involve the use of rotation apparatus, are described in Chapter 7. These include a method by which values of γ, which are too high to be determined directly, may be obtained by an indirect procedure. Universal stage methods of determining refractive indices are described in the appropriate works listed in Appendix I.

6   THE STEREOGRAPHIC PROJECTION

Drawings of various kinds, either in perspective or in plan, are useful for giving a picture of the external appearance or habit of crystals, but it is convenient to be able to show accurately the angular relations of the crystal faces (and hence the crystal symmetry), by means of the more highly abstract graphical representation afforded by geometrical projections. Various types of these have been used, but as an effective means of displaying crystal symmetry and the geometrical relationships of the optical properties to external morphology, as well as being an indispensable tool in many optical investigations, the stereographic projection occupies a unique place. For these reasons, and as it is easily constructed with a few simple drawing instruments, it is the only one that will be used in this book. Some examples of its use are given at the end of this chapter.

Fundamental Principles of the Stereographic Projection. Consider a sphere (Fig. 6.1), of which NS is the vertical diameter, and ABCD the plane normal to this diameter through the centre of the sphere. This plane cuts the sphere in a circle XYX'Y' known as the *primitive circle* or briefly, the *primitive*. If any point p on the surface of the sphere is joined to S by a straight line, the intersection P of this line with the equatorial plane is the stereographic projection of p. Points such as p situated on the surface of the upper hemisphere are always projected in this way, but points on the lower hemisphere such as p' (which for the purpose of this demonstration is regarded as being vertically below p), may be projected by joining to N, the pole of the upper hemisphere (in which case it plots also at P), or by being projected from S on to the plane ABCD as at P'. The first method is adopted in showing the relationships of crystal faces, and the second is necessary for certain geometrical constructions, as will be shown later. Fig. 6.2 is a vertical section through Npp'S of Fig. 6.1 and will make the two methods of projection plain. It should be noted that projection on any plane parallel to ABCD (e.g. to P'' on EFGH), by the methods detailed above will give a stereographic projection, but on a different scale.

For the cartographer who wishes to map the surface of the earth by using this method of projection, the features to be shown are already

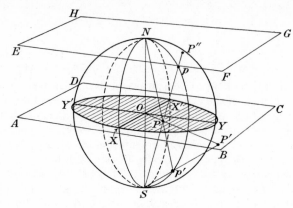

Fig. 6.1

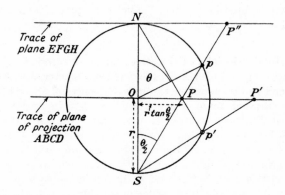

Fig. 6.2

disposed on the surface of a sphere, but for the crystallographer it is necessary first of all to make a *spherical projection* of the relevant crystal properties. For this purpose the crystal is imagined to be oriented within a sphere so that, for example, an important set of edges is parallel to the N–S axis as in Fig. 6.3. From the centre of the sphere, lines are imagined to radiate in directions normal to the planes represented by each crystal face, and where these *face normals* pierce the sphere, *face poles* are located. These face poles are then projected on to the plane of projection within the primitive circle in the manner already described and are referred to as face poles in the projection. Faces occurring on the upper half of the crystal are represented conventionally in the projection by points, and those on the lower half by small open circles.

The face normals will not necessarily pass through the crystal face which they represent, but often through the face produced, as shown

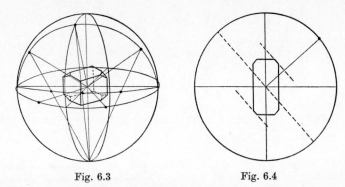

Fig. 6.3   Fig. 6.4

in Fig. 6.4. As a matter of fact, it is better to regard each crystal face as being translated parallel to itself until its plane intersects the centre of the sphere of projection, for the following reason. It is often necessary to represent a crystal face or other plane not only by its pole, but also by projecting the trace of the intersection of the plane with the sphere. This is shown in Fig. 6.5. The plane XLX′M is represented by its face pole p, which is projected to P, and also by the arcs XlX′ and XmX′ which are the stereographic projections of the upper and lower parts of the circle XLX′M respectively. Further, P is not only the projection of the face pole p, but may also be taken to represent the *direction* Op, which might be, for example, an optic axis of the crystal or the pole of a zone of crystal faces (see below). The representation of a plane by projecting the circle in which it intersects the sphere is often called the *cyclographic projection* of the plane.

Great Circles and Small Circles. *Great circles* are the intersections with the sphere of planes which pass through its centre. In the discussion above it was pointed out that crystal faces and other planes are to be regarded as moving parallel to themselves until they pass through the centre of the sphere of projection. It will be clear therefore that all planes such as crystal faces, cleavage planes, symmetry planes, and the like, when shown in cyclographic projection will be the stereographic projections of great circles.

Small circles are formed by the intersection of the sphere by planes which do not pass through its centre (Fig. 6.5). They form the locus

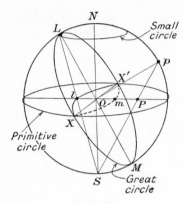

Fig. 6.5

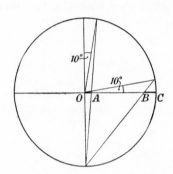

Fig. 6.6. Distances OA and BC represent 10° at centre and margin of projection, respectively.

of points at an equal angular distance from a point on the surface of the sphere, or stated alternatively, the intersection with the sphere of a cone of directions making equal angles with the axis of the cone.

Properties of the Stereographic Projection. 1. *The projection of a circle on the sphere is a circle.* This is a property which makes the drawing of the projection easy. Vertical great circles will project as straight lines (circles of infinite radius), through the centre of the projection. Other great circles will project within the primitive circle as arcs of circles, and the line joining diametrically opposite points where these arcs cut the primitive will pass through the centre, being a projection of the diameter of the great circle. Small circles entirely within either the north or south hemisphere will project as complete circles within the primitive; those which lie in both hemispheres will project as arcs of circles.

2. *Angular truth is preserved in the projection.* This means that the angle between the planes of two great circles which intersect on the sphere is the same after projection on to the equatorial plane. It is this

property which makes the stereographic projection so valuable a means of checking calculations involving the solution of spherical triangles, and in such problems as the estimation of the extinction angle on any face of a crystal (p. 256), as well as being a more rapid substitute for calculations where the utmost accuracy is not required. It will be seen from Fig. 6.6 that the *linear* value of a degree in the projection is greater near the primitive than near the centre of the projection, but this causes no difficulty in measurement.

The proofs of the above statements are not presented here, but the reader who is interested will find them in the *Manual of Petrographic Methods* by A. Johannsen, 2nd edn., McGraw-Hill, 1918, pp. 8–9.

Some Necessary Constructions. The following graphical constructions are sufficient to enable the student to make for himself stereographic projections from angular values of the face poles, to solve problems such as the graphical determination of extinction angles, and to understand the construction of stereographic nets. The only *necessary* instruments are a pair of compasses with an extension bar, a protractor of not less than 5 in. diameter, a scale in millimetres and a pair of set-squares. Special protractors and scales have been devised to help in the drawing of projections. They are not necessary, but effect a saving of time. However, after a time, linear scales engraved on celluloid become inaccurate because of contraction. In any case, it is good that the student should first undergo the discipline of going through all the constructions without these special aids. Reference may be made to the works in Appendix I (*a*), for descriptions of these instruments.

All the constructions may be done on the plane of the primitive circle. This is possible because any great circle can be imagined to be revolved into the plane of the primitive. Consider Fig. 6.7. Suppose it is desired to plot a pole *p* which lies 45° above the primitive on the East–West vertical great circle B*p*NB′. This plots at P. The same result is obtained by doing the construction on the primitive circle, which for this purpose may be regarded as the vertical circle revolved around the horizontal diameter BOB′ which it has in common with the vertical circle. X becomes the 'south pole' for the purpose of the construction, and *p*′, 45° from B on the primitive, plots at P also.

1. *The Primitive Circle.* This should be drawn with a radius of 5 cm. Any larger size becomes inconvenient when constructing circles with a small inclination from the centre of the projection, and on so small a circle with careful work an accuracy of half a degree may be attained. Generalised nets to be described later, may be used with a much greater radius.

2. *To draw a great circle through two poles, one lying on the primitive.* In Fig. 6.8, which is a projection on the equatorial plane, A and B are the two poles. Join A to O at the centre and produce to C on the primitive. AOC is the projected diameter of the required circle.

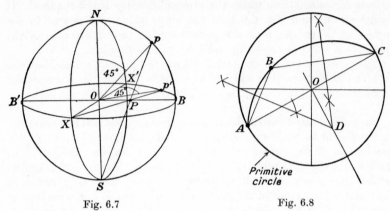

Fig. 6.7   Fig. 6.8

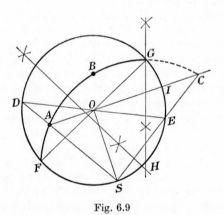

Fig. 6.9

Bisect the chords AB and BC. The intersection D of the perpendicular bisectors then marks the centre of the projected circle. This centre, around which the circle ABC may be drawn, lies on the normal to AC from O.

3. *To draw a great circle through two poles, both lying within the primitive.* The principle underlying this construction is to find a point diametrically opposite to either of the given poles. In Fig. 6.9, which,

like Fig. 6.8, shows the projection on the equatorial plane, A and B are the given poles. Through A and O draw a diameter and produce, then construct the normal to AO from O, meeting the primitive at S, which becomes the 'south pole' for the purpose of the construction. Project A to the primitive at D from S. Draw the diameter DOE to find E which is thus 180° from D. The stereographic projection of E is located at C (cf. Fig. 6.1). Thus three points on the required great

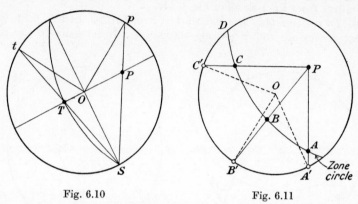

Fig. 6.10   Fig. 6.11

circle have been found. Its centre is located at H by the usual construction and the circle drawn in.

4. *Given a pole, to draw the corresponding great circle*, i.e. *the great circle to which it is normal*. In Fig. 6.10, P is the given pole. Draw the diameter through P and O and the normal to it, OS. Project P to the primitive at p. Locate t, 90° from p and project back to S thus finding T, 90° from P in the projection. The great circle through T and S can now be found by the construction shown in Fig. 6.8. The reverse of this problem, to locate P given a great circle, is obvious from the figure.

The faces of crystals occur in sets which intersect (or their planes produced intersect) in parallel edges. Such a group of faces is called a zone. It will be appreciated that all the face poles of these faces will lie on a great circle. It is appropriate to point out here an important property of the pole of a zone, which is the projection of the normal to the circle on which the face poles lie. Thus, the true value of the angle between any two faces of a zone may be measured by projecting the two face poles from the pole of the zone to the primitive, where the arc thus cut off gives the correct angle. In Fig. 6.11, P is the pole of the zone circle ABCD, on which A, B and C are poles of the faces of the zone. If now the poles are projected from P to the primitive, the angles between the faces may be measured around the primitive circle as shown by the dotted lines from O. The converse of this construction is a very useful way of plotting the faces of a zone if the polar angles and the inclination of the zone circle are known.

5. *To measure the angle between two poles.* Pass a great circle through the two poles as described in sections 2 and 3. Locate the pole of this circle as shown in 4 above, and measure the angle by projecting to the primitive from the pole as in Fig. 6.11.

6. *To measure the angle between two great circles.* In Fig. 6.12, two great circles are shown passing through P. If tangents to the two

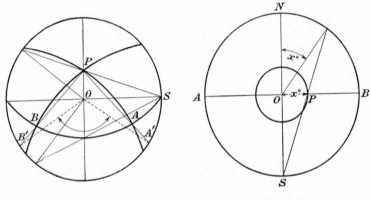

Fig. 6.12   Fig. 6.13

circles are drawn at P, the angle between them is equal to the angle between the two great circles. Another, and usually more accurate, method is to pass a circle 90° from P (the construction of section 4 being shown by thin lines) over the two circles between which the angle is to be measured. This cuts off two equal segments PA and PB each of 90° arc. Now P is the pole of the circle just drawn so that the angle will be given by projecting A and B from P to the primitive, the angle being measured in the manner described above, as shown by the dotted lines from O in the figure.

Small Circles

7. *To construct a small circle $x°$ from the centre of the projection.* Measure the angle $x°$ along any diameter, such as AOB in Fig. 6.13, by laying off from N, normal to the diameter as shown, and project on to the diameter by joining to S. The required radius is OP.

8. *To draw a small circle with a radius of $x°$ from a point on the primitive* (Fig. 6.14). Draw the diameter from the point (P), and the normal to this diameter from O to S. Lay off $x°$ in opposite directions from P (i.e. in the figure, $\angle BOP = \angle DOP = x°$), and project one of these points, say B, on to the diameter. Three points, B, A and D, on the required circle have now been found, and the centre C is found by the method of bisection of the chords BA and AD. Another method is

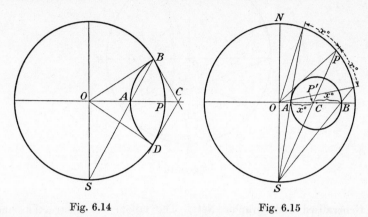

Fig. 6.14   Fig. 6.15

to draw tangents at B and D to the diameter produced. This method is in practice not as accurate as the first.

9. *To draw a small circle of $x°$ around a point within the primitive* (Fig. 6.15). P′ is the given point. Draw the diameter through it and then the normal OS. Project P′ to p. Lay off in opposite directions from p around the primitive, angles of $x°$, and project the angle $2x°$ back on to the diameter. This marks the diameter AB of the small circle, and it is only necessary to bisect this line to get the centre C of the required circle. Notice that the geometrical centre is not coincident with the angular centre P′.

10. *To locate a pole given its angular distance from two other points.* The two given points A and B may be on the primitive, as shown in Fig. 6.16. Draw diameters from each point, and as already described (section 8) construct small circles of the required angular radius around each point. In the case shown in the figure, the required pole P is located 70° from B, and 50° from A.

When the two given points are within the primitive, draw the two small circles corresponding to the required angles $x°$ and $y°$ around the two points, as demonstrated in section 9. These small circles intersect at two points. This means that geometrically there are two solutions to the construction, one or both of which may represent real poles in the particular case under consideration. There is usually no difficulty in deciding this point from a knowledge of the other measurements.

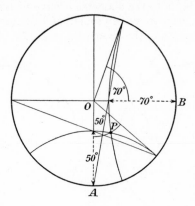

Fig. 6.16

Generalised Stereographic Nets. The labour of construction and measurement is greatly reduced by the use of printed stereographic nets, two types of which are in general use. The first, the so-called Wulff net (Fig. 6.17), consists of a series of great circles, usually at 2° intervals, drawn between two diametrically opposite points on the primitive, and around these two points is a series of small circles at the same angular interval. The second, the Federov net (Fig. 6.18), is like two Wulff nets at right angles, superposed upon one another, and has in addition a series of small circles described about the centre of the projection as well as a series of vertical great circles. The angular distance between adjacent circles on the Federov net is 5°; closer spacing would result in confusion. The nets may be printed on card or paper and the plotting done upon them directly, or tracing paper may be pinned to the centre of the net, the paper being revolved above it to bring the appropriate great or small circle into position, when it may be traced. Alternatively, the nets themselves are printed on tracing paper, and pinned by the centre to a sheet of stout paper below, when the appropriate circles or poles may be pricked through and subsequently inked in.

The direct plotting of face poles and other data such as optical vectors may be done on small Federov nets having a diameter of

5 cm.* If sufficient data are available it is usually possible to plot face-poles of non-triclinic crystals (Chapter 1) without having to draw circles other than those printed on the net, but for triclinic crystals

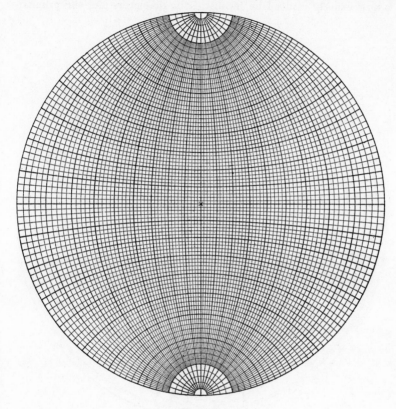

Fig. 6.17

and for the solving of optical problems (p. 256) it is most convenient to use tracing paper above a Wulff net of 20 cm. diameter, as follows.

The Wulff net is fixed flat upon a drawing board by means of thin strips of sellotape along its edges. (Drawing pins used for this usually interfere with the rotation of the tracing paper.) A piece of strong tracing paper is cut a little larger than the net, and on it are drawn the primitive circle of 20 cm. diameter and two diameters at right angles.

* Obtainable from J. H. Steward, 406 Strand, London, W.C.2.

The centre of the tracing paper is reinforced by means of a small piece of gummed thin card or stout paper and the two diameters drawn in across it to locate the centre of the primitive circle. The tracing paper is now exactly centred by means of the diameters and the primitive

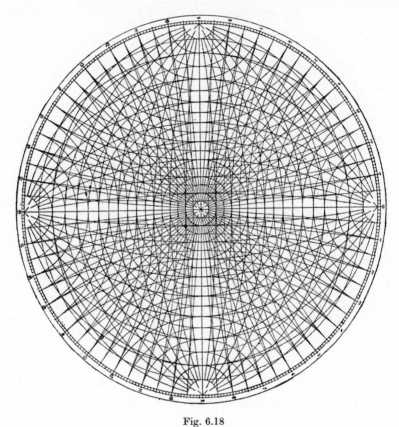

Fig. 6.18

circle, and a thin pin is pushed through its centre. One of the diameters is marked at the end with an arrow so that the projection may be brought back to its original position after rotation.

A few examples will make clear the method of using this simple apparatus. A great circle may be drawn through any two points within the primitive by rotating the tracing paper until the two points lie on one of the great circles of the net, when it can be sketched in.

The angle between two such points may be estimated by counting the number of degrees between the small circles which cut the great circle at right angles. Small circles around any point on the primitive are readily drawn in by rotating the point until it lies at one end of the diameter from which the great circles diverge and drawing in the required small circle. Face-poles distant by a given number of degrees from two points on the primitive may thus be readily located by constructing the two appropriate small circles (problem 10, p. 250). The diameter of any small circle within the primitive may be read off along the N–S diameter of the net and the circle drawn in with compasses after bisecting the diameter to find the *geometric* centre of the circle. The student will find no difficulty in adapting the net to the solution of other constructions.

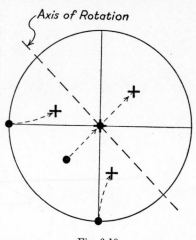

Fig. 6.19

It is sometimes necessary to rotate a projection through a given angle around a horizontal axis. The generalised net is very useful for this purpose. Each pole in the projection is turned through the appropriate angle along a small circle lying normal to the axis of rotation. The procedure is shown in Fig. 6.19. The axis around which rotation of the projection is to take place is brought parallel to the N–S axis of the net, and each pole or point is moved the correct number of degrees along a small circle in the appropriate direction.

The poles in their new positions may be marked in differently coloured ink or ringed around with a coloured pencil.

The Zonal Relationships of Crystal Faces. This subject is dealt with very briefly here since it has a direct relationship to the problems arising in the plotting of crystal faces in the projection, and to defining the directions of extinction in optical problems.

It has already been stated (p. 247) that the faces in any one zone (termed *tautozonal* faces) lie on a great circle, the pole of which (the pole of the zone) gives the direction of the edges between the faces of the zone. The orientation of the zone axis with respect to the crystal axes is defined by means of a zone symbol consisting of three numbers enclosed in square brackets to indicate a *direction* and not a crystal face. The three numbers represent co-ordinates along each axis in turn as will be explained by means of Fig. 6.20. In general terms the zone

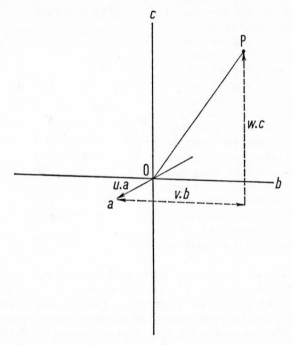

Fig. 6.20. Illustrating the operation of the zone symbol [*uvw*]. PO is the axis of the zone [*uvw*].

symbol may be expressed in the form [*uvw*]. In the figure *a*, *b* and *c* are unit lengths of the crystal axes and the direction of the zone axis is found by taking a distance *u.a* from the origin along the *a* axis followed by a distance *v.b* parallel to the direction of the *b* axis and then a distance *w.c* in the direction of the *c* axis. The point thus arrived at joined to the origin O gives the direction of the zone axis.

The numerical values for the co-ordinates *u*, *v* and *w* are derived from the Millerian indices of any two faces of the particular zone by the following procedure which is based on determinant notation. If the indices are (*hkl*) and (*h'k'l'*) respectively, they are written down twice thus—*hklhkl*, and below these *h'k'l'h'k'l'* as shown below,

$$
\begin{array}{c|cccc|c}
h & k & l & h & k & l \\
 & \times & \times & \times & \\
h' & k' & l' & h' & k' & l'
\end{array}
$$

the first and last columns being discarded. They are then cross-multiplied as shown, and for each cross the product corresponding to the thin stroke is subtracted from that corresponding to the thick one, giving expressions for the co-ordinates as follows:

$$u = (kl' - k'l), \ v = (lh' - l'h), \text{ and } w = (hk' - h'k)$$

To take a concrete example, if the two faces concerned are (121) and (111), then

$$
\begin{array}{c|cccc|c}
1 & 2 & 1 & 1 & 2 & 1 \\
 & \times & \times & \times & \\
1 & 1 & 1 & 1 & 1 & 1
\end{array}
$$

$u = (2 - 1)$, $v = (1 - 1)$ and $w = (1 - 2)$ and the zone symbol is $[10\bar{1}]$.

Now if any two faces in a zone will provide the zone symbol, it follows that all the faces in a zone will have a definite relationship to the zone symbol. It can be shown that this relationship is expressed in the formula (the *Weiss Zone Law*):

$$ux + vy + wz = 0$$

where x, y and z represent the Millerian indices of any face in the zone of which $[uvw]$ is the zonal axis. It follows that a face situated at the intersection of two zones must satisfy the conditions for each zone. Or stated differently the point of intersection is the pole of a possible face. The indices of such a face may be derived by cross multiplying the two zone symbols in the way described above. For example, the symbol for the zone containing the faces (110) and (111) is $[\bar{1}10]$ and that for the zone containing (100) and (10) is [010]. Cross multiplication of these two zone symbols gives the Millerian indices of the face common to both zones as (001).

In arranging the Millerian indices or the zone symbols for cross multiplication there is a choice as to which set of figures occupies the top line. In either case the result gives the same indices or symbols, but one or other of the figures may be positive in one case and negative in the other. Examination of the stereogram should reveal which of the two are appropriate.

The mathematical relationships of the faces of a crystal result in another property that is of great practical use in deciding the sign of a face and its position with respect to others. If the indices of two faces are added together index by index the resultant Millerian indices are those of a face which will bevel the edge between the two original faces. For example, in the following exercises it will be apparent that addition of (110) and (010) gives (120); addition of (100) and (010) gives (110); and addition of (101) and (010) gives (111) and so on.

In dealing with the hexagonal and trigonal systems, one of the horizontal axes is omitted and the remaining three axes are used to determine zonal and facial indices in the way given above. The missing index is then computed from the fact that in these systems the sum of the first three indices is always zero.

It must always be borne in mind that although the indices of a face and those of a zone appear superficially alike, they mean very different things. The zonal symbol gives the co-ordinates for determining a *direction* whereas the Millerian indices are divisors of the axial ratios of the crystal and define a plane.

EXERCISES IN THE USE OF THE STEREOGRAPHIC PROJECTION

For speed and accuracy, problems such as those of the following exercises are done using tracing paper over a Wulff net as described on p. 251, but the student should also familiarise himself with the relevant geometrical constructions described previously.

1. $MgSO_4,7H_2O$ is orthorhombic (sphenoidal, class 222, Fig. 1.31, p. 25). The angle (010):(110) is 45·3°, and the angle (010):(011) is 60·3°. The optic axial plane is (001), the X (or α) axis of the indicatrix is parallel to b^*, the sign is negative, and 2V = 51°. Plot on the stereographic projection the forms {010}, {110}, {011}, and {111}. Determine the vibration directions (for light of perpendicular incidence) on (111), and the angles they make with the (111): (110) edge of the crystal. (The smaller of these angles is known as the *extinction angle* of the face with reference to the edge in question.)

* *Dana's System of Mineralogy*, 7th edn., Vol. II (Wiley, New York; Chapman and Hall, London) p. 511, and E. S. Larsen, *Microscopic Determination of the Non-opaque Minerals*, 2nd. edn., Bull. 848, U.S. Geol. Surv., 1934, p. 149, both give X = a, but A. N. Winchell, *Microscopic Characters of Artificial Minerals*, 1931, (Wiley, New York; Chapman and Hall, London), p. 226 and also in *Elements of Optical Mineralogy*, Part II, 4th. edn., 1951 (Wiley, New York; Chapman and Hall, London), p. 155, give X = b. It would be useful for the student to work out what difference is made in the extinction angles on (111) from those derived here, by the orientation X = a.

Draw the primitive circle and insert two diameters at right angles in the N–S and E–W positions (Fig. 6.21). The faces (010) and (0$\bar{1}$0) are plotted at the east and west ends of the horizontal diameter respectively. The four faces of {110} are next inserted 45·3° around the

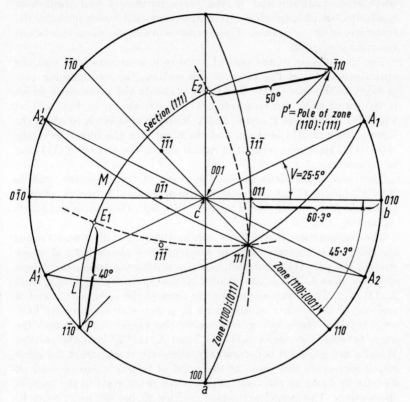

Fig. 6.21. Extinction angles in $MgSO_4$, $7H_2O$.

primitive from the (010) faces. A small circle around (010) of 60·3° is now drawn and for this, if a net is used, swing (010) round to the south end of the vertical diameter and sketch in the appropriate small circle. The pole of (011) obviously lies on the east-west diameter where this circle cuts it as it lies in the zone (010):(001). It is now possible to insert the (111) face because it is common to the two zones (110):(001), and (100):(011), as may be proved by the Weiss zone law (p. 255). These two zone circles are now drawn. The first is a vertical great circle from the pole of (110) through the centre of the projection and the second is the great circle around the north-south diameter passing through the pole of (011). The face (111) lies at the intersection of these two zone circles. The other faces of this form plot in the upper north-west quadrant and in the *lower* north-east and south-west quadrants (small open circles; p. 243) in conformity with the holoaxial symmetry of the substance. The absence of symmetry planes is obvious from the projection.

For the solution of the optical problem it is necessary to plot the optical vectors and the trace of the section (the cyclographic projection), of the face (111). The latter is clearly the great circle which is 90° away from the face pole (111) and is shown in Fig. 6.21 at PE_1E_2P'. The points P and P' lie 90° from the zone circle to which the faces (110) and (111) belong, and therefore give the direction of the (110):(111) edge from which the extinctions on the section of (111) will be measured.

The optic axial plane lies in the plane of the primitive, and as $X = b$ which is the acute bisectrix, the optic axes A_1 and A_2 may be plotted 25·5° on either side of the pole (010) with their antipodal points A_1' and A_2'.

The construction that follows applies the rule of Biot and Fresnel (p. 182). It is necessary first to construct two planes both of which contain the pole (111) but each contains a separate optic axis. These are now drawn. They are shown in the figure by $A_1(111)A_1'$ and $A_2(111)A_2'$. These two circles cut the trace of the section at L and M and one of the extinction directions E_1 occurs stereographically halfway between these two points where the plane which bisects the angle between the circles $A_1(111)A_1'$ and $A_2(111)A_2'$ cuts the section. When a net is used it is not actually necessary to construct the circle which represents this plane as the point of bisection can be read off directly by bringing the small circles of the net normal to the trace of the section. The second extinction position E_2 lies 90° away from E_1 along the line of the section. The angles of extinction are read between the extinction directions E_1 and E_2 and in each case the nearer of the poles P or P'. The values are $E_1:P = 40° \pm 1°$, and $E_2:P' = 50° \pm 1°$.

2. *β*-Sulphur is monoclinic class 2/m. The *β* angle is 95·75°, the angle (110):(1$\bar{1}$0) is 89·5°, and the angle (100):(210) is 26·4°. The optic axial plane is (010), X is inclined at 44° to c^* in the obtuse

---

* There is some doubt about this value since in *Dana's System* already referred to, Vol. 1, p. 145, and in Winchell (*op. cit.*), p. 23, the value X' to c on (1$\bar{1}$0) = 44° is given. The value of the exercise is, however, not impaired.

angle β, the sign is negative and $2V = 58°$. Determine the extinction angles on (010), (110), (210) and (100) with reference to the c axis.

Two methods of plotting monoclinic data are commonly in use. In the first the projection is made on the plane normal to the c axis, poles of vertical faces lying on the primitive and the basal pinacoid plotting forward (or 'southwards') from the emergence of the c axis in the centre of the projection. The second method is to take (010) as the projection plane, the c axis being arranged along the vertical diameter, and the pole of (010) being centrally placed. This exercise will illustrate both methods of projection.

In the first method (Fig. 6.22), the primitive is drawn with its two diameters at right angles, the c axis being placed in the centre but the (001) face lies 95·75° from the position of ($\bar{1}$00) along the north-south diameter, or 5·75° forward of c. The vertical faces are inserted on the primitive, (010) due east of c, the others, (110) and (210), being measured from (100), since the angle (110):($\bar{1}$10) lies across the symmetry plane, and (100):(110) is half this angle. The cyclographic projections of the faces (110) and (210) are drawn, being vertical great circles 90° from the respective face poles.

The optical data are now inserted. First locate X, the acute bisectrix 44° from c towards (100), and lay off the optic angle $V = 29°$ on each side of X, designating the optic axes A_1 and A_2. The Biot and Fresnel rule is now applied as in exercise 1, great circles being passed from the face pole (110), for example, through each optic axis to where they cut the trace of the section at L and M in the figure. The angular distance between these two points is bisected at the point E_{110} which is the point of emergence of an extinction direction. The extinction angle on the face (110) may now be measured between E_{110} and c along one of the diameters of the net, and is $39° \pm 1°$. The same construction is applied in the case of (210), the extinction angle being about 32°. It is evident that the extinction on (010) must be 44° since the optic axial plane is parallel to (010), and that the extinction on (100) must be straight since its section lies normal to the optic axial plane.

When the data are plotted on (010) (Fig. 6.23) the vertical diameter of the projection is the c axis, (100) and ($\bar{1}$00) plot at the left and right extremities of the east–west axis respectively and (010) lies in the centre of the field. All (hk0) faces plot along the east–west diameter 0 at the appropriate angular distances measured from either (010) or (100). The face (001) lies 95·75° from ($\bar{1}$00) or 5·75° from c towards (100).

Insert the above faces in the projection and plot the faces (110) and (210) measuring from (100).

The optical vectors may now be inserted. X (or α) falls 44° away from *c* towards (100), that is in the obtuse angle β, and the optic axes

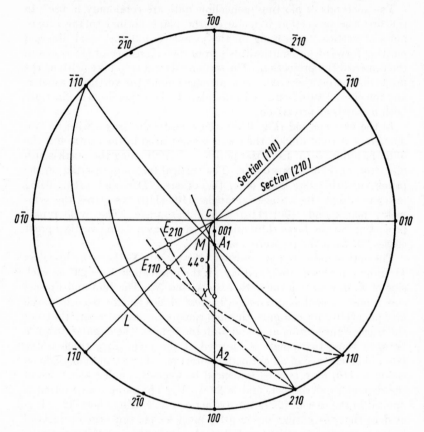

Fig. 6.22. Extinction angles in β-Sulphur. Projection ⊥ to *c*.

A_1A_1' and A_2A_2', lie at the angle V on either side of the bisectrix. The principles of the construction are exactly as before, the only difference being that the cyclographic representations of the sections are arcs of circles and not straight lines. There is no need therefore to give further detail, the various constructions being clearly shown in the figure, the great circles through (110) and the optic axes being in solid lines, and those for (210) being dashed. The extinction angles $E_{110}:c$ and $E_{210}:c$ are about 39° and 32°, respectively, as before, being measured conveniently to the negative end of c by the small circles normal to the great circles on which the extinction positions lie.

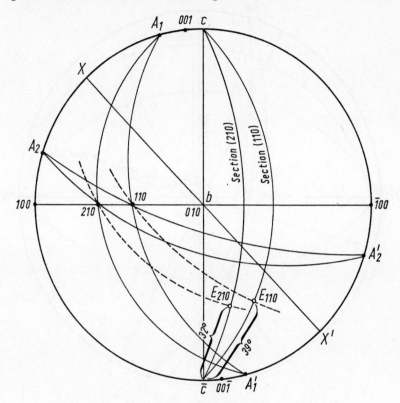

Fig. 6.23. Extinction angles in β-Sulphur. Projection on (010).

3. Kyanite, $Al_2O(SiO_4)$, is triclinic, class $\bar{1}$. The angle (010):(001) = 86·75°; (010):(100) = 73·9°; and (100):(001) = 78·5°. Cleavage {100} perfect, {010} good. The crystal is optically negative. Bx_a (α) emerges very steeply on (100) and 2V = 82°. Assuming that the usual convention is adopted in the projection of plotting c in the centre, and therefore the face poles (010) and (100) on the primitive, the positions of the optic axes in the projection are given in terms of two co-ordinate angles, ϕ and ρ, as follows. ϕ is measured round the

primitive from (010), the clockwise direction being positive, and ρ is the polar angle measured from the centre of the projection (c) along the radius in the direction determined by ϕ. (They can be

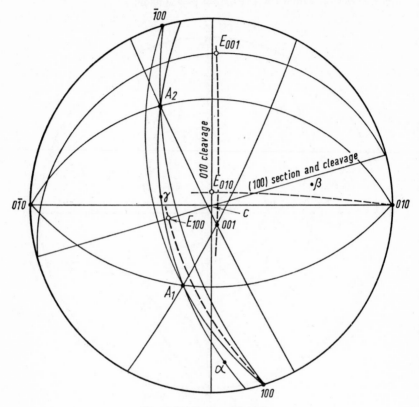

Fig. 6.24. Optics of kyanite.

regarded as longitude and co-latitude of any point in the projection.) For A_1, $\phi = 110°$, $\rho = 48°$; and for A_2, $\phi = -118°$, $\rho = 63°$.

Find (i) the extinction angle on (100) with respect to c; (ii) the extinction angle on (010) with respect to c; (iii) the extinction angle on (001) with respect to the trace of the (010) cleavage.

Plot the faces (010) and (100) around the primitive and fix the position of (001) by finding the intersection of the two small circles values of which are given above from (010) and (100) respectively (see

Fig. 6.24). Draw the traces of the sections of the three faces already plotted, those of the vertical faces being straight lines through the centre of the projection and that of (001) is the great circle 90° from the pole (001). Plot the optic axes, A_1 and A_2 from the above data. For each face in turn make the Biot and Fresnel construction, passing two great circles through the pole and each optic axis. Where these two circles cut the appropriate section the bisector of the angle cut off between the circles will be the required extinction direction. The approximate values are $E_{100}:c = 30°$, $E_{010}:c = 7°$ and E_{001} to the trace of the (010) cleavage is nearly straight (*ca.* 2°). All values are $\pm 1°$.

7   PREPARATION, MOUNTING AND MANIPULATION OF MATERIAL

Crystalline material is normally studied under the polarising microscope in one of two forms: (a) as small separate particles which may, for example, be micro-crystals prepared by some recrystallisation procedure, or crystal fragments obtained by crushing coarser material; (b) as a thin section or film, examples being sections of rocks and refractories prepared by grinding down thin slices, and polycrystalline films of organic compounds obtained by the crystallisation of a thin layer of the melt. The specimen is supported on a glass *slide*, usually 3 in. by 1 in. (*ca.* 76 mm. by 25 mm.) and 1 to $1\frac{1}{2}$ mm. thick, and is protected by a *cover slip*, the thickness of which for optimum resolution should be 0·17 mm. (p. 123). Except in the case of films of crystals from the melt, the specimen is immersed or embedded in an inert isotropic medium, which is usually a liquid for separate particles, and Canada balsam or one of the more modern synthetic mounting media for thin sections. If this were not done, small separate particles might appear practically opaque (unless they were very 'platy'), owing to the scattering of the light at their surfaces. There are also the further important advantages, which we have noted, that by using selected media of known refractive index the deviation of the light by irregularly shaped particles may be avoided (p. 101), and the refractive indices of the material determined (pp. 157–169, and 237–240). In the case of a thin section the main function of the embedding medium is to anchor the specimen to the glass, but it also suppresses any scattering of the light by small-scale irregularities on the surfaces of the section.

In the routine study of such preparations (the making of which will be dealt with in the first part of this chapter) the information obtainable is determined by the optical sections presented by the crystals as they happen to be oriented on the slide. Particles mounted in a liquid can often be rolled into other positions by making use of the shearing effect produced on the liquid when the cover slip is gently shifted with a needle (Fig. 7.1 c), but if they are of a pronounced platy habit they will always be likely to settle on the slide in the same orientation, and the information gained from this may be insufficient. In such circumstances

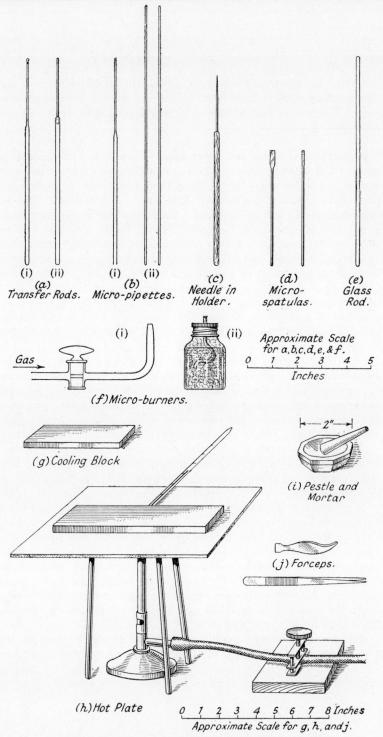

Fig. 7.1. Apparatus for preparing and mounting material.

265

it will be necessary to resort to a method by which crystals of the material may be turned and held in other and more favourable orientations. The second part of this chapter will deal with some of these methods.

Preparation of Slides and Cover Slips. These must be thoroughly cleaned and dried before use. This is most important, for much time may be wasted in studying specks of birefringent dust in mistake for part of the specimen, and in the determination of refractive indices, an inaccurate result will be obtained if the immersion liquid is contaminated with the remains of former liquids, or diluted with water. New slides may be prepared for use by washing them in hot soapy water, then in hot distilled water, and finally drying and polishing them with a clean linen cloth, or a piece of well-washed cambric, holding them by the edges only. To prepare new cover slips it is usually sufficient to breathe on both sides and then dry and polish by gently rubbing them in a fold of well-washed cambric held between the finger and thumb. Once cleaned they must be handled by the edges only, or more conveniently, especially if they are small, by means of forceps (Fig. 7.1 *j*).

For cleaning slides after use, it is convenient to have two wide-mouthed glass-stoppered bottles on the working bench, one containing benzene and the other alcohol. Slides on which oily immersion liquids have been used are dropped into the benzene bottle, and after the lapse of a few hours are transferred by means of crucible tongs to the alcohol bottle. Slides contaminated only with aqueous immersion media (as when crystals have been examined in an aqueous mother liquor; see below) may be placed at once in the alcohol bottle. The slides are removed as required from this bottle, and cleaned and dried as described above.

It is hardly worth while to attempt to recover and clean used cover slips, particularly very small ones.

Cover slips are made in various sizes, both square and circular, the choice between these two shapes being largely a matter of personal taste. For most optical crystallographic work in which particles are mounted in a liquid, the slips need not be larger than $\frac{1}{4}$ to $\frac{1}{2}$ in. in diameter. As some immersion liquids are expensive, small cover slips make for economy in material and encourage neatness in practice. They have other advantages (p. 279).

Large cover slips may readily be divided into smaller sizes by the following method. The large slip is placed on two or three thicknesses of filter paper laid on the working bench so as to form a slightly yielding surface. The ground edge of a 3 × 1 in. slide held in a slanting position is then pressed firmly and evenly on the slip. This results in a neat straight fracture along the line of pressure.

Methods

Methods of preparing and mounting crystalline material fall broadly into two groups according to whether they involve recrystallisation of the material or not. If recrystallisation is possible, then it usually pays to undertake it, for it is commonly found that the particles of the material as received are not sufficiently well developed to enable the optical characters to be related to the external crystalline form without ambiguity. Recrystallisation may, however, be forbidden by the nature of the material or of the problem, or both. Thus for example it may be necessary to examine a substance for the presence of a suspected impurity. In this case, recrystallisation will obviously defeat the object of the investigation. Many other problems arise, the essence of which is that the material must be examined, at least in the initial stages, 'just as it is', except in so far as it may be necessary to reduce its particle size by crushing, or in the case of massive material perhaps, to prepare a thin section of it.

Some of the simpler items of apparatus used in the preparation of material for optical examination are shown in Fig. 7.1. A few of these have already been mentioned, and the function of the remainder and any necessary further description of them will appear in what follows.

I. Preparation and Mounting without Recrystallisation.

(*a*) *As separate particles.* The particles should not be larger than about 0·2 mm. in average diameter, for if they exceed this size they are difficult to cover with the immersion liquid, and are generally too thick to give characteristic polarisation colours between crossed polars. On the other hand, their average diameter should not be appreciably less than 0·01 mm., for crystals much below this size cannot be usefully studied with the polarising microscope.

Crystals of chemical material that are too large may be crushed by gently pounding them (not grinding) in a small agate mortar (Fig. 7.1 *i*), or in a glass block with a hemispherical cavity, as used by botanists as a dissecting dish, the pestle in this case being a piece of stout glass rod, the ends of which have been rounded in a bunsen flame. Massive petrological and refractory materials are best crushed in a steel percussion mortar by tapping the steel pestle smartly with a hammer.

If sufficient material is available from the crushing operation, it is advisable to sieve it to separate the fraction consisting of particles between about 0·1 and 0·05 mm. in size.* Standard sieves are made for such size-grading operations, and the fraction required in the present case is that which passes a sieve with *ca.* 140 meshes per inch and is held by one with *ca.* 300 meshes per inch. Many substances, however, tend to stick to the meshes of a sieve, and in such cases, or where sieves are not available, the material may be broken down until the average particle diameter is about equal to that of a human hair (approximately 0·05 mm.) which, in order to make the comparison, may be mounted with a portion of the powder and viewed under the microscope. Alternatively, a calibrated eyepiece scale (p. 158) may be used.

A minute amount of the powdered material is placed in the centre of a slide by means of a micro-spatula (Fig. 7.1 *d*, and below), and is then covered with a cover slip, which is gently pressed down with a slight rotary motion to spread out the crystal grains so that they do not overlie one another. This is best done with a rubber-tipped glass rod, or a small cork. A small drop of the immersion liquid is then brought to the edge of the cover slip by means of the dropping rod (with which bottles to hold immersion liquids are usually provided) when it will run in by capillary action. Further small drops are added if necessary until the space under the cover slip is just filled. Excess of liquid is to be avoided, as this results in a messy preparation, and the liquid may find its way to the top of the cover slip, where, besides interfering with observation, it is liable to contaminate objectives which have a small working distance.

The bulk of material taken should not in general exceed the size of a pin's head, and with a fine powder may be considerably less, for it is pointless, and may be confusing, to have an excessively large number of particles to view.

Suitable micro-spatulas for this work are those sold for micro- and semimicro-chemical analysis. Alternatively, they may be made very easily by hammering out the end of a piece of brass, or better, nickel wire of suitable gauge, and trimming it to shape by filing or on a fine grinding wheel. The surfaces of the blade must be quite flat, and the end must be trimmed to a fine edge, otherwise it will be difficult to pick up and retain the material on it. It is convenient to have two sizes, one with a blade $\frac{1}{8}$ to $\frac{3}{16}$ in. wide, and one with a blade about $\frac{1}{16}$ in. wide.

It is sometimes necessary to examine wet crystals, e.g. a crude reaction product, or a solid phase in a phase equilibrium study, suspended in its mother liquor. In such a case a drop of the material is

* Particles which it is intended to 'roll' in a viscous mounting medium (see p. 279) should be smaller than this, say about 0·02 mm.

simply placed on a slide, and covered with a cover slip. The liquid in the material acts as the immersion medium. The crystals may, of course, first be reduced in size by crushing, if they are too large to mount satisfactorily. Alternatively it may be possible, after putting the drop on the slide, to remove the liquid by means of filter paper and mount the crystals in a liquid of known refractive index, as described in II. 1 below.

With powdered inorganic material containing more than one compound, e.g. a crushed rock, a separation or partial separation of the ingredients by gravity methods may first be made. For this purpose, a small conical separating funnel is partly filled with a heavy liquid such as bromoform (sp. gr. 2·9), and a few grams of the sieved material are poured into the funnel. The lighter material will float and the heavier will sink, and can be drawn off after the separation is complete. Methylene iodide (sp. gr. 3·3) is also very useful for this purpose. To adjust the liquid to any desired specific gravity, bromoform may be mixed with methylene iodide, or either may be mixed with benzene to give less dense solutions. Clerici solution* having a specific gravity of about 4·2 may also be used, and lower values may be obtained by dilution with water. While separation is in progress the material must be agitated with a glass rod from time to time to free heavy substances entangled amongst the lighter fraction. The heavier fraction is easily caught on a filter paper held in a conical funnel under the separating funnel, whilst the lighter fraction may be collected in the same way after removing the heavy material, and running off the major portion of the liquid. The use of the organic liquids mentioned above has the advantage that they evaporate without leaving any residue, and the grains do not need washing before mounting for the microscopic examination.

(*b*) *As a thin section.* Rocks and hard industrial materials of complex composition, such as refractories, slags and concrete, may be prepared in this form. The study of a thin section reveals the texture, particle size, form, and relative abundance of the ingredients, and it is possible to determine a number of the optical properties of the various substances present. The method is particularly suitable in the study of thermal changes as for example, those undergone by silica brick when used as a furnace lining. The determination of the optical properties under the microscope is circumscribed, however, by the fact that the optical section presented by any individual crystal is random, and cannot be altered except by the use of the universal stage (p. 280), and also

---

* A concentrated aqueous solution of equal weights of thallium malonate and thallium formate.

by the fact that the refractive indices cannot be determined except in a comparative way with adjacent substances. In many cases these limitations do not matter, because the possible ingredients are known in advance and differ so markedly in their optical properties, colour or cleavage, that they can be readily distinguished whatever the orientation of the grains. But with material about which little is known, or where ambiguities arise, the thin section method must be supplemented by crushing and the examination of the separate constituents as described in the previous section.

A thin section may be prepared as follows. A parallel-sided slice about $\frac{1}{16}$ in. thick is cut from the specimen by means of a power-driven wheel which may be simply a soft iron disc into the edge of which has been forced diamond dust, or a more elaborate one of steel to the edge of which is riveted a copper band impregnated with diamond dust. One surface of the slice is smoothed with fine carborundum powder before mounting on a 3×1 in. glass slide as described below. If no cutting machine is available it is possible to begin with a small chip about 1 in. square struck from the edge of the specimen with a hammer, and a smooth surface is prepared on one side by grinding with successively finer carborundum powder on a metal lap or plate, or on a sheet of plate glass. Different plates must be used for the various grades of abrasive and the chip carefully washed when changing from one grade to another. Water is used as a lubricant unless any of the constituents is water soluble, when a thin oil may be used. A small quantity of natural Canada balsam is placed on a glass slide and heated slowly on a hot plate (Fig. 7.1 h, and below) to a temperature of about 80° until it is 'cooked', that is until a small portion removed on a needle-point or the pointed end of a matchstick and pressed against a hard surface such as the thumb-nail, has just lost its stickiness and hardens almost immediately. The prepared surface of the chip, which has been previously warmed, is now pressed down on the warm balsam with a glass rod (Fig. 7.1 e) so that all bubbles are excluded, and left to cool, when it will be found that the balsam has set quite hard. The other side of the specimen is now ground down in the same way until it is about 0·03 mm. thick. This can be judged by examining the slice from time to time under the microscope until some substance such as quartz (or any other substance of low double refraction), shows a grey or pale yellow of the first order of Newton's scale (p. 176). Dirty balsam around the slice is cleaned off with a warm knife-blade and a little absolute alcohol or methylated spirit applied with a small stiff brush. The section is now covered with a cover glass. This is done by cooking a little balsam on a cover slip and inverting it upon the section, or by pouring a little warm balsam, already cooked, upon it. A warmed cover slip is now allowed to fall from one edge upon the section and gently pressed down. After cooling, the balsam which has been squeezed out around the cover slip is cleaned off with alcohol, and the preparation is ready for examination.

The hot plate used in the above procedure may take many different forms. In petrological laboratories, for example, where considerable numbers of thin sections have to be prepared, large plates with thermostatic control are commonly used. The one shown in Fig. 7.1 h is, however, simple and easy to make, and may be used for other preparative procedures as will appear below (e.g. recrystallisations by sublimation, and from a melt). It consists of a metal slab about $8 \times 3 \times \frac{1}{2}$ in. made of iron, copper, or brass, drilled to take a thermometer, and placed on a sheet of thin asbestos board supported on a tripod above a bunsen burner, the gas supply to which is controlled by the screw clip device shown. The purpose of the asbestos sheet is to shield from the flame the stem of the thermometer and also the projecting portions of slides which are not lying wholly on the plate. The upper surface of the plate must be smooth and flat, and, if the plate is of iron, should be coated with copper by first polishing with fine emery paper and then rubbing copper sulphate solution over it with a wad of cotton wool. This will prevent rusting, or at least retard it very considerably. A circular hole about 2 in. in diameter should be cut in the asbestos sheet immediately above the burner, so that there is no undue lag in raising the temperature of the plate.

Sections of friable material, which disintegrates under the grinding process, may be made after preliminary treatment as follows.* A chip is placed in a dish or small beaker and covered with bakelite varnish diluted with methyl alcohol and a few drops of acetone. The dish is allowed to stand for several hours in an evacuated desiccator, after which the specimen is removed and heated in an oven at a temperature of 70° for about four hours to remove the solvents. The temperature is then raised and maintained at 100° for several days, or if the material is stable enough, at 200° for a few hours. The hardened specimen can now be ground in the usual way.

II. Methods of Preparation and Mounting which include Recrystallisation.

Material which may be broadly described as 'chemical' may often with advantage be recrystallised before it is examined optically, and in this section we shall describe methods by which this may be done. Since one of the most important features of microscopical examination is

* See also Fowler, J. W. and Shirley, J., *Geol. Mag.*, 1947, **84**, 354.

that it can be applied to very small amounts of material, we shall confine our attention to those methods of recrystallisation which can be carried out on a very small scale, and usually on the microscope slide itself.

It will first be convenient to give some explanatory notes about those items of apparatus shown in Fig. 7.1 which have not already been noticed above, and which are specifically required for recrystallisation procedures. (The letters following the headings in these notes correspond with those in the figure.)

Transfer rod (a). This is used for transferring minute amounts of solid material, or small drops of solvent to the microscope slide. (Very small particles of solid will adhere to the rod if it is breathed on first.) It is also used as a micro-stirring rod. It may be made either by drawing out a piece of narrow glass rod, and rounding off the end to a ball about the size of a pin's head (i); or by sealing a piece of stout platinum wire into a glass handle, and slightly roughening the end of the wire (ii).

Micro-pipette (b). This is used for adding liquid to, or withdrawing it from, the slide. It is made as shown by drawing out one end of a piece of narrow glass tubing (i). Alternatively a number of glass capillaries about 8 in. to 10 in. long may be made (ii). These are sealed at each end to prevent the entry of dirt. When required for use, the sealed ends are broken off. After use the capillary is thrown away.

Micro-burner (f). This is used for heating a drop of solution on a slide in the technique of micro-recrystallisation from solution, and also for micro-sublimation, as will be described later. The burner should be capable of adjustment to give a flame not more then $\frac{1}{4}$ in. high. The type shown in (i) is made from a pyrex glass tap with one limb bent upwards and drawn out to a jet, the best size of which may be found by trial. The jet should not be very fine, otherwise the flame will be too pointed and will crack the slide. The other limb of the tap is attached to the gas supply. A readily made burner using methylated spirits is shown at (ii). It consists of a small ink-bottle with a screwed metal cap which is drilled in the centre to fit a cigarette-lighter wick. The bottle is loosely filled with cotton wool. This burner gives a round 'soft' flame, which has no tendency to crack the slide if the latter is kept in gentle motion.

Cooling block (g). This is also used when crystallising material on the slide, its purpose being to cool the slide rapidly after it has been heated over the micro-burner, and thus to arrest evaporation of the solvent. The upper surface must be smooth and quite flat, and its dimensions somewhat greater than those of the slide, so that the whole area of the latter can, if necessary, be brought into contact with the metal. The block should be about $\frac{3}{16}$ in. thick or more, and should preferably be made of copper or aluminium.

1. Recrystallisation from Solution. We will consider first the recrystallisation from water of a non-deliquescent substance, the solubility of which is moderate at ordinary temperatures and shows the usual increase with rise of temperature.

By means of the glass rod or the micro-pipette, a drop of distilled water 5 to 7 mm. in diameter is placed in the centre of the slide. Minute quantities of the powdered solid are added by means of the transfer rod, and dissolved by stirring, taking care, however, not to spread the drop. Spreading of the drop is avoided by holding the rod in a nearly vertical position. If necessary the dissolving of the solid may be hastened by *gently* warming the slide over the micro-burner, keeping it in continual motion in a horizontal plane and about 1 in. above the flame to avoid any risk of cracking it. Addition of solid is continued until no more appears to dissolve. The slight excess remaining is taken up by further warming, or by the addition of a trace of water on the transfer rod. The object is to obtain a solution saturated at, or slightly above, room temperature.

If sufficient material is available, the above procedure can be avoided by making up a few cubic centimetres of the solution in a test tube, filtering from any suspended matter, and transferring a drop to the slide by means of the glass rod. It is worth emphasising, however, that the quantity of material required in the first method is extremely small, and this is likely to be an important consideration in many problems.

If the drop prepared in either of the above ways is warm, it may begin to deposit satisfactory crystals spontaneously on cooling. If examination under the microscope (using a low-power objective, e.g. 1 in.) shows, however, that no crystals have formed, crystallisation may be induced as follows. The slide is warmed over the micro-burner to hasten the evaporation of solvent. Presently a crust will appear at the edges of the drop. This crust is of no value for study, for having grown inwards from the surface of the solution, it consists of poorly formed crystals matted together. The slide is immediately placed on the cooling block, and by means of the transfer rod the crust is broken up and gently stirred into the centre of the drop so as to inoculate it. It may happen that the crust dissolves when this is done, indicating that the original solution was not fully saturated. In this case, the drop must be evaporated further over the micro-burner and the operation repeated. Stirring is continued, again taking care not to spread the drop, and also not to rub the tip of the rod on the slide, for the latter action is likely to result in the formation of a multitude of very minute crystals along the tracks of contact. When crystallisation in the interior of the drop appears to be well under way, the slide is transferred to the microscope. If the crystals are well formed and are not so numerous that they overlie one another, their growth is watched until they have reached a suitable size for study. A cover slip is then placed over the drop to arrest further evaporation of the solvent, and the preparation is ready.

If, however, the crystals are unsatisfactory, they should be partially redissolved by adding a minute drop of water on the transfer rod and the solution stirred again, the undissolved solid acting as seed crystals. Alternatively a larger drop of water sufficient to cause the whole of the solid to redissolve may be added with the micro-pipette, and the solution concentrated by the use of the micro-burner as before.

If it is desired to mount the crystals in a liquid of known refractive index, it will be necessary to remove the mother liquor and this may be done as follows. As soon as the crystals have grown to the right size, the edge of the drop is touched with the end of the micro-pipette (dry) when most of the liquid will be drawn off by capillary action. The preparation is then gently dabbed with strips of filter paper applied edgeways, until microscopic examination shows it to be practically dry. (It is particularly important not to leave the crystals surrounded by small pools of liquid, for in the final drying these will deposit a confused mass of solid material which may interfere with observations of the crystal-liquid border after the immersion medium has been added.) The last traces of moisture are removed by gently warming the slide on the hot plate, or, if the material will not withstand this treatment, leaving it to dry off in the air. A cover slip is now placed over the crystals, and the immersion liquid run in from the edge as previously described.

If the substance is a hydrate, great care must be taken not to overheat it nor to prolong the drying unnecessarily, otherwise dissociation may occur. Moreover in the crystallisation stage, the temperature of the drop must not be allowed to rise above the transition point at which the hydrate ceases to be stable, otherwise crystals of the next lower hydrate or of the anhydrous compound may be deposited. If the transition point is low, it is better to use the hot plate instead of the micro-burner for preparing the solution, so that the temperature can be kept under control.

Sparingly soluble substances may be recrystallised by the above method, but only very small crystals are likely to be obtained. When preparing the solution, only the minimum amount of material should be added to the drop of water, for a large excess cannot be got rid of and is likely to hinder the examination of any crystals which do form from the solution. Crystallisation must be made to take place very slowly, either by allowing the drop to evaporate at room temperature, or cooling it very slowly by placing it on the hot plate, the temperature of which is gradually lowered.

Very soluble substances are apt to be troublesome because once the solution is saturated, a small further evaporation or fall of temperature may result in deposition of a relatively large mass of crystals overlying one another, which will be useless for study. This is particularly likely to happen if the solution supersaturates and then suddenly crystallises. The solution should therefore not be saturated at too high a temperature, otherwise the rate of cooling and of evaporation, and thus the rate of deposition of solid, will be rapid. Supersaturation must be prevented as far as possible, either by introducing a trace of the solid on the transfer rod, or in some cases by gently scratching the slide with the rod just at the edge of the drop.

Recrystallisation on the slide from organic solvents may also be carried out by the methods described above for aqueous solutions. Solvents that are very volatile or mobile should be avoided, however, otherwise rapid evaporation or the uncontrollable spreading of the drop will occur, resulting in the deposition of imperfect crystals or continuous films of solid material, which will be of little value for study. Spreading of the drop may sometimes be prevented by previously surrounding the site with a film of vaseline. Alternatively a slide with a cavity ground in it may be used.

Supercooled thymol (1-isopropyl:2-hydroxy:4-methyl benzene) is a useful solvent for many organic substances, for it does not spread on a slide. The freezing-point of this substance is 50°, but it may be supercooled to room temperature and will remain indefinitely in that condition if the melt has been heated to about 90°. Moreover the supercooling is not readily relieved when the liquid is stirred with a clean transfer rod. To recrystallise a substance from this solvent, the slide is placed on the hot plate and a few fragments of the solid thymol are placed in the centre of the slide. The thymol is melted and its temperature raised to 90° and then adjusted to the value at which it is desired to saturate the liquid, say about 60°. (This temperature will depend on the temperature coefficient of solubility of the substance, and the optimum value will have to be found by trial.) By means of the micro-spatula the powdered substance is added, a little at a time, to the drop of thymol, and is stirred in after each addition with the transfer rod. When no more will dissolve, the excess is taken up by raising the temperature again, or alternatively it may be left to act as seed crystals, particularly if the substance is prone to form supersaturated solutions. The slide is then removed from the plate and the drop is stirred until crystals make their appearance, when the slide is transferred to the microscope stage for observation. If the crystals are satisfactory, a cover slip is placed over the drop.

In all the above methods of recrystallisation, crystallisation is brought about by the cooling or evaporation, or both, of a saturated solution of the substance in a single solvent. Other methods depending on *variation in the composition of the solvent medium* are also available in certain cases. For example, some substances may be brought into solution as complex ions by the addition of volatile acids or ammonia, and then crystallised out by allowing the volatile constituent to escape slowly. Thus silver chloride may be dissolved in ammonia, and if a drop of this solution is placed on a slide, the chloride will be deposited as the ammonia evaporates. (The slide should not be placed on the microscope stage until volatilisation is complete, or sufficiently so for the drop to be covered with a cover slip, otherwise the corrosive fumes will attack the instrument.) Substances soluble in alcohol but not in water may in some cases be caused to crystallise satisfactorily by allowing a drop of water to diffuse into a drop of the alcohol solution. Use may also be made of the principle of 'salting out'. Thus sodium benzene sulphonate may be crystallised from a drop of its aqueous solution by adding a little solid sodium chloride or a drop of a saturated solution of this salt.

2. Recrystallisation by Sublimation. This method is particularly useful for organic substances and for volatile inorganic compounds, e.g. mercuric iodide, ammonium halides, and arsenious oxide. It also affords a means of separating a volatile constituent from a mixture. It must be borne in mind, however, that overheating, particularly in the case of organic material, may cause decomposition, and that with polymorphous substances a form which is unstable at room temperature may be deposited from the vapour. For example, the sublimation of mercuric iodide may yield crystals of the yellow form which is only stable above 127°, and these crystals are liable to undergo transformation into pseudomorphs of the stable red modification, particularly if they are touched or subjected to shock.

Microsublimation may be carried out in many ways. The simplest is to sublime the material from one slide to another held just above it, the

former being heated with the micro-burner, or, with better control of
the temperature, on the hot plate. It is advantageous first to fix the
material to the slide by moistening it with a drop of water and then
evaporating this off. Alternatively the substance may be dissolved in a
suitable solvent and successive drops evaporated from the same place
on the slide until a sufficient amount of solid has been accumulated.
This brings the substance into more intimate contact with the glass,
and prevents it being blown away by stray air currents, or scattered by
accidental disturbance of the slide. If the micro-burner is used for
heating, the slide carrying the material is held in one hand, and the
receiver slide in the other, so that it lies across the former with one edge
resting on it to keep the two steady in relation to one another. The
vapour then diffuses across a wedge-shaped space between the two
slides, and this space should be made as narrow as possible without
allowing the receiver actually to touch the material. Heating should
at first be cautious and as soon as the first sign of a sublimate appears,
the slides should be raised well above the flame to reduce the rate of
vaporisation, otherwise a very finely divided deposit is likely to be the
only result. By moving the receiver into different positions a series of
sublimates may be collected on it. If the hot plate is used, the receiver
slide may be supported on strips of thin glass. Heating in this case
should be even more cautious than when the micro-burner is used, at
least until the optimum temperature for the substance has been ascertained, for it is not possible rapidly to reduce the temperature of the
plate if sublimation should be proceeding too quickly.

With very volatile substances it may be necessary to cool the receiver.
This may be done by putting drops of cold water on it from time to
time by means of the micro-pipette; or a chilled block of copper or
aluminium may be used. On the other hand with substances which tend
to form a very finely divided deposit, it may be advantageous to reduce
the rate of crystallisation by warming the receiver, and this may be done
by placing on it a warmed block of carbon, e.g. a piece cut from the ordinary charcoal block used in qualitative analysis, or from an arc electrode.

When only a very little of the material is available, losses from the
vapour phase may be avoided by subliming in an enclosed space. For
this purpose the substance may be heated in a shallow glass capsule
with a carefully ground upper edge on which the receiver slide is laid.
If these are held together with a suitable metal clip, the capsule can be
heated over the micro-burner. Alternatively if the hot plate is used
as described above, the two slides may be separated by a shallow glass
ring cut from a piece of wide glass tubing and having its upper and lower
surfaces ground perfectly flat.

3. Recrystallisation from a Melt. Substances having a low melting-point may with advantage be examined in the form of a thin film obtained by melting them between a slide and a cover slip. To make such a preparation the slide with a cover slip on it is placed on the hot plate and a small pile of the powdered material is put at one edge of the cover slip by means of a micro-spatula. The temperature is then raised until the substance melts and fills the space between the slide and slip. The slide is then removed from the plate and the melt allowed to solidify, scratching the edge of the film with a needle, if necessary, to relieve supercooling. The crystals thus obtained, having grown rapidly, will probably be too small or narrow for convenient study, and in this event larger crystals may be obtained as follows. The bulk of the film is remelted by placing the slide partly on and partly off the hot plate, leaving an unmelted strip along one side. The source of heat is then turned off, and as the plate cools the melt will crystallise slowly, supercooling being entirely prevented by the presence of the unmelted strip.

The parallel-sided plates formed by this method admit of good microscopic examination being made without the use of an immersion liquid. A disadvantage is that the outward form of the crystals is largely obscured, because mutual interference along their boundaries during growth produces anhedral outlines, but the relation of the optical properties to prominent cleavage directions, when these exist, or to a direction of elongation, is easily made out.

Better shaped crystals may be obtained by a modification of the procedure, known as 'melt-back' or 'mixed fusion'. For this only sufficient of the substance is taken to occupy a part of the area under the cover slip, or alternatively the slide is removed from the hot plate and cooled before the molten substance has had time to spread over all of this area. After the substance has solidified, a non-volatile solvent is allowed to run in to fill the unoccupied space, or a solid with a melting point much lower than that of the substance and known to form with it a eutectic which is liquid at room temperature, is melted in. Possible solvents are benzyl alcohol, nitrobenzene, tricresyl phosphate, medicinal paraffin, immersion oil (p. 131), or if the preparation is warmed, Aroclor (p. 279), or Canada balsam. The slide is then placed on the hot plate at a temperature just below the melting point of the substance, and left for some minutes to allow a layer of saturated solution to form at the interface between solid and solvent. The slide is then allowed to cool slowly, e.g. by leaving it on the plate and turning out the gas, when a crop of well-formed crystals should grow outwards from the main mass of the solid into the layer of solution. Better control of the crystallisation process is possible if the microscope is fitted with a *hot stage** on which the melting back and subsequent cooling operations can be carried out while the specimen is kept under observation.

For further information about methods of preparation and mounting material, the reader should consult the appropriate works in the list in Appendix I.

METHODS OF CHANGING THE ORIENTATION OF CRYSTALS UNDER EXAMINATION

'Crystal-rolling'. As already mentioned on p. 264, crystals or crystal fragments mounted in a liquid may often be rolled from one orientation to another by gently shifting the cover slip with a needle. The number of different stationary orientations obtainable by this means will be all the greater the more equant the particles are in shape, while the rolling operation itself is facilitated by having a fairly deep layer of immersion liquid, this condition being favoured by the use of small cover slips. It is evident that it is not possible to roll a particle in a direction with respect to which its maximum dimension is greater than the distance between the slide and the cover slip. Thus needle-shaped crystals with a length greater than this distance can only be rolled about the needle axis. It sometimes helps to mix the particles with powdered glass of similar particle size. The glass fragments help to turn the crystals over and support them in otherwise unstable positions, and being isotropic they do not interfere with the optical examination.

By using a very viscous immersion medium, the crystals may be held in unstable positions for long periods, and rolling is more easily controlled. For inorganic substances natural Canada balsam may be used for this purpose, but a much better medium is 'Aroclor 1260', which is one of a range of chlorinated diphenyls manufactured by the Monsanto Chemical Company (St. Louis, U.S.A., and Victoria Street, London). It is a thermoplastic resin with a refractive index of about 1·64, which is extremely viscous at room temperature, but becomes quite fluid when gently warmed. The following notes on its use are based on advice received from Dr. W. C. McCrone (McCrone Associates, Chicago, U.S.A., and c/o Malies Instruments Ltd., Southwick, Sussex), who has used the crystal-rolling technique for many years, and to whom the authors wish to express their thanks.

The method of immersing the crystals in the Aroclor is not critical, the main consideration being the avoidance of mess due to the viscous

* Some of these are described by Hartshorne and Stuart, *Crystals and the Polarising Microscope*, 3rd edn. (Arnold, London, 1960), and by McCrone, *Fusion Methods in Chemical Microscopy* (Interscience, 1956).

and sticky nature of the medium. McCrone finds the following procedure satisfactory. The crystals are placed at the centre of the slide and a drop of Aroclor on a needle is applied to the slide immediately adjacent to the crystals, and perhaps touching some of them. The needle is rotated in contact with the slide so as to pile up the drop, and is then drawn with some of the drop across the crystals and touched down on the other side of them. It is rotated so as to free it from Aroclor as far as possible, and withdrawn. A *circular* cover slip less than $\frac{3}{4}$ in. in diameter is placed over the crystals, the preparation is warmed until the Aroclor is quite fluid, and the crystals are thoroughly mixed with the medium by moving the cover slip around with a pencil rubber, taking care not to press too hard so that a fair thickness of the medium will be maintained.

For the rolling, a clean needle is of course used. The use of a circular cover slip ensures that the shifting movements can be made in all directions symmetrically. Unrestricted rotation of the crystals in all directions requires that they be of more or less equant shape with a maximum diameter not exceeding about 0·02 mm. (taking the thickness of the medium in an average preparation as being about 0·025 to 0·03 mm.).

For organic crystals, McCrone has used the 'aqua resins' manufactured by Glycol Products Inc., 26 Court Street, Brooklyn, N.Y., U.S.A. These are viscous glyceryl- or glycol-boriborates with a refractive index of about 1·47. They are freely miscible with water, and insoluble in hydrocarbons. The resin-water mixtures will dissolve large amounts of potassium mercuric iodide ($KHgI_3$, p. 166), and use has been made of this property to prepare a range of viscous media of known refractive index, by means of which crystals insoluble in these media may be rolled into principal orientations, and their principal refractive indices determined. McCrone recommends that the series be based on a resin-water mixture with an index of 1·45, in which increasing amounts of potassium mercuric iodide are dissolved to give values up to about 1·60; thereafter increasing amounts of mercuric iodide will raise the index to nearly 1·75. If the complex salt is used throughout the whole range, the higher index members deposit potassium iodide crystals.

Rotation Apparatus. The standard commercially available apparatus for rotating crystals under the microscope into different orientations is the *universal stage*, originally invented by Federov. With this apparatus the preparation, supported between glass hemispheres, may be rotated through measured angles about vertical and horizontal axes

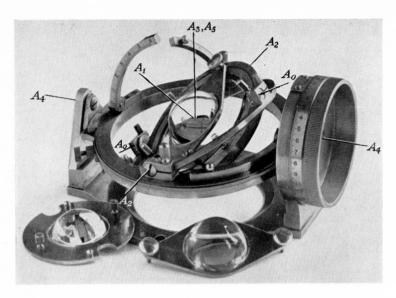

PLATE II. 5-Axis universal stage.

(See page 281)

[to face page 281

so as to bring the symmetry planes of the indicatrix in turn parallel to the axis of the microscope. The most elaborate type of universal stage (due to Emmons[*]) has five axes of rotation, three horizontal and two vertical, with the microscope stage adding yet another vertical axis of rotation. This instrument is shown in Plate II (opposite).

Angles of rotation about horizontal axes on a universal stage have to be corrected for the difference between the refractive index of the hemispheres and those of the crystal. Since the latter vary with direction, it is usual to use either the β index or the mean index of the crystal when making this correction, whatever the direction of the light, and this approximation is good enough when dealing with crystals of low or medium birefringence, say, below 0·05. When the birefringence is high, however, this procedure can lead to considerable errors which can only be avoided by adopting somewhat involved methods. The use of the apparatus in the study of such crystals is therefore rather restricted.

From the practical point of view, the universal stage is more suited to the study of rigid preparations such as rock sections (p. 269) than to that of separate crystals mounted in a liquid medium, and since, in addition, most minerals have birefringences below 0·05, it is in the fields of mineralogy and petrology that the universal stage finds its greatest application. Details of the theory and use of the instrument lie, however, outside the scope of this book. For these the reader must consult more advanced texts, such as those cited in Appendix I.

In the much simpler *single-axis rotation apparatus*, a single crystal is mounted on the end of a needle or thin spindle, which is parallel to the microscope stage and may be rotated about its own axis, the crystal being at the same time immersed in a liquid of known refractive index. If the latter is the same as one of those presented by the crystal in a given position, then this component of the light passes straight through the crystal without deviation by refraction at its surfaces, and by making use of this principle and changing the liquid as required, angles of rotation of the needle become true angles between directions of propagation within the crystal, whatever its birefringence.

Another important fact on which the use of the single-axis apparatus is based is that even if the crystal is mounted in a random orientation, every radius vector of the indicatrix becomes parallel to the stage of the microscope, and the corresponding refractive index therefore becomes determinable, once in a rotation of the needle through 180°. Of particular interest of course are those vectors corresponding to the principal refractive indices. The biaxial case is shown in Fig. 7.2, in

*Emmons, R. C., *Amer. Min.* 1929, **14**, 441.

which XOX' (α), YOY' (β), and ZOZ' (γ) are the principal axes of the indicatrix projected along the direction of the axis of rotation O; by rotations of θ, ϕ and ψ, respectively, each of these axes is brought into the horizontal plane. In each of these positions, which we shall call

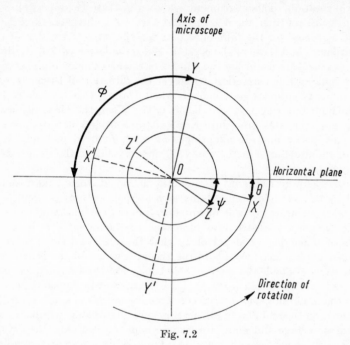

Fig. 7.2

principal positions in what follows, an optical symmetry plane is vertical.

With a uniaxial crystal, a radius of the circular section of the indicatrix (corresponding to ω) is parallel to the stage at every position of rotation, so that there is an infinite number of 'principal positions'. The one of most practical interest, however, is that at which the ε axis (optic axis) is parallel to the stage, in which position the crystal shows both principal indices.

Single-axis Rotation Apparatus.

Examples. Many forms of single-axis rotation apparatus have been described,* and they may be broadly divided into two groups according

---

* For example: Bernal, J. D. and Carlisle, C. H., *J. Sci. Instr.* 1947, **24**, 107; Hartshorne, N. H. and Swift, P. McL., *J. Roy. Microscop. Soc.* 1955, **75**, 129;

as they (i) lack, or (ii) incorporate, means of measuring angles of rotation. Much useful exploratory work of a qualitative or semi-quantitative nature can be done with very simple apparatus of type (i), particularly if it allows objectives with a small working distance and thus a large N.A. to be used, so that wide-angle interference figures can

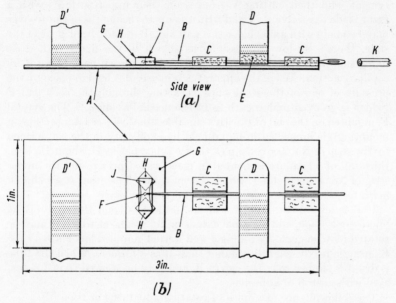

Fig. 7.3

be obtained. Thus with suitably oriented crystals the morphology and the general relationship between the optics and the morphology may be studied, while from conoscopic observations estimates of 2V and information about the dispersion of the optic axes may be obtainable. Moreover if the positions in which an optical symmetry plane is vertical can be clearly recognised conoscopically (see below), it will be possible to determine the principal refractive indices with such apparatus.

Figs. 7.3 *a* and *b* show a very simple rotation apparatus of type (i),

Rosenfeld, J. L., *Amer. Min.* 1950, **35**, 902; Tatarskii, V. B., *Zapiski Vsesoiuznogo Mineralogicheskogo Obshcestva*, 1951, second series, part 80, 293; Wilcox, R. E., *Amer. Min.* 1959, **44**, 1272; *Proceedings of the International Microscopy Symposium*, Chicago, 1960 (Edited by W. C. McCrone, McCrone Associates, Chicago) p. 180; also private communication. Wood, R. G., and Ayliffe, S. G., *J. Sci. Instr.* 1935, **12**, 194. Hartshorne, N. H., *Min. Mag.* 1963, **33**, 693; *The Microscope and Crystal Front*, 1964, **14**, 81.

which can be made without any workshop facilities whatever. A 3 × 1 in. microscope slide A, as thin as possible (1 mm. or less), carries a large sewing needle B, about 5 cm. long, on two cork bearings C. These bearings are made by cementing cork blocks about $\frac{5}{16}$ in. square and $\frac{3}{32}$ in. thick to the slide with 'Durofix',* or some other insoluble cement, and then cutting V-grooves on their upper surfaces with a razor blade to receive B. Final adjustments to the depths of the grooves may be made with a fine file, e.g. a nail file. B must be well clear of the slide, though as low as possible, as shown in the figure, otherwise immersion liquid from the cell (below) will be drawn back along it by capillary action. When the apparatus is in use, B is held in place by the pressure of one of the stage clips D, acting through the cork pad E (which is grooved underneath to fit the needle) as shown. The crystal F, mounted on the end of B with a suitable adhesive (see later section on mounting), is immersed in liquid held by capillarity in the cell formed by the strip of No. 2 cover slip G, the two glass blocks H, about 1·5 mm. thick, all of which are cemented in place with Durofix, and the upper strip of No. 1 cover slip J, which is removable. The other stage clip D' helps to secure the apparatus to the microscope stage.

If B is only 5 cm. long it will not project beyond the edge of the microscope stage, and a simple extension by means of which it may be rotated may be made by rolling a well wetted gummed label into a tube K, using a needle slightly thinner than B as a former. When the tube is dry it is slipped over the eye of B, and may be secured to it if necessary with a drop of adhesive.

The following are examples of rotation apparatus of type (ii).

Fig. 7.4 shows a recent model of a type of 'spindle stage' designed by R. E. Wilcox of the U.S. Geological Survey (refs. in footnote on p. 283). The stainless steel base-plate A, 0·050 in. thick, carries the needle or spindle B, made from a straight piece of 0·025 in. piano wire. This is tapered for about a quarter of an inch at the end carrying the crystal, though blunted at the extreme tip, and is bent at the other end to form a pointer to the transparent plastic half-circle H, which is graduated in 5° intervals. It rests in a groove C in the base-plate, and is held in position by the turn-clips D. The bottom and walls of the immersion cell consist of a glass disc E, cemented into a hole with a lower retaining rim in the base-plate, and two short lengths F of the same wire as is used for the needle. When in use the cell is completed by placing a small piece of cover slip on top, as in the apparatus shown in Fig. 7.3.

---

* 'Durofix' consists essentially of nitrocellulose dissolved in amyl acetate with other additives, and is manufactured by the Rawlplug Company Ltd., Cromwell Road, London, S.W.7.

A shallow pit G hinders the creeping of liquid along the spindle, especially if a drop of water is placed in the pit. The half-circle H is held in a slot in the base-plate, and is easily removed to allow the spindle to be mounted and dismounted. The apparatus is held on the microscope stage by the ordinary stage clips. It is made to order by Lyman Nichols, Cherryhurst, Fort Collins, Colorado, U.S.A.

Fig. 7.5 *a* shows a rotation apparatus designed by N. H. Hartshorne, which is a simplified and thinner version of an earlier one designed by

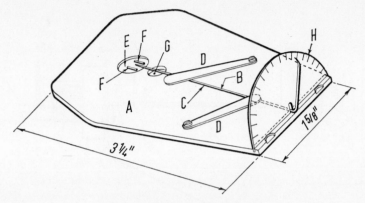

Fig. 7.4. Wilcox's spindle stage.

N. H. Hartshorne and P. McL. Swift (ref. in footnote on p. 282). The needle A, of $\frac{1}{32}$ in. or 0.040 in. steel rod, is tapered at the end carrying the crystal B (and slightly flattened at the tip), and rests in a V-groove cut in the upper surface of the brass or light alloy plate C, which is $\frac{1}{16}$ in. thick or slightly less, say, $\frac{3}{64}$ in. A is held in the groove by the three turn-clips D. The depth of the groove is such that the axis of A is level with the upper surface of C. At E, C is recessed to a depth of 0·045 in.* over a diameter of $\frac{3}{4}$ in. and a central hole $\frac{3}{8}$ in. wide is drilled through the plate. This recess accommodates a $\frac{3}{4}$ in. No. 2 cover slip and two glass blocks, *ca* 1·5 mm. thick, which are cemented in place with Duro-fix, to form the bottom and sides of the immersion cell. In use this is completed by a strip of cover slip laid on the blocks, as in the apparatus shown in Fig. 7.3. Rotation angles are measured to the nearest degree by the light alloy drum, 1 in. in diameter and graduated at intervals of 2°, which can be clamped to the needle by means of the milled head G

---

* This depth is important. If it is appreciably less, the needle is too close to the base of the cell, and liquid is drawn along the needle by capillary action.

which is tapered internally and, when screwed up, binds on the split and tapered shank of F, (see *b*) in a similar manner to the chuck on a hand drill. Angles are read against the fixed mark on the quadrant H. Two legs J, about $\frac{5}{8}$ in. long, project downwards from the plate to

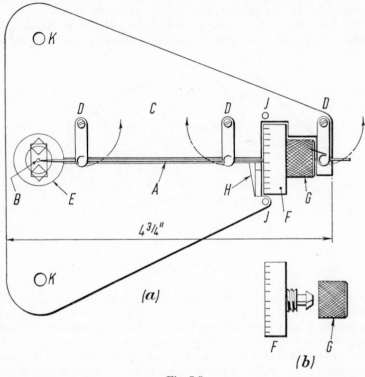

Fig. 7.5

protect the drum from collision with the microscope stage clamp or vernier when the stage is being rotated,* and also from contact with the working bench when the apparatus is removed from the microscope and laid down. The apparatus is clamped to the microscope stage by two finger screws (not shown) passing through the holes K, which are

* It must be possible to rotate the stage sufficiently to bring the crystal into two adjacent extinction positions whatever angles these positions make with the needle axis, i.e. through at least 180°. Considerably more than this is possible with the apparatus now described, while the Wilcox device (Fig. 7.4) and that shown in Fig. 7.3 permit unrestricted rotation of the stage.

drilled oversize to allow for centring, as on the usual type of universal stage. It may be obtained from McCrone Associates, c/o Malies Instruments Ltd., Ann's Place, Albion Street, Southwick, Sussex.

All the devices described above may be used with objectives having N.A's. of at least 0·65, and if special care is taken to make the depth of the immersion cell as small as possible, and only very small crystals are used, objectives of N.A's. 0·80 or 0·85 may be focussed.

Mounting the crystal. A crystal to be studied on a single-axis rotation apparatus has to be large enough to be manipulated, so that it can be mounted properly on the needle of the apparatus. The minimum size that can be dealt with depends very much on the skill and experience of the operator, but its average value may be put at about 0·2 mm. for the dimension normal to the axis of rotation. This is appreciably greater than the dimensions of particles suitable for ordinary preparations (p. 268), and the crystals are usually too thick to show low-order polarisation colours, except at wedge-shaped borders, or when the light is travelling nearly parallel to an optic axis, unless the birefringence is low.

R. E. Wilcox (footnote, p. 283) has discussed the mounting of the crystal, and mentions a number of adhesives which have been used by different workers. He draws attention to the properties which a suitable adhesive should possess, namely that its setting time should be such that it remains tacky long enough for contact to be made between crystal and needle, but sets quickly thereafter, and, of course, that it must be insoluble in the immersion media to be used. He himself favours a mixture of about '4 parts of common water-soluble carpenter's glue (such as Lepage's 'Liquid Glue') and one part of crude ('black-strap') molasses'. Vedeneeva* has used waterglass, and Tatarskii (footnote, p. 283) freshly melted Rochelle salt, or sugar melted with a little water. The present authors find that 'Durofix' diluted with about an equal volume of amyl acetate is satisfactory. Dental wax has been used for a special mounting technique (to be explained below) in which the crystal is first oriented on a goniometer head, and then transferred in the same orientation to the needle of the rotation apparatus (Wood and Ayliffe, Hartshorne and Swift, footnote, pp. 282, 283; Hartshorne and Stuart†).

Before mounting the crystal it should be ascertained by examination under a low-power microscope that it is free from adhering smaller

* Vedeneeva, N. E., *Trudy Vses. Nauch.-Issled. Inst. Mineral. syr'ia*, 1937, **124**, 1.

† Hartshorne, N. H. and Stuart, A., *Crystals and the Polarising Microscope*, 3rd edn. (Arnold, London, 1960), p. 396 *et seq.*

crystals or debris, which would interfere with the optical examination on the rotation apparatus. If it is to be mounted in a *random orientation*, the procedure is simple. The crystal is transferred to a glazed tile or a smooth card, the colour of which contrasts with that of the crystal, so that the latter stands out clearly. The needle, its tip armed with adhesive (see below), is then carefully approached to the crystal so as to attach it as nearly as possible in line with the axis of the needle. This operation may be carried out with the aid of a hand lens,

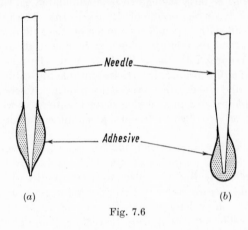

(a)   (b)

Fig. 7.6

or under a low-power binocular microscope, and with the light of a nearby lamp falling on the crystal obliquely from the front. By watching the shadow of the needle in relation to the needle itself, it is easy to judge when it is about to make contact with the crystal.

To apply the adhesive to the needle, a drop is placed on a flat surface, and the extreme tip of the needle is dipped into it. Adhesives which wet the metal, such as the Durofix-amyl acetate mixture mentioned above, are apt to draw away from the tip as shown in Fig. 7.6 *a*, and to overcome this the needle should be dipped into the drop a number of times and withdrawn rather slowly, so as to build up a small bead completely covering the tip as in Fig. 7.6 *b*. In all cases the amount of adhesive taken on to the tip should be as small as possible, so as not to mask the crystal.

By a method originally due to Wood and Ayliffe (footnote, p. 283), and slightly modified by Hartshorne and Stuart (footnote, p. 287), a well-formed crystal can be mounted in a *definite orientation*, such that the axis of rotation is coincident with some prominent morphological direction, e.g. the axis of elongation in the case of a bladed or acicular crystal. When this direction is also that of one of the axes of the indicatrix (which will often be the case except with triclinic crystals), such a setting of the crystal has many advantages, as will appear later. The method consists in first mounting the crystal with soft wax on the needle of an ordinary reflecting goniometer arranged with its axis vertical, and bringing it to the desired orientation by means of the adjustments on the goniometer head. A small quantity of white dental wax is melted on to the needle of the rotation apparatus about ¼ in. from its point, and the needle is then fixed vertically above the crystal so that its point nearly touches it (Fig. 7.7). This adjustment may be conveniently made by sighting on a plumb line. The upper part of the needle is now gently

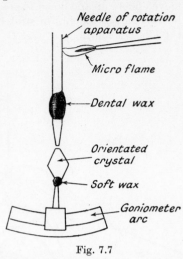

Fig. 7.7

heated by means of a small flame, whereby the dental wax is made to run down to the tip of the needle, so gripping the crystal firmly on cooling. The goniometer head is now gently lowered, thus breaking the soft wax connection between the crystal and the goniometer needle.

A mounting apparatus, incorporating the goniometer head and needle holder, for the more convenient application of the above method has been described by Hartshorne and Swift (footnote, p. 282; see also Hartshorne and Stuart, footnote, p. 287). For details the reader should consult either of these accounts.

A much simpler apparatus by means of which an elongated crystal may be mounted so that its long axis coincides with the axis of rotation, with sufficient accuracy for many purposes, is shown in Fig. 7.8 a. The holder for the needle A consists of the vertical bracket B (ca. 2½ in. high) attached to the baseboard C (ca. 6 in. square), both made of hardwood. B is cut away in front to form the two beds D,D, which have vertical V-shaped grooves against which A is lightly held by means of the rubber band E acting through the hardwood block F. F has a V-groove registering with the needle, and is hinged to the bracket B on the far side with a strip of adhesive tape. E is attached to a small screw on the far side of B, and when in use is looped over the screw G as shown, the operation being facilitated by knotting E so as to leave a free loop H for handling. The length of E must be chosen so that it gives sufficient pressure to hold A firmly on D,D, while allowing it to be moved freely up and down. Some change in the tension can be effected by varying the amount of stretch given to E before it is passed round the block F and looped over G. The grooves in D,D and F may be

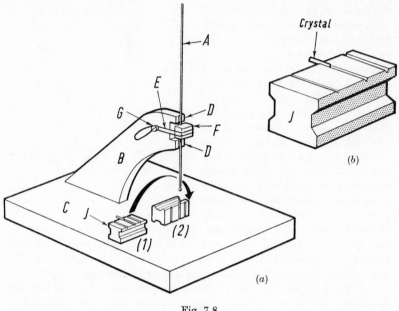

Fig. 7.8

lubricated with graphite by rubbing the point of a soft pencil along them, to give smoother longitudinal movement of the needle.

The crystal is placed on the block J (position 1), which is made of hard rubber or plastic, and has been previously electrified by rubbing on a cloth. J has a number of grooves of different depths to suit different sizes of crystals (Fig. 7.8 *b*), and by means of a finely pointed glass rod the crystal is manoeuvred into one of these and pushed along until it overhangs the edge as shown. The block is then carefully turned into position 2 (Fig. 7.8 *a*), so that the crystal, held by the charge on the block, is now upright. The block is moved so that the end of the crystal is exactly under the tip of the needle when the latter is pushed down so as nearly to make contact with it. The needle is then withdrawn a little, its tip is armed with adhesive as described above, and it is then cautiously brought down to make contact with the crystal. After the adhesive has set, the needle and crystal are withdrawn from the block.

The apparatus can also be used to mount a plate-like crystal so that the plane of the plate is normal to the axis of the needle. In this case the crystal is merely laid on the flat surface of the block, which need not be electrified, and, after positioning the block to bring the crystal under the needle, the latter, armed with adhesive, is pushed down and the crystal picked up after the adhesive has set.

Other apparatus for mounting crystals on the needle has been described by N. H. Hartshorne (last reference, footnote, p. 283).

Adding and changing the immersion medium. The liquid can be run into the cell quite conveniently by means of the dropping rod used in making ordinary preparations between a slide and cover slip (p. 268), but if the cell contains the remains of a former liquid, the rod must be wiped clean with filter paper before returning it to the bottle so that there will be no risk of contaminating the contents. Liquid can be withdrawn from the cell by applying either small pieces of filter paper, or a dry micro-pipette (p. 272). Additions and withdrawals can also be made with a dropper, i.e. a capillary pipette of the type shown in Fig. 7.1 *b* (*i*) but fitted with a rubber teat, but with this some care and practice are needed in controlling the flow of liquid.

When changing the immersion medium, the first lot of the new liquid to be run in should be withdrawn, and the process of running in and withdrawing repeated once or twice to flush out as much of the former liquid as possible. When the refractive index of the liquid must be accurately known, as when a match between crystal and liquid has been secured, a little of the liquid should be withdrawn and its value determined on a refractometer. As a check on the homogeneity of the liquid in the cell (which may take a little time to establish when changing viscous liquids, even when the flushing-out procedure above is followed), it may be advisable to remove the rest of the liquid, and test this also on the refractometer.

Methods of Using Single-Axis Rotation Apparatus.

(*a*) *Methods in which the crystal is mounted in a random orientation.* The primary object in this case is to determine the principal refractive indices. It is first necessary to identify the principal positions (p. 282), and the vibration directions at these positions which correspond to the principal refractive indices. Each of these indices is then determined in the usual way by changing the immersion liquid until a match is obtained. It may happen that the orientation is such as to bring one or both of the optic axes into the conoscopic field on rotation of the crystal, in which case additional data may be obtained, e.g. the optical sign by direct determination with a compensator, or the dispersion of the optic axes.

In theory the principal positions and the vibration directions corresponding to the principal refractive indices may always be identified *conoscopically* as explained on pp. 217–218. However, biaxial crystals having a small or moderate optic axial angle, and oriented so that the acute bisectrix makes only a small angle with the needle, give such broad and diffuse isogyres that is it not possible to set them in their principal positions very precisely by this method. This is because such cases approximate more or less closely to that of a uniaxial crystal rotated about its optic axis; this would give an optic normal figure with its characteristically broad and diffuse isogyres at all positions of rotation. One way out of this difficulty is to mount another crystal of the substance so that its acute bisectrix makes a larger angle with the needle axis. Wilcox (footnote, p. 283) discusses such cases in detail, and also the errors in the values of the refractive indices resulting from imprecise settings of the crystal. These errors naturally increase with increase in the birefringence of the crystal, but Wilcox shows that even when this is as high as 0·10, the maximum theoretical error that could result from a setting which was wrong by 4° would be within the limits of accuracy of the immersion method as ordinarily applied. For further details of this discussion the original paper must be consulted.

When the crystal is uniaxial, it is only necessary to rotate it so that it presents an $\varepsilon\omega$ section, as shown by its giving an optic normal figure. Both principal indices can be determined in this setting. The precision of this setting will be all the greater the greater the angle which the optic axis makes with the needle axis.

The conoscopic method can be used with simple apparatus of type (i) (p. 283), since it is not necessary to know the angles between the principal positions. It must be remembered, however, that in a rotation of the needle through 360° the crystal assumes a given principal position twice, at settings 180° apart, and care must be taken that these duplicate settings are not taken as representing different principal positions. A simple means of following the amount of rotation of the needle roughly, e.g. by making distinctive ink marks on the paper needle holder (K) in the apparatus shown in Fig. 7.3, will avoid any such confusion. When using apparatus of type (ii), the principal positions can be noted on the angle-measuring device and no confusion will arise. In Wilcox's spindle stage (Fig. 7.5), the rotation of the needle is restricted to 180° and no duplication of the principal positions is possible.

The principal positions can also be identified *orthoscopically*, and we shall describe a method due to N. Joel.* (For another method, and

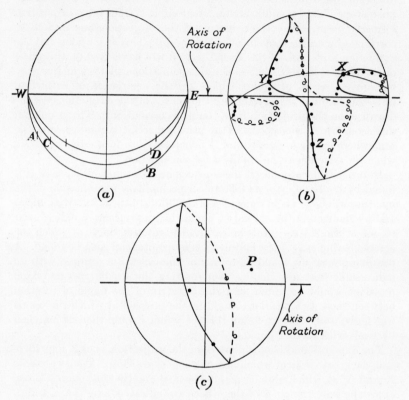

Fig. 7.9. (After Joel.)

references to yet others, see Wilcox's first paper, footnote p. 283). The procedure is as follows. At first no immersion liquid is used. For each section which comes into position as the crystal is rotated there are two extinction directions. These are determined in relation to the axis of rotation and plotted on a stereographic projection for a complete revolution. For example, in Fig. 7.9 *a*, the primitive circle represents

* *Min. Mag.* 1950, **29**, 206.

the horizontal circle in the starting position. The two extinction directions are measured from the horizontal cross wire (the axis of rotation) and plotted on the primitive circle as shown at A and B in the figure, 90° apart.* Now suppose that the crystal is rotated, say, 10° in a direction which turns the top of the crystal towards the observer at the microscope. This would bring the great circle WCDE into the position formerly occupied by the primitive if the projection was rotated to correspond with the movement of the crystal. This is not done, but the extinction directions of the second section will be plotted on this great circle as at C and D. Successive determinations plotted in this way will give a series of points which are the emergence of extinction directions around the crystal and the curves of the extinctions can be drawn in on the projection for a complete revolution.† The extinction directions which correspond to the principal refractive indices must lie somewhere on these curves and it is necessary to locate one of these, when the others may be obtained by construction.

In order to locate one of these principal directions, either α or γ is found by trial and error as follows. A preliminary examination of the material will have given some idea of the limits of the refractive indices, and by immersing the crystal in liquids having refractive indices near to one of these, say γ, this index and the rotation angle at which the corresponding axis of the indicatrix is horizontal can soon be found. A possible procedure would be to mount the crystal in a liquid with an index somewhat less than γ. On rotating the needle two matching positions would be found, and the bisectrix of the angle of rotation between these two positions would be the position at which the γ-axis was horizontal. Having found this the γ index could then be matched by trials with further liquids.

The axis so found is now plotted on the projection as at Z Fig. 7.9 b, and the great circle of which it is the pole is drawn in. The two points X and Y at which this circle intersects the extinction curves locate approximately the poles of the other two indicatrix axes, i.e. α and β, if the axis first located was γ. The two poles are only located approximately by this construction because the extinction curves were obtained with the dry crystal, and their positions were affected to some extent by the deviation of the incident light which occurred whenever the

* For setting the needle parallel to the horizontal cross wire, a low-power objective should be used, and the needle pushed across the field if necessary to bring more of it into view. The microscope stage reading is then noted, and this is the zero from which the extinction directions are measured.

† Another way of expressing this is that the great circles WCDE, etc. are the cyclographic projections (p. 243) of a series of optical sections of the crystal, having a common diameter WE and inclined at intervals of 10° to one another.

crystal presented an inclined surface to it. However, the two points of intersection will be sufficiently near to the true poles to enable these and the values of the indices α and β to be found by trial. The best procedure is first to locate and measure α by a method similar to that used for γ. β must then be at the pole of the great circle containing α and γ, and so can be accurately fixed and determined.

With a positive crystal it is best to find γ first, as above, while with a negative crystal α should be found first. The great circle drawn to locate the other two poles approximately will then intersect the extinction curves at a large angle, and the points of intersection will be more closely defined than if the reverse procedure is adopted.

When a uniaxial crystal is examined in the same way as that just described it is seen that the one refractive index direction which is always normal to the optic axis plots in a great circle (Fig. 7.9 c), the pole of which is the optic axis. The ordinary refractive index, which may be found on any section, is now determined, the course of the great circle is confirmed with the crystal immersed, and the pole located accurately. The direction of the optic axis may now be brought horizontal and the value of ε found.

Instead of determining the extinction curves with a dry crystal as stated above, it is more satisfactory to do this with the crystal immersed in a liquid which matches approximately its mean refractive index, some idea of which can usually be gained from a preliminary examination of the substance in ordinary mounts between a slide and cover slip. The extinction positions will be more sharply defined, and the course of the curves more accurate, if this is done.

Wilcox has shown* that *a good estimate of 2V can be made from the extinction curves*, if its approximate value is known from a preliminary examination of the substance or otherwise. The method consists in plotting possible positions of the optic axes on the αγ great circle, and then by applying the Biot–Fresnel construction (p. 258) finding which of these positions best fits the extinction curves.

(*b*) *The crystal is mounted with an optical symmetry plane vertical.* If a preliminary examination of the substance has shown that an axis of the indicatrix is co-directional with some prominent morphological feature, such as an axis of elongation, it will be possible to mount the crystal by one of the methods dealt with on pp. 288–291 so that an optical symmetry plane is perpendicular to the axis of rotation. A particularly favourable case is that in which the symmetry plane in question is the optical axial plane. It is evident that in this orientation

* Wilcox, R. E., *Amer. Min.* 1959, **44**, 1290; *Geol. Soc. Amer., Bull.* 1960, **71**, 2003.

the values of $\alpha \beta$, γ and 2V can all be found directly, at least in principle, by immersing the crystal successively in liquids of increasing refractive index, because as it is rotated, it presents sections giving a constant refractive index β along the axis of rotation, and, at right angles to this, values which will vary between α and γ. The optic axes become vertical in turn during the rotation, and these positions can be recognized conoscopically. The main advantage of this particular orientation is, however, that it enables γ to be determined *indirectly*, in cases

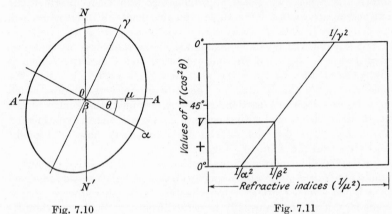

| Fig. 7.10 | Fig. 7.11 |

Values of $1/\mu^2$ increase towards the left of the figure.

in which this index is too high to be matched by any accessible liquid, as was first shown by Wood and Ayliffe.* The theory of the method is as follows. Fig. 7.10 represents a section of the biaxial indicatrix of a crystal mounted in this way, the axis of rotation being β, normal to the paper, and NN' being the axis of the microscope. AOA' is the trace of an elliptical section of the indicatrix parallel to the microscope stage, having β as one axis and μ as the other. Light travelling normally to the section AOA' will be resolved into components having refractive indices β and μ. θ is the angle through which the crystal has been turned from a position in which the $\alpha\beta$ section was horizontal (and in which the refractive indices α and β may be measured). The mathematical relationships between α, β, μ and θ, are expressed by the equation:

$$\frac{1}{\mu^2} = \frac{1}{\gamma^2} + \left(\frac{1}{\alpha^2} - \frac{1}{\gamma^2}\right) \cos^2 \theta.$$

* Wood, R. G. and Ayliffe, S. H., *Phil. Mag.* 1936, (7), **21**, 324.

In such an equation, $\dfrac{1}{\mu^2}$ varies linearly with $\cos^2 \theta$. If now values of $\dfrac{1}{\mu^2}$ and $\cos^2 \theta$ are plotted along the abscissa and ordinate respectively $\dfrac{1}{\alpha^2}, \dfrac{1}{\beta^2}$, and $\dfrac{1}{\gamma^2}$ plot on a straight line as shown in Fig. 7.11.

The method of Wood and Ayliffe was to immerse the crystal mounted as described in liquids of successively greater refractive index, and turn it until a match was obtained. By this means a number of values for θ and corresponding refractive indices were obtained. $\cos^2 \theta$ was plotted against $\dfrac{1}{\mu^2}$ for each pair of values, and the straight-line graph thus obtained gave $\dfrac{1}{\alpha^2}$ on the lower line, $\dfrac{1}{\gamma^2}$ on the upper line, and a value of $\dfrac{1}{\beta^2}$ when $\theta = V$ for a positive crystal, or $(90° - V)$ for a negative crystal,* their angles being measured in a liquid of refractive index β.

In making observations such as those just described, it is obviously necessary to fix the zero position from which to measure the angles. This may be done in a number of ways, but the simplest is to turn the crystal till the acute bisectrix is vertical, each melatope being centred in turn and the mean position taken. If the sign is now determined the orientation of all the principal vibration directions is known, β lying along the axis of rotation. The $\alpha\beta$ section may now be placed in the horizontal position. Alternatively, if the crystal is immersed in a liquid with a refractive index somewhat above α, two positions of matching will be found on either side of the α direction and at equal angles to it. It is then easy to set this direction in the horizontal position.

It is evident that this method could be used not only for the indirect determination of γ, but also for the indirect determination of α in cases in which this index is too low to be conveniently matched directly.

It is easy to construct diagrams like that in Fig. 7.11, in which the values of the refractive indices themselves are plotted against values of V. This is facilitated since F. E. Wright† (in a paper which contains graphical solutions for many crystallographic formulæ) has given tables of $\cos^2 \theta$, and values (to six decimal places) for $\dfrac{1}{\mu^2}$ from $\mu = 1\cdot40$

---

* It will be remembered that V is conventionally used to denote one-half of the *acute* angle between the optic axes (see p. 90).

† Wright, F. E., 'Methods in Microscopical Petrography', *Amer. J. Sci.* 1913, **36,** 509.

to 2·48. On such a diagram the plots may be drawn direct without the necessity of calculating values of $1/\mu^2$.

A diagram of this kind has been used by the authors for many years, and is included as a folder at the end of this book. Mertie* published

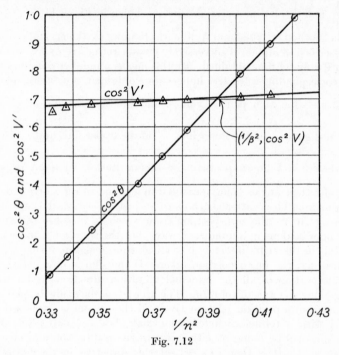

Fig. 7.12

a similar one in 1942 but did not mention the paper here quoted of Wood and Ayliffe, though he gives other references to various types of graphical solutions to the same problem.

Such a diagram has a number of uses in addition to that of finding the value of γ by extrapolation. It can be used to test the compatibility of experimentally determined results for the optical constants of a crystal. Further it can be used to demonstrate that small errors (of the order of $\pm0\cdot002$ in refractive indices, and $\pm4°$ in the value for 2V) will result in large errors in the determination of γ by calculation, especially if α and β are very near to one another, 2V small, and the optical sign positive. A little intelligent experimentation with the diagram will demonstrate the size of the errors to be expected when

* Mertie, J. B. Jr., *Amer. Min.* 1942, **27**, 538.

calculating one constant from a knowledge of the other three, using formulæ such as those given on p. 234.

Swift* has described a method by which all the optical vectors may be determined indirectly. The crystal is set as before with the optic axial plane vertical, and is mounted in a series of liquids having indices between α and γ. For each liquid the rotation angle θ, at which a match is given, is determined. The zero position from which the angles are measured is found as described above. $\cos^2 \theta$ is plotted against $1/\mu^2$ (or θ and μ are plotted directly on the nomogram at the back of this book), giving a straight line at the extremities of which lie the values for $1/\alpha^2$ and $1/\gamma^2$ (Fig. 7.12). For each point at which a match is obtained the apparent optic axial half-angle V' is also determined by bringing each optic axis in turn to the cross-hairs. $\cos^2 V'$ for positive crystals, or $\cos^2 (90 - V') = \sin^2 V'$ for negative crystals, is then plotted against $1/\mu^2$. This plot will intersect the former one at the point where $V' = V$ and $\mu = \beta$ (see figure). It will be seen that it is not necessary to have measured β exactly as in the method of Wood and Ayliffe. If many determinations of θ are made the accuracy of the values of α and γ will be satisfactory.

To give an idea of the accuracy of the results obtainable by this method, Swift's values for hippuric acid are compared below with those listed in A. N. Winchell's *Optical Properties of Organic Compounds* (Academic Press, New York, 1954, p. 113), and the experimental data are plotted in Fig. 7.12.

	From the Graph	From Winchell
α	1·537	1·5348
β	1·594	1·5921
γ	1·762	1·7598
2V	65·7°	65° 49·5′

Since the equation on p. 296 is based solely on the geometry of the ellipse, it can be modified to apply to the cases in which (i) the $\alpha\beta$ section, and (ii) the $\beta\gamma$ section are vertical by substituting β for γ in (i) and β for α in (ii), and the method of Wood and Ayliffe can be used to extrapolate to the value of α in the former case and to that of γ in the latter case, where these values are inaccessible directly. If in either of these settings an acute bisectrix figure appears in the conoscopic field, additional data will be obtainable, such as the value of 2V by the Mallard method (p. 235). The method can also be applied to vertical $\varepsilon\omega$ sections of uniaxial crystals.

* Swift, P. McL., *Amer. Min.* 1954, **39**, 838.

8 DETERMINING OPTICAL CRYSTALLOGRAPHIC PROPERTIES: SOME PRACTICAL EXAMPLES

The exact procedure for determining the optical crystallographic properties of a substance depends very much on its state of division, crystal system and habit, and on whether it is possible, or is permitted by the nature of the problem, to recrystallise the substance In this chapter we shall outline the appropriate procedures in a number of simple cases. All the substances concerned are readily available, and their study on the lines indicated would form a useful series of experiments for the beginner. Emphasis has been placed mainly on the properties that can be determined on ordinary mounts of the substances between a slide and a cover slip.

1. **Ammonium dihydrogen phosphate, $NH_4H_2PO_4$.** Tetragonal, class $\bar{4}2m$. Optically negative, ε_D 1·479, ω_D 1·525. Crystallises from water as four-sided prisms with pyramidal terminations (Fig. 8.1), thus apparently holohedral, and concealing the true symmetry class.

The uniaxial character can be readily confirmed on randomly oriented particles obtained by crushing larger crystals and mounting the powder in any ordinary immersion liquid (p. 268). Among those particles showing the lowest polarisation colours will be found some giving inclined, or even possibly centred uniaxial interference figures (Fig. 5.3, p. 204). The negative sign may be deduced from the effect of an appropriate compensator on these figures (p. 228).

By micro-recrystallisation from water on a slide (p. 273), crystals as in Fig. 8.1, though with varying degrees of distortion, will be obtained. These almost without exception will lie on a prism face, giving straight extinction with respect to the edges of the face. They also give optic normal interference figures showing that they present $\varepsilon\omega$ sections. The vibration direction parallel to the optic axis (ε), i.e. the direction of falling colours in the figure (Fig. 5.9, p. 208), will prove to be that parallel to the prism faces. This is also the 'fast' direction (thus confirming the optical sign as negative), as may be found on thinner crystals by means of the quarter wave mica plate, or on thicker crystals showing 'high whites' by observing the movement of the colour bands on the pyramidal terminations as a quartz wedge is inserted (p. 192).

ε and ω may be determined on such recrystallised specimens after removal of the mother liquor, as described on p. 274.

As an alternative to this compound, the isomorphous potassium salt KH_2PO_4 may be studied. This crystallises from water in the same habit, and has ε_D 1·468, ω_D 1·509.

2. Urea, $CO(NH_2)_2$. Tetragonal, class $\bar{4}2m$. Optically positive. As given by different authors, ε_D is 1·600 to 1·602, and ω_D 1·474 to 1·484. Melting point 132°.

The uniaxial character is conveniently revealed on a 'melt' preparation (p. 278), which will show a variety of orientations, including some sections parallel to {001}, or near, which give uniaxial interference figures. From these the optical sign may be determined.

Micro-recrystallisation from water on a slide is not particularly easy, since the solid tends to come out suddenly as a crust, but by cautious evaporation and fairly vigorous stirring with the transfer rod, elongated prisms and needles giving straight extinction may be obtained. These give optic normal interference figures, and thus present $\varepsilon\omega$ sections. The direction of elongation is 'slow', and is also that of the optic axis (direction of falling colours in the interference figure), thus confirming the positive optical sign. ε and ω may be determined on such crystals after removal of the mother liquor, or on any elongated crystals in the original specimen which show optic normal interference figures, and are of suitable size.

Fig. 8.1.
Crystal of
$NH_4H_2PO_4$.

3. Potassium chlorate, $KClO_3$. Monoclinic class $2/m$. Optically negative. $2V_D = 27°$. α_D 1·408, β_D 1·517, γ_D 1·523. The Z (or γ) axis of the indicatrix is parallel to b, and so the optic axial plane (O.A.P.) is normal to (010). The X (or α) axis of the indicatrix is at 56° to c in the obtuse angle β, which is 100°. In tables of optical data this information about the optic orientation would be given more concisely, e.g. as follows: Z $= b$, X : $c = 56°$ in obtuse angle β. It may also be expressed graphically as in Fig. 8.2 a.

Micro-recrystallisation from water yields thin plates parallel to (001), bounded by {110}, and having an acute profile angle of 80°. This is shown in Fig. 8.2 *b*, which for simplicity gives the profile of the (001) face, without showing the narrow faces of the bounding form, which would not be prominent in the microscopic image. Forms {10$\bar{1}$}, {011} and {01$\bar{1}$} may also be developed, and the intersections of these with

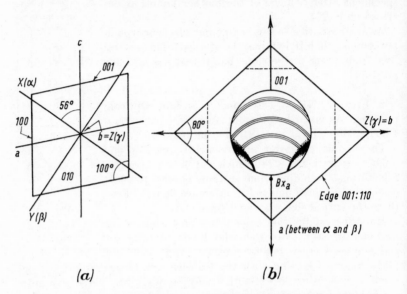

(a)   *(b)*

Fig. 8.2. Potassium chlorate. Optic orientation (*a*), and 'common view' (*b*) showing interference figure in 45° position.

{001} are indicated by the broken lines in the figure.* The crystal plates naturally lie flat on the slide, and the resulting 'common view', as we may call it, gives symmetrical extinction and a laterally displaced acute bisectrix interference figure with Bx_a just outside the edge of the field if an objective of N.A. 0·85 is used, as shown within the central circle in the drawing. On very thin plates giving diffuse isogyres, it may be difficult to decide whether the substance is biaxial or uniaxial from the interference figure, but on thicker crystals showing a number of colour bands and sharper isogyres, as in the drawing, the biaxial character can be clearly made out; the inner bands are distinctly oval,

* Twinning on (001) often occurs. Such crystals give abnormal interference figures, since the light is passing through two or more differently oriented individuals, and afford no useful optical information.

and the separation of the isogyres in the 45° position is evident and corresponds to a small value of 2V. The use of an oil immersion objective would bring Bx_a well into the field, and would confirm these facts. In the extinction position a single straight isogyre will bisect the field and be coincident with a cross hair, showing that an optical symmetry plane is vertical (p. 218). From the negative optical sign determined on the interference figure it may be deduced that the principal refractive index shown by the section is γ, and corresponds to the vibration direction which is parallel to the longer diagonal of the plates. This index can be determined in the usual way after removal of the mother liquor.

To determine the other principal indices and 2V, a rotation apparatus would be most convenient (p. 282). 2E could be determined by the Mallard method, if the plates were rolled in a viscous medium (p. 279) so as to bring Bx_a to, or near to, the centre of the conoscopic field, and 2V could be calculated from this if an independent value of β were available, say, from the study of preparations of randomly oriented particles obtained by crushing larger crystals from stock.

4. Zinc sulphate heptahydrate, $ZnSO_4,7H_2O$. Orthorhombic, class 222. Optically negative. $2V_D = 46°$. α_D 1·457, β_D 1·480, γ_D 1·484.

By micro-recrystallisation from water, elongated prisms are obtained. The heptahydrate changes to the hexahydrate at 39°, and so the recrystallisation must be carried out below this temperature. The best way to proceed is to shake up an excess of the salt with a few c.c. of water, maintained at about 30°, until no more appears to dissolve, and then to place a drop of the clear solution on the slide. If no crystallisation begins after a few minutes, even on stirring with the transfer rod, the normal evaporation procedure over the micro-burner (p. 273) must then be followed, great care being taken not to overheat the drop.

The crystals present two common views as shown in Fig. 8.3 *a* and *b*. (In these drawings the end faces have been omitted, as they are usually very small and are not relevant to the present discussion.) These two views represent different positions of rotation about the axis of elongation as is shown by the fact that the refractive index for light vibrating parallel to this axis (β) is the same in the two cases. Calling this axis *c*, view (*a*) is given by crystals lying on a prism face, possibly (110), and view (*b*) by those lying on a pinacoid, which we will take as (010). This follows from the nature of the interference figures in the two cases, that in (*a*) being an inclined single optic axis figure, and the one in (*b*) a centred acute bisectrix one. The O.A.P. is normal to *c*, and it will be noted that the sign of elongation is positive in (*a*) and negative in (*b*). This is because we are looking into the obtuse optic angle in (*a*) and into the acute optic angle in (*b*).

Crystals showing view (*b*) give a much sharper extinction than those presenting view (*a*), and their polarisation colours are usually very low owing to the values of β and γ being very close together.

The negative sign may be determined on the interference figures, and crystals showing view (*b*) yield values of β and γ, and 2V by the

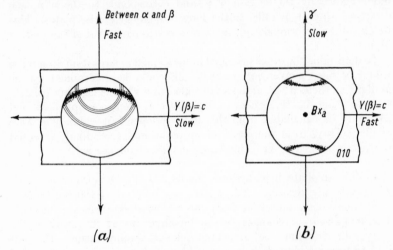

Fig. 8.3. Common views of $ZnSO_4,7H_2O$. Interference figures in 45° position.

Mallard method. From these results a value of α may be calculated, or read off from the nomogram at the end of this book, but it is likely to be subject to considerable error, since the difference between β and γ is near to the limit of accuracy of the immersion method as ordinarily applied (see data above), but at least it will be possible to estimate the limits between which α must lie. The salt is, however, an ideal example for study on a single-axis rotation apparatus, since by rotation about the β axis (easily recognisable for mounting purposes as the axis of elongation of the crystals), all the principal indices and 2V can be accurately determined. For this it would be necessary to prepare somewhat larger crystals than those which grow on a slide, or with some specimens, suitable crystals could no doubt be found in the stock bottle.

5. Hippuric acid, N-benzoylglycine, $C_6H_5.CO.NH(CH_2.COOH)$. Orthorhombic, class 222. Optically positive. $2V_D = 66°$. α_D 1·535, β_D 1·592, γ_D 1·760. Melting point 188°.

When crystallised from water, it usually appears as long prisms or needles, elongated parallel to c and with forms {100} and {110}, though the face development is often not very clear owing to a tendency to grow as parallel clusters. $Y(\beta) = c$, and $Z(\gamma) = a$, so that the O.A.P. is normal to c. (The assignment of crystallographic axes is that given in A. N. Winchell's *The Optical Properties of Organic Compounds*, Academic Press Inc., New York, 1954.) The optic orientation and habit are thus similar to those of zinc sulphate heptahydrate above, and the common views are also similar. Most frequently the crystals lie on (110) or near, and give figures like that in Fig. 8.3 a, but some (100) sections are also presented, giving centred acute bisectrix figures as in Fig. 8.3 b, though with the melatopes just outside the field for a N.A. of 0·85, since 2V is large. The principal indices α and β are presented by this latter section since the sign is positive. A 'melt' preparation should show the same sections, and possibly give clearer interference figures.* The use of an oil immersion objective will bring the melatopes of the acute bisectrix figure into the field.

The information obtainable from the above preparations consists of the optical sign, the indices α and β, and 2V by the Mallard method if an oil immersion objective is used. From these results a value for γ may be obtained. Using an objective of N.A. 0·85, it will be possible to make a rough estimate of 2V from the angular aperture of the field. Like zinc sulphate heptahydrate, however, the substance is very suitable for study on a single-axis rotation apparatus, and some results obtained by this method have already been given on p. 299.

6. Copper sulphate pentahydrate, $CuSO_4 5H_2O$. Triclinic, class $\bar{1}$. Optically negative. $2V_D = 56°$. α_D 1·514, β_D 1·537, γ_D 1·543.

Micro-recrystallisation from water yields crystals the majority of which are developed as plates parallel to $(1\bar{1}0)$ (Fig. 1.20, p. 21), and the more important properties of the resulting common view are shown in Fig. 8.4. The extinction is oblique, and the interference figure shows the emergence of an optic axis just outside the field for a N.A. of 0·85. In the extinction position, as in the drawing, the isogyre is curved, showing that the section is not normal to an optical symmetry plane, and thus does not present any of the principal refractive indices. In fact, owing to the low symmetry of the substance, recrystallisation affords no help in determining these indices, though on the other hand the properties of the common view are characteristic and could be

---

* Melt preparations if crystallised very slowly may give spherulites with a radially twisted texture, which have been discussed by Hartshorne, *Nature*, 1961, **190**, 1191.

useful as data by means of which the salt could be identified. The principal indices may be determined on preparations of randomly oriented grains, obtained by crushing larger crystals, by the method described on p. 239. From optic axial (β) sections in these preparations, the optical sign may be found, and a rough estimate of 2V made from the curvature of the isogyre in the 45° position. A more satisfactory method of determining the principal indices is, however, to mount a small crystal or grain on a single-axis rotation apparatus in a random

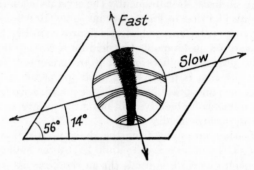

Fig. 8.4. Common view of $CuSO_4,5H_2O$ (figure in extinction position).

orientation, and to follow one or other of the procedures described on pp. 291–295.

7. Quartz, SiO_2. Trigonal, class 3*m*, (Fig. 1.16, p. 19). Optically positive. ε_D 1·553, ω_D 1·544.

Study first a thin section of quartzite, which is composed almost entirely of quartz grains either interlocking or cemented with secondary silica. The mineral is colourless with very low relief, its refractive indices being very close to that of the mounting medium (Canada balsam, 1·54, or a resin with comparable index). Using the Becke test at the margin of the section, compare the two refractive indices with that of the mounting material. One will be slightly above and the other a very close match in white light. The substage diaphragm should be closed down to emphasise the Becke lines. Between crossed polars the low double refraction is immediately apparent, the highest colours being those (in a good slice) of a pale yellow of the first order, the others being between this and the black of the isotropic basal sections. A number of sections may show white of the first order. To confirm this (and to compare with the 'high whites' of the next study), turn the polariser parallel to the analyser and notice the resultant colour (p. 178).

In many rocks the quartz crystals show undulose extinction. Rotate the slice and look for this property, which shows that the mineral has suffered stress. The extinction angle cannot be measured on the anhedral crystals as there is no cleavage. The isotropic sections reveal in convergent light a diffuse uniaxial cross, which owing to the small relative retardation is not surrounded by coloured rings. Use of the gypsum plate will give the optic sign which is positive, showing that the higher of the two principal indices is ε.

A mount of crushed grains (about 0·2 mm. in size) enables the refractive indices to be determined directly, and as the mineral has no good cleavage the grains present a random orientation. Between crossed polars the contour-like interference colours are seen up to about the third or fourth order on sections with maximum birefringence, and ε and ω may be determined on these. However, every grain will give ω. On irregular grains such as these, the Schroeder test is most convenient as many fragments may be examined at once.

It is instructive to examine the small doubly-terminated idiomorphic crystals which occur in some limestones and which may be recovered by dissolving the rock in weak acid. Especially good ones of suitable size are to be found in the limestone from Talacre, Flintshire. These, lying with the optic axis horizontal, give the two principal refractive indices, and show that the mineral has straight extinction. The sign of elongation (positive) determined with the quartz wedge confirms the optical sign, and every grain gives in convergent light a 'flash' figure.

8. Calcite, $CaCO_3$, Trigonal, class $\bar{3}m$, (Fig. 1.71, p. 35). Perfect ($10\bar{1}1$) cleavage parallel to the rhomb face (Fig. 1.45, p. 29). Sometimes lamellar twinning on ($01\bar{1}2$). Optically negative with high birefringence, ε_D 1·486, ω_D 1·658.

Prepare a sample of the crushed mineral having a particle size of about 0·05 to 0·1 mm. diameter. Iceland spar is best, since the varieties of calcite which are white contain many inclusions which make the grains almost opaque and the determination of refractive indices more difficult. The two directions of vibration bisect the angles of the rhomb-shaped fragments, one direction giving ω and the other (the shorter diagonal) ε', which has a value of 1·566. Every grain lying on a rhomb face gives these two indices. However, substances with even perfect cleavages may lie in a variety of ways because the grain may have stepped cleavage and thus lie so as to give a different value of ε'. It is necessary therefore in determinations on such material to make sure that the fragment being examined (if the true values of ω and ε' are being sought) lies on a rhomb face. It should show a uniform polarisation colour (a stepped one would have a greater relative retardation in the thicker parts), and it should not be resting with its edge on another grain. Between crossed polars the high birefringence results in 'high whites'. To test this, turn the polariser through 90° as in the study of quartz, and it will be found that the colours are unchanged. (Contrast with quartz above.) The extinction is symmetrical as stated above. In convergent light the centre of the cross is displaced towards the margin of the field (Figs. 5.11 e to h, p. 210) in the direction of the obtuse angle of the rhomb. The sign of the substance is best found by using the quartz wedge, as there are numerous closely spaced interference rings in the figure.

The angle between (0001) and (10$\bar{1}$1) in calcite is 44° 37′, and this is the amount by which the optic axis is displaced from the axis of the microscope in a rhomb lying truly parallel with the stage. It is the angle between the normal to the rhomb face and the optic axis. Since this angle is known and also the values of ω and ε', the diagram at the back of the book may be used to find the approximate value of ε, the direct determination of which is usually precluded in practice by the persistent habit of the mineral. Draw a straight line from the value of ω on the top line through the point which marks the intersection of the vertical line having the value ε' and the horizontal line at 44·6° from the top line. Project this line to the base where it will give a value for ε, the accuracy of which will depend on those of the values of ε' and ω.

9. Topaz, $Al_2(F, OH)_2SiO_4$. Orthorhombic, class *mmm*. Perfect basal cleavage. O.A.P. and $Bx_a(Z)$ are normal to (001); $X = a$. Optically positive. $2V_D = 48° - 68°$. α_D 1·606 − 1·629, β_D 1·609 − 1·631, γ_D 1·616 − 1·638, depending on the proportion of F to OH.

Prepare a crushed sample as before and immerse the material in a fluid of refractive index about 1·61 which is somewhere near the α and β values. It will be seen that most of the particles lie parallel to the only cleavage (001). They show a poor relief in the immersion fluid and a grey or white polarisation colour of the first order. The direction of the refractive index β may be found from the interference figure, for it lies normal to the O.A.P. The identity of the index corresponding to the other vibration direction in the trace of the O.A.P. becomes apparent when the optical sign is determined. This is found to be positive, Z emerging vertically and hence the direction normal to β must be α. These refractive indices may now be measured, and as the optical properties vary with the composition it is important that they be determined as accurately as possible in sodium light. The optic axial angle should now be measured. With an objective of numerical aperture, say, 0·85 it will be found that the melatopes come, with most specimens, just outside the field, and it may be necessary to resort to an oil immersion lens before a measurement can be made using Mallard's formula. Occasionally stepped cleavage brings one optic axis parallel to the microscope axis and an estimate may be made from the curvature of the brush (p. 237). Such sections may be recognised by being isotropic in the thinner sections, or by remaining evenly illuminated throughout a rotation of the stage.

It is very difficult in ordinary immersion media to induce sections to become oriented so that γ can be measured directly, but if the other indices have been determined to $\pm0'001$ it will be possible to find a value for this index using the nomogram in this book from the values of β, α and V. V must of course be calculated from the measured value of E by the formula given on p. 236.

The optical properties change in sympathy with the replacement of (OH) by F, thus, with an increase in F the refractive indices decrease and the optic angle increases. An accurate determination of the optical properties therefore enables an estimate to be made of the chemical composition of the mineral. Winchell* and Deer, Howie, and Zussman† give data showing the relations between the optics and the chemical composition. The molecular percentage OH/(OH + F) varies from 0 to 30. Find the position in the series of the specimen which has been studied.

10. Barite, BaSO$_4$. Orthorhombic. Class *mmm*. Perfect (001) and (110) and poor (010) cleavages. The angle (110):(1$\bar{1}$0) = 78° 22'. The O.A.P. is (010); Z = a. Optically positive, $2V_D = 37°$ 30', α_D 1·636, β_D 1·637 and γ_D 1·648.

The crushed mineral presents a variety of sections owing to the two perfect and one poor cleavages (Fig. 8.5). Since their maximum double refraction is only 0·012 the grains show low colours mainly of the first order, if the sizes are as recommended above. Look for the the sections with preferred orientation. For example the basal section will show edges and traces of cleavage with an included angle of about 78° and will show in convergent light the Bx$_0$ figure. As 2V is small, this figure will be very like that shown on a section parallel to the optic axial plane. The extinction is symmetrical with respect to the (110) cleavage. The refractive indices β and γ may be determined on this face,

* Winchell, A. N., *Elements of Optical Mineralogy*, Part 2, 4th. edn. (Wiley, New York, 1951) p. 510.
† Deer, W. A., Howie, R. A., and Zussman, J., *Rock Forming Minerals*, Vol. 5, *Non-Silicates*, (Longmans, London, 1962), pp. 146–148.

the former normal to the optic axial plane and the latter parallel to it.

The (110) sections will tend to be rectangular with straight extinction, α being one vibration direction. On this section the acute optic angle will appear on the margin of the field (see Fig. 8.5) laterally displaced from the centre, but certain sections with stepped cleavages will bring the optic angle into positions in which the optic sign may be determined and 2E may be estimated by the Mallard method. True (110) sections

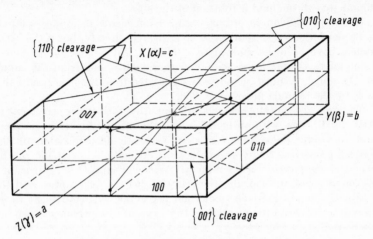

Fig. 8.5. Optic orientation and cleavages of barite.

will often show traces of the (001) cleavage, but only if the refractive index liquid does not match. Cleavages disappear with the border phenomena when a match is made. (010) sections, occasionally seen will show a flash figure, and will have two cleavages at right angles, those of (001) and the trace of (110), the edges of the fragments being determined by these. It goes without saying that every fragment will not be neatly bounded by straight edges as would appear from the Fig. 8.5. Fracture in crushing plays a good part as well as cleavage in determining the shapes of individual particles.

$BaSO_4$ is isomorphous with celestite, $SrSO_4$, and if there is any of the latter present in solid solution the refractive indices will be lower than those listed above, and the value of 2V will be higher.

Pure celestite has the refractive indices α_D 1·622, β_D 1·623 and γ_D 1·631. 2V is 50° and the sign is positive.

11. Augite. $Ca(Mg,Fe)Si_2O_6$ with some $(Mg,Fe)SiO_3$ and a little Al_2O_3 in solid solution. Monoclinic, class $2/m$. The cleavage is prismatic

{110} at an angle of 87°. The O.A.P. is (010), Z:c is about 41° in the obtuse angle β, 2V = about 60°, and the mineral is optically positive. α_D 1·686, β_D 1·692 and γ_D 1·711. These are typical values for augite, marked changes taking place with change in composition.

As the members of the mineral family to which augite belongs (the pyroxenes) display a great variety of isomorphous relationships, and as the examples available to different students would certainly differ in their properties, only general directions will be given here.

The good prismatic cleavage of augite induces crushed grains to lie in an orientation presenting (110) sections. None of the principal vibration directions lies in this section and so the student is advised to use thin sections of the mineral as well as crushed grains. Thin slices have certain advantages in that all the sections are of equal thickness and a number of orientations may occur, which are difficult or impossible for cleaved fragments to assume. On the other hand refractive indices cannot be determined in thin slices permanently mounted.

Material for study may be had by taking a coarse-grained basic rock such as gabbro and, after slices have been cut from it, separate fragments of augite may be gouged from the rock, or the rock may be crushed and the pyroxene separated by means of heavy liquids from the feldspar.

In thin section common augite will show either a pale brown tint or greenish brown although the colour varies a good deal, and it will be non-pleochroic in thin section unless it is a titaniferous variety when it presents a purplish or violet tint.

Characteristic sections are recognised in thin slices (Fig. 8.6). Basal (001) sections show two cleavages at 87° which do not appear to move laterally on raising and lowering the objective, this showing that they are vertical. This section should present one optic axis emerging at a high angle. From this an estimate of the value of 2V may be made from the curvature of the brush, and the dispersion of the optic axis noted. The extinction is symmetrical and the O.A.P. bisects the angle between the cleavages.

The (100) section may be recognised by its parallel traces of the prismatic cleavage and its straight extinction. An optic axis emerges through the pinacoid, displaced from the centre of the field but in the symmetry plane, and once again 2V may be estimated and the dispersion of the second axis noted. The amount of dispersion may be quite different in the two axes.

The (010) section is recognised by its parallel cleavage and oblique extinction which is the maximum on this face, the slow direction Z being 41° from the trace of the vertical cleavage which is the c direction.

All the sections in the slice ought to be looked at in conoscopically.
A chance section parallel to (101) would give a view of the acute optic
angle.

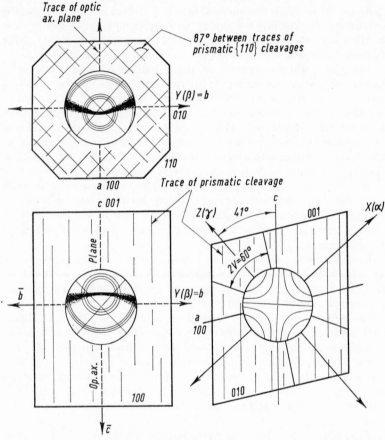

Fig. 8.6.
Characteristic sections of augite.

Crushed grains will present a majority of (110) sections which, as has
been said, are not parallel to any of the principal vibration directions,
but the extinction angle on (110) is a very useful criterion since, with a
knowledge of the cleavage angle and the size of the optic angle, the
extinction on (010) may be calculated. In this connection see Johann-

sen, *Manual of Petrographic Methods*, 1918, p. 402, where Harker's table of extinction angles on (110) have the corresponding maxima on (010) listed for various sizes of the optic axial angle. A useful paper by Gazzi* deals with the problem of the determination of monoclinic amphiboles and pyroxenes in crushed grains and gives diagrams for estimating $Z:c$ from the extinction angle $Z':c$ on {110} fragments.

There are usually sufficient sections with a random orientation due to stepped cleavage to enable the three principal refractive indices to be measured. The sections required are easily recognised and should be one of the things first looked for, and a flash figure given by a grain showing the highest colours in the mount will give α and γ. If a series of mounts is made with progressively higher indices, the desired data will gradually accumulate.

It should not be forgotten that the orientation of grains in a liquid mount may often be altered by 'rolling' (p. 279), and if all these methods fail, the study of a cleavage flake mounted on the single rotation apparatus described on p. 282 will probably provide all the necessary data.

* Gazzi, P., *Amer. Min.*, 1963, **48**, pp. 422–429.

APPENDIX

I. BOOKS RECOMMENDED FOR FURTHER READING

The works given below are classified according to the main topics on which the reader of this book will need to seek further information, if he proposes to carry his knowledge of the subject to a more advanced stage. Under each heading are given a selection of texts which either deal mainly with that topic, or include an authoritative treatment of it.

(a) *Morphology of Crystals and Graphical Methods of Representation (e.g. Stereographic Projection)*.

Tutton, A. E. H., *Crystallography and Practical Crystal Measurement*, Vol. I (Macmillan, 1928).

Miers, H. A., *Mineralogy* (Macmillan, 1929).

Phillips, F. C., *An Introduction to Crystallography* (Longmans, London, 2nd edn. 1956).

Porter, M. W. and Spiller, R. C., *The Barker Index of Crystals*, Vol. I, Part I (Heffer, Cambridge, 1951).

Barker, T. V., *Graphical and Tabular Methods in Crystallography* (Murby, London, 1922).

Terpstra, P. and Codd, L. W., *Crystallometry* (Academic Press, New York, 1961).

(b) *Optical Properties of Crystals*.

Rosenbusch, H. and Wülfing, E. A., *Mikroscopische Physiographie der Mineralien und Gesteine*, Vol. I (Schweitzerbart, 1924).

Niggli, P., *Lehrbuch der Mineralogie*, Vol. I (Gebruder and Bornträger, 1924).

Johannsen, A., *Manual of Petrographic Methods* (McGraw-Hill, New York and London, 2nd. edn., 1918).

Rinne, F. and Berek, M., *Anleitung zu Optischen Untersuchungen mit der Polarisations Mikroskop*, 2nd edn., revised by C. H. Claussen, A. Driesen, and S. Rösch (Schweizerbart, 1953).

Weissberger, A. (ed.), *Physical Methods of Organic Chemistry*, Vol. 1, Chap. XI, by E. E. Jelley (Interscience, London, 1945). [This

314

chapter includes a useful section on the optics of strongly absorbing crystals.]

Jenkins, F. A. and White, H. E., *Fundamentals of Optics* (McGraw-Hill, New York and London, 1957).

Longhurst, R. S., *Geometrical and Physical Optics* (Longmans, London, 1957; later impressions 1960, 1962).

Shubnikov, A. V., *Principles of Optical Crystallography* (translated from the Russian, Consultants Bureau, New York, 1960).

(c) *Crystal Structure (including Relation of Optical Properties to Structure)*

Bragg, W. L., *The Crystalline State* (G. Bell, London, 1933).

Bunn, C. W., *Chemical Crystallography* (University Press, Oxford, 2nd. edn. 1961).

(d) *The Polarising Microscope and Microscopy Generally*

Johannsen, A., *Manual of Petrographic Methods* (see b above).

Chamot, E. M. and Mason, C. W., *Handbook of Chemical Microscopy* Vol. I (Wiley, 3rd edn. 1958).

Hallimond, A. F., *Manual of the Polarising Microscope* (Cooke, Troughton and Simms, Ltd., 2nd edn. 1953, reprinted 1956).

Martin, L. C. and Johnson, B. K., *Practical Microscopy* (Blackie, London, 3rd edn. 1958, reprinted 1959).

Barer, R., *Lecture Notes on the Use of the Microscope* (Blackwell, 1953).

Payne, B. O., *Microscope Design and Construction* (Cooke, Troughton and Simms, York, 1954).

Longhurst, R. S., *Geometrical and Physical Optics* (see b above).

(e) *Index Variation Methods. The Universal Stage.*

Winchell, N. H. and A. N., *Elements of Optical Mineralogy*, Part I (Wiley, 5th edn. 1948).

Hallimond, A. F., *Manual of the Polarising Microscope* (see d above).

Hartshorne, N. H. and Stuart, A., *Crystals and the Polarising Microscope* (E. Arnold, London, 3rd. edn. 1960).

(f) *Determination of Path-difference. (Relative Retardation.)*

Hallimond, A. F., *Manual of the Polarising Microscope* (see d above).

Hartshorne, N. H. and Stuart, A., *Crystals and the Polarising Microscope* (see e above).

(g) *Preparation of Material.*

(i) *General.*

Chamot, E. M. and Mason, C. W., *Handbook of Chemical Microscopy* Vol. I (see d above).

(ii) *Rocks, Refractories, Ceramics.*

Johannsen, A., *Manual of Petrographic Methods* (see *b* above).

Krumbein, W. C. and Pettijohn, F. J., *Manual of Sedimentary Petrography* (D. Appleton-Century, New York, 1938).

Holmes, A., *Petrographic Methods* (Murby, London, 1921).

Weatherhead, A. V., *Petrographic Micro-technique* (Arthur Barrow Ltd., 1947).

Rigby, G. R., *The Thin-section Mineralogy of Ceramic Materials* (British Ceramic Research Association, 2nd edn., 1953).

II. TABLES AND COLLECTIONS OF OPTICAL
CRYSTALLOGRAPHIC DATA

Groth, P., *Chemische Kristallographie*, Vols. I–V (Engelmann, 1906–19). Both morphological and optical data are given in this work.

International Critical Tables, Vol. I, pp. 165, 279, 320; Vol. VII, pp. 12, 16.

Winchell, A. N., *Microscopic Characters of Artificial Inorganic Solid Substances or Artificial Minerals* (Wiley, New York and London, 1931).

Winchell, A. N., *Elements of Optical Mineralogy*, Part II, 4th edn. Descriptions of Minerals with Special Reference to their Optical and Microscopic Characters (Wiley, New York and London, 1951).

Winchell, A. N., *Elements of Optical Mineralogy*, Part III, 2nd edn., 2nd Printing. Determinative Tables (Wiley, New York and London, 1939).

Larsen, E. S., *Microscopic Determination of the Non-opaque Minerals*, Bull. Geol. Survey U.S.A., No. 848 (1934), pp. 47 *et seq.*

Winchell, A. N., *The Optical Properties of Organic Compounds*, 2nd Edn. (Academic Press, New York and London, 1954).

Landolt-Börnstein, *Physikalisch-Chemische Tabellen*, Vol. II, Part 8, 6th Edn. (Springer Verlag, Berlin, 1962). Pp. 43–560 (includes glasses and liquid crystals).

Tables Annuelles Internationelles de Constanes &c. (Paris).

Fry, W. H., *Tables for the Microscopic Identification of Inorganic Salts*, Bull. Dept. Agr. U.S.A., No. 1108 (1922).

Porter, M. W. and Spiller, R. C., *The Barker Index of Crystals* (Heffer, Cambridge). Vol. I, Parts I and II, 1951. Vol. II, Parts I, II and III, 1956. Vol. III (in the press).

Kordes, E., *Optische Daten zur Bestimmung anorganischer Substanzen mit dem Polarisations-Mikroskop* (Verlag Chemie. GMBH. Weinheim/Bergstr., 1960).

Journals.

From 1948 to 1962, optical and morphological descriptions of a number of important inorganic and organic compounds appeared in *Analytical Chemistry* as a regular series. In late 1962, the series was transferred to *The Microscope and Crystal Front*, beginning with the issue Vol. 13, No. 10. The series is edited by W. C. McCrone, McCrone Associates, Chicago, Illinois, and Southwick, Sussex.

Optical descriptions of substances have often appeared in the following:

American Journal of Science; American Mineralogist; Mineralogical Magazine and Mineralogical Abstracts; Zeitschrift für Kristallographie; Acta Crystallographica.

III. SOURCES OF CERTAIN MATERIALS MENTIONED IN THE TEXT

Index immersion media:

Baird & Tatlock (London) Ltd., Freshwater Road, Chadwell Heath, Essex.

British Drug Houses Ltd. (B.D.H. Laboratory Chemicals Group), Poole, Dorset.

R. P. Cargille, 118 Liberty St., New York 6, N.Y., U.S.A.

J. T. Rooney, P. O. Box 358, Buffalo, N.Y., U.S.A.

Mineral, rock, and oriented crystal sections:

Gregory, Bottley, & Co., 30 Old Church St., Chelsea, London, S.W.3.

W. Harold Tomlinson, 260 N. Rolling Rd., Springfield, Pa., U.S.A.

Ward's Natural Science Establishment Inc., P.O. Box 24, Rochester 9, N.Y., U.S.A.

Stereographic nets:

Thomas Murby & Co., 40 Museum St., London, W.C.1.

J. H. Steward Ltd., 406 Strand, London, W.C.2.

INDEX

INDEX

Aberrations of lenses, 114 *et seq.*
Absorbing crystals, 94 *et seq.*
Absorption, 170
  coefficient, 95
  formula, 171
  modulus, 95
  spectrum, 95
Achromatic doublet, 120
Acute bisectrix, 90
Allotriomorphic crystals, 34
Ammonium dihydrogen phosphate, study of, 300
Amplitude of vibration, 49
Analyser, 125
Anhedral crystals, 34
Anisotropic crystals, 47
Anisotropism, 172
Aplanatic points, 121
'Aqua resins', 280
Augite, study of, 310
Axes, crystal, 5, 7
  of symmetry, 10
  rotation-inversion, 12

Barite, study of, 309
Barker, T. V., 5
Basal sections of uniaxial crystals, between crossed polars, 181
  in convergent light, 203, 204
Bausch and Lomb 'LD' microscope, 136
'Becke line', explanation of, 160
Becke method of refractive index determination, 159 *et seq.*
Bertrand lens, 126, 200, 201
Biaxial crystals, optics of, 82 *et seq.*
Birefringence, 176, 178
  determination of, 192
  Michel–Levy's chart of, 180
  of a section, 178
Bond polarisabilities, 108
Brachy-axis, 17
Brachy-pinacoid, 17
Bragg, W. H., 1
Bragg, W. L., 1, 108
Bravais, A., 1

Bravais cells, 2
Bravais plate, 188
Brewster's Law, 75
Brookite, crossed-axial-plane dispersion of, 227
Bryant, W. M. D., 227
Buckley, H. E., 197
Bunn, C. W., 108

Calcite polarising prisms, 127
Calcite, study of, 307
Cauchy's equation, 96
Central illumination, 160
Change in optical sign, 94, 227
Chromatic aberration, 115
Circularly polarised light, 58
Cleavage, 40
  terms descriptive of, 41
  under the microscope, 155
Clino-pinacoid, 18
Coherent sources, 63
Combination of wave motions, 55 *et seq.*
Composition plane, 42
Compound microscope, the, 117 *et seq.*
  magnification of, 119 *et seq.*
Condensers, 137 *et seq.*
  centring, 136
Conoscope, 199
Contact twins, 42
Copper sulphate pentahydrate, study of, 305
Cover slips, 266
Critical angle, 127
'Critical' illumination, 140 *et seq.*
Crossed-axial-plane dispersion, 94, 226
  of brookite, 227
Crossed (or rotated) dispersion, 225
Crystal, angles, measurement of, 6
  classes, 20 *et seq.*
  elements, 8
  form under the microscope, 156
  systems, 5, 12, 20
'Crystal-rolling', 279
Cubic (isometric) system, 32
  forms, 33

321